GUIDE TO FOOD STORAGE

Follow this guide for food storage, and you can be sure that what's in your freezer, refrigerator, and pantry is fresh-tasting and ready to cook.

IN THE FREEZER
(At –10° to 0° F)

DAIRY
Cheese, hard	3 months
Cheese, soft	2 weeks
Egg substitute	6 months
Egg whites	6 months
Egg yolks	8 months
Ice cream, sherbet	1 month

FRUITS AND VEGETABLES
Commercially frozen fruits	1 year
Commercially frozen vegetables	8 to 12 months

MEATS, POULTRY, AND SEAFOOD
Beef, Lamb, and Veal
Ground, uncooked, and all cuts, cooked	3 months
Roasts and steaks, uncooked	9 months

Pork
Ground, uncooked, and all cuts, cooked	3 months
Roasts and chops, uncooked	6 months

Poultry
All cuts, cooked	1 month
Boneless or bone-in pieces, uncooked	6 months

Seafood
Bass, perch, trout, and shellfish	3 months
Cod, flounder, and halibut	6 months

IN THE REFRIGERATOR
(At 34° to 40° F)

DAIRY
Buttermilk, low-fat	1 to 2 weeks
Cheese, grated Parmesan	1 year
Cheeses, Cheddar and Swiss	3 to 4 weeks
Cream cheese, ⅓-less-fat and reduced-fat.	2 weeks
Eggs and egg substitute	1 month
Margarine	1 month

MEATS, POULTRY, AND SEAFOOD
Beef, Lamb, Pork, and Veal
Ground and stew meat, uncooked	1 to 2 days
Roasts, uncooked	2 to 4 days
Steaks and chops, uncooked	3 to 5 days

Chicken, Turkey, and Seafood
All cuts, uncooked	1 to 2 days

FRUITS AND VEGETABLES
Apples, beets, cabbage, carrots, celery, citrus fruits, eggplant, and parsnips	2 to 3 weeks
Apricots, berries, peaches, pears, plums, asparagus, cauliflower, cucumbers, mushrooms, okra, peas, peppers, salad greens, and summer squash	2 to 4 days
Corn, husked	1 day

IN THE PANTRY
Keep these at room temperature for six to 12 months.

BAKING AND COOKING STAPLES
Baking powder
Biscuit and baking mix
Broth, canned
Cooking spray
Honey
Mayonnaise, regular, light, and nonfat (unopened)
Milk, canned evaporated skimmed
Milk, nonfat dry powder
Mustard, prepared (unopened)
Oils, olive and vegetable
Pasta, dried
Peanut butter, reduced-fat
Rice, instant and regular
Salad dressings, bottled (unopened)
Seasoning sauces, bottled
Tuna, canned

FRUITS, LEGUMES, AND VEGETABLES
Fruits, canned
Legumes (beans, lentils, peas), dried or canned
Tomato products, canned
Vegetables, canned

Holiday Herbed Pork Roast, page 172
Citrus Cran-Apple Relish, page 173
Garlic-Roasted Brussels Sprouts, page 173
Brown Sugar-Crusted Sweet Potato
Casserole, page 173
Pear Upside-Down Cake with Pecans,
page 38

Chicken Tenders Satay, page 18
with Red Curry Peanut Sauce and
Peanut Dipping Sauce, page 19

Classic French Onion Soup,
page 154

Tiramisu,
page 40

Weight Watchers®

ANNUAL RECIPES
for SUCCESS
2005

compiled and edited by
Holley Contri Johnson, M.S., R.D.

OXmoor
HOUSE®

©2004 by Oxmoor House, Inc.
Book Division of Southern Progress Corporation
P.O. Box 2463, Birmingham, Alabama 35201

ISBN: 0-8487-2796-7
ISSN: 1526-1565
Printed in the United States of America
Second Printing 2005

Be sure to check with your health-care provider before making any changes in your diet.
Weight Watchers® and **POINTS**® are registered trademarks of *Weight Watchers* International, Inc., and is used under license by Healthy Living, Inc.

OXMOOR HOUSE, INC.

Editor-in-Chief: Nancy Fitzpatrick Wyatt
Executive Editor: Katherine M. Eakin
Art Director: Cynthia R. Cooper
Copy Chief: Allison Long Lowery

WeightWatchers® ANNUAL RECIPES
FOR SUCCESS 2005
Editor: Holley Contri Johnson, M.S., R.D.
Successes Writer: Heather Averett
Editorial Assistants: Shannon Friedmann, Dawn Russell
Designer: Jay Parker
Director, Test Kitchens: Elizabeth Tyler Luckett
Assistant Director, Test Kitchens: Julie Christopher
Test Kitchens Staff: Kristi Carter, Nicole Faber, Elise Weis, Kelley Self Wilton
Senior Photographer: Jim Bathie
Photographer: Brit Huckabay
Senior Photo Stylist: Kay E. Clarke
Photo Stylists: Amy Wilson, Ashley J. Wyatt
Publishing Systems Administrator: Rick Tucker
Director of Production: Phillip Lee
Associate Production Manager: Leslie Wells Johnson
Production Assistant: Faye Porter Bonner

CONTRIBUTORS
Copy Editor: Dolores Hydock
Indexer: Mary Ann Laurens
Photographers: Ralph Anderson, Lee Harrelson
Photo Stylists: Mindy Shapiro, Katie Stoddard
Recipe Development: Gretchen Brown, Maureen Callahan, Martha Condra, Caroline Grant, Nancy Hughes, Ana Kelly, Jean Kressy, Rebecca D. Lang, Karen Levin, Joyce Lock, Kathleen Royal Phillips
Editorial Interns: Leighton Batte, Jessica Dorsey, Sheila Egts
Test Kitchens: Tamara Goldis, Jan A. Smith
Test Kitchens Interns: Natalie Gavin, Elizabeth Grezaffi, Julie Perno
Nutrition Interns: Monica McArthur, Megan Smalley

To order additional copies of this publication or any others, call 1-800-765-6400.

For more books to enrich your life, visit
oxmoorhouse.com

COVER: Mint Brownie Ice Cream Bars, page 50

CONTENTS

Welcome 8
About Our Recipes 10

RECIPES

Appetizers & Beverages 11
Breads...........................25
Desserts 31
Fish & Shellfish 51
Meatless Main Dishes..................61
Meats............................81
Poultry 95
Salads............................117
Sandwiches........................125
Side Dishes........................141
Soups & Stews 151

SUCCESSES

The Challenge........................41
It's All About Health.....................48
A Friend For Life 65
Success Speaks Volumes 72
Thin Feels Good 89
All About Attitude 109
Beating The Odds 116
A Picture Is Worth A Thousand Words...........133
Shopping Once Again 140
Comfortable At Last....................157

SPECIAL OCCASION MENUS

Easy Weeknight Supper 164
Simple Sunday Brunch 166
Off the Grill.........................168
A Taste of Italy 170
Family Holiday Dinner 172

WEEKLY MENU PLANNERS

Weeks 1-4........................174

General Recipe Index 182
POINTS® Value Recipe Index...................190

Welcome!

Discover the pleasures of mealtime without sacrificing the foods and flavors you love most.

WeightWatchers *Annual Recipes for Success 2005* is your complete guide to delicious food, healthy living, and weight loss success. In this *Weight Watchers* book you'll find:

- Over 300 **great-tasting recipes**
- More than 70 **color photographs** of our most favorite recipes
- Step-by-step recipe instructions, how-to photography, and **Test Kitchens Secrets**
- Five **Special Occasion Menus** with a game plan for preparing each meal
- Four weeks of **7-Day Menu Planners** that incorporate many recipes from the cookbook, plus a few new ones, too. Each day has a **POINTS** value of 24 or less!
- Ten truly inspiring **Weight-Loss Success Stories** from people just like you
- Plus, **Our Favorite Recipes**—all the recipes are healthy and delicious, but these recipes are the "best of the best"

Our Recipes

All recipes in **WeightWatchers** *Annual Recipes for Success 2005* carry the Test Kitchens' seal of approval. Each recipe is tested at least once—sometimes two or three times—to ensure that it's easy to prepare, tastes terrific, and is supremely healthy.

The Test Kitchens staff notes the exact time it takes to prepare each dish, from start to finish.
- **Prep** is the time it takes to cut, measure, and weigh ingredients before cooking.
- **Cook** is the time when heat is applied to the ingredients (such as sautéing, grilling, or baking).
- **Other** is the additional "hands-off" time when the ingredients marinate, cool, chill, freeze, rise, or stand.

Smart Cooking

Our goal is to help you master meal preparation. We encourage you to experiment with new flavors and ingredients and to be practical, too. For example, **Chicken and Black Bean Taco Salad with Chipotle Dressing,** page 124, calls for 1 chipotle chile in adobo sauce. Since you have to purchase an entire jar to get just 1 pepper, we've planned ahead and identified other recipes in the book that use this ingredient like **Spicy Andouille Posole,** page 163, and **Bean and Roasted Vegetable Burritos,** page 64.

Special Occasion Meals Made Easy

Planned meals help you stay within your daily **POINTS** value range yet still allow your favorite foods. Beginning on page 164, you'll find five *Special Occasion Menus* (each with a **POINTS** value of 12 or less) designed to guide you through those times when it's hard to resist overeating. Each menu comes complete with a "Game Plan" to help you get the meals on the table as efficiently as possible, plus quick tips, and make-ahead ideas. Try our **Family Holiday Dinner** menu, page 172-173. The recipes are so flavorful that your family  and guests will never guess they're healthy for you. Best of all, the meal has a **POINTS** value of only 12. Compared to the 20 **POINTS** value or more found in a traditional holiday feast, this menu is a blueprint for success. For a healthy, hassle-free, and kid-friendly meal, try our **Easy Weeknight Supper** menu, page 164-165. Spaghetti Pie never tasted so good!

Weekly Menu Planners

We offer four *7-Day Menu Planners*, pages 174–181, with fabulous ideas for breakfast, lunch, dinner, and a snack—all with a **POINTS** value of 24 or less. Each day's menu provides at least two servings of milk and at least five servings of fruits and/or vegetables. You can make adjustments as needed to accommodate your daily **POINTS** value plan.

Real Life Success Stories

Trying to shed extra pounds can be overwhelming. But don't give up! Maybe all you need is a little inspiration. In WeightWatchers® *Annual Recipes for Success 2005*, you'll find the stories of 11 extraordinary people, such as Carrie Meyer, who have had tremendous success following the *Weight Watchers* weight-loss program. As Carrie says,

"I'm smaller now than I ever was in high school and well within my healthy weight range. I've learned how to manage and how to eat real food."

(Read the rest of Carrie's story on page 157)

Carrie Meyer

For each success story you'll find **before and after photographs** along with **helpful tips** and **inspirational quotes** highlighting personal struggles and victories. Each person has a unique story and hopes that his or her success will, indeed, inspire you.

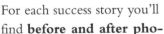 *Annual Recipes for Success 2005* shows how to make a healthy lifestyle not only attainable but fun. We hope it will become a trusted resource for you to turn to when you're searching for delicious, one-of-a-kind recipes.

OUR FAVORITE RECIPES

We judge the merits of every recipe, and only the best ones make the cut. These recipes are so outstanding they've become our personal favorites. We hope they'll be your favorites, too!

Mocha Dark Chocolate Chunk Brownies, 2 *POINTS* value (page 32). Brownies aren't just for kids anymore. We've added coffee and chopped dark chocolate chunks to the simple made-from-scratch brownie batter to create a rich, indulgent after-dinner treat.

Molasses-Bourbon Grilled Salmon, 5 *POINTS* value (page 168). No matter whether you use your gas or charcoal grill or even a grill pan, this salmon is delicious!

Crunch Pecan Greens with Fresh Berries, 4 *POINTS* value (page 119). Crunchy ramen noodles, pecans, sweet strawberries, and blueberries make a perfect topping for these delicate salad greens—and make this an all-time favorite salad as well.

Overnight Caramel-Pecan Bread, 3 *POINTS* value (page 28). These gooey, pull-apart, caramel rolls won top honors in our Test Kitchens for their make-ahead convenience and for their all-round yum factor.

Roasted Italian Pork Tenderloin, 3 *POINTS* value (page 94). Once your family has tasted this pork roast, it may replace the traditional favorite, roast turkey, at your next holiday meal.

Fresh Green Veggie Salsa, 1 *POINTS* value (page 13). The crunchy combination of cucumber, celery, tomatillos, and green onions, makes this one of our favorite salsas ever! Fresh cilantro and a splash of lime juice give it a refreshing kick. And when served with our favorite "Dippers," **(page 12),** it's the perfect party snack food.

About Our Recipes

WeightWatchers® *Annual Recipes for Success 2005* gives you the nutrition facts you need to make your life easier. We've provided the following useful information with every recipe:

- A number calculated through the **POINTS**® Food System (a component of the **POINTS** Weight-Loss System) from Weight Watchers International, Inc.
- Diabetic exchange values for those who use them as a guide for planning meals
- A complete nutrient analysis per serving

POINTS FOOD SYSTEM

Every recipe in the book includes a number calculated using the **POINTS** Food System. This system uses a formula based on the calorie, fat, and fiber content of the food. Foods with more calories and fat (like a slice of pepperoni pizza) receive high numbers, while fruits and vegetables receive low numbers. For more information about the *Weight Watchers* program and a meeting nearest you, call 1-800-651-6000 or visit online at www.weightwatchers.com.

DIABETIC EXCHANGES

Exchange values are provided for people with diabetes and for those who use them for calorie-controlled diets. All foods within a certain group contain approximately the same amount of nutrients and calories, so one serving of a food from a food group can be substituted or exchanged for one serving of any other item on the list. The food groups are starch, fruit, vegetable, milk, meat, and fat. The exchange values are based on the *Exchange Lists for Meal Planning* developed by the American Diabetes Association and The American Dietetic Association.

NUTRIENT ANALYSIS

Each recipe has a complete list of nutrients, including calories, protein, fat, saturated fat, carbohydrates, dietary fiber, cholesterol, iron, sodium, and calcium. This information makes it easy for you to use the recipes in any weight-loss program that you may choose to follow. Measurements are abbreviated g (grams) and mg (milligrams). Numbers are based on these assumptions:

- Unless otherwise indicated, meat, poultry, and fish refer to skinned, boned, and cooked servings.
- When we give a range for an ingredient (3 to 3½ cups flour, for instance), we calculate using the lesser amount.
- Some alcohol calories evaporate during heating; the analysis reflects that.
- Only the amount of marinade absorbed by the food is used in calculation.
- Garnishes and optional ingredients are not included in an analysis.

Nutritional values used in our calculations either come from The Food Processor, Version 7.5 (ESHA Research) or are provided by food manufacturers.

Appetizers & Beverages

ROSEMARY-WHITE BEAN HUMMUS

prep: 10 minutes • cook: 3 minutes
other: 10 minutes

2½   teaspoons olive oil
2   garlic cloves, thinly sliced
1½   teaspoons chopped fresh
     rosemary
½   teaspoon ground cumin
1   (15-ounce) can cannellini or
     other white beans, rinsed and
     drained
3½   tablespoons water, divided
1½   tablespoons fresh lemon juice
1   teaspoon tahini (sesame seed
     paste)
¼   teaspoon salt
     Rosemary sprigs (optional)

1. Heat oil in a small nonstick skillet over medium heat. Add garlic, rosemary, and cumin. Sauté 1 to 2 minutes or until garlic begins to brown. Remove from heat; let stand 10 minutes.
2. Place beans, 2 tablespoons water, lemon juice, tahini, and salt in a blender or food processor; process until smooth. Add garlic mixture and 1½ tablespoons water, if needed, until spread is desired consistency. Place spread in a small bowl and garnish with rosemary sprigs, if desired. Serve at room temperature, or cover and chill until ready to use. Serve with pita bread or fresh cut vegetables. YIELD: 10 servings (serving size: 2 tablespoons).

POINTS value: 1; **Exchange:** ½ Starch;
Per serving: CAL 43 (33% from fat); PRO 1.6g;
FAT 1.6g (sat 0.2g); CARB 5.6g; FIB 1.5g;
CHOL 0mg; IRON 0.6mg; SOD 100mg; CALC 14mg

LENTIL HUMMUS

prep: 4 minutes • cook: 5 minutes
other: 15 minutes

½   cup red lentils
3   cups water
½   cup rinsed and drained canned
     chickpeas (garbanzo beans)
3   tablespoons olive oil
2   tablespoons fresh lemon juice
½   teaspoon salt
¼   teaspoon ground cumin
2   garlic cloves, peeled and
     crushed

1. Rinse lentils. Combine lentils and water in a saucepan; bring to a boil. Boil 3 minutes; remove from heat, cover, and let stand 15 minutes. Drain.
2. Place lentils, chickpeas, and remaining ingredients in a blender or food processor; process 2 minutes or until smooth. YIELD: 12 servings (serving size: 2 tablespoons).

POINTS value: 1; **Exchanges:** ½ Starch, ½ Fat;
Per serving: CAL 66 (48% from fat); PRO 2.3g;
FAT 3.6g (sat 0.5g); CARB 6.6g; FIB 1.6g;
CHOL 0mg; IRON 0.6mg; SOD 112mg; CALC 11mg

HUMMUS WITH AVOCADO AND LIME

prep: 3 minutes

Liven up store-bought hummus with fresh avocado and lime juice. Your guests will never know you started with a convenience product.

1   (7-ounce) container prepared
     hummus (such as Athenos)
1   ripe avocado, seeded
½   cup low-fat sour cream
2   tablespoons fresh lime juice
1   teaspoon ground cumin
½   teaspoon salt
2   garlic cloves, minced

1. Process all ingredients in a blender or food processor until smooth, stopping to scrape down sides. YIELD: 14 servings (serving size: 2 tablespoons).

POINTS value: 1; **Exchanges:** ½ Starch, ½ Fat;
Per serving: CAL 58 (65% from fat); PRO 1.9g;
FAT 4.3g (sat 1.2g); CARB 4.0g; FIB 2.0g;
CHOL 4mg; IRON 0.4mg; SOD 143mg; CALC 22mg

DIPPERS

Regular potato or corn chips have a high *POINTS* value per serving and are loaded with sodium. Plus, the recommended serving size is small and often not very satisfying. Enjoy these healthy variations with your favorite dips. They offer as much texture and taste satisfaction as regular chips, but with a lower *POINTS* value.

• **Fresh vegetables:** cucumber slices, sugar snap peas, red bell pepper strips, carrots, broccoli or cauliflower florets. Serving size: 1 cup *POINTS* value: 0
• **Corn Tortilla Wedges:** Cut each corn tortilla into 8 wedges. Place wedges in a single layer on a baking sheet coated with cooking spray. Coat wedges with cooking spray. Bake at 350° for 13 to 15 minutes or until crisp. Serving size: 8 wedges *POINTS* value: 1
• **Pita Crisps:** Cut each pita bread round into 8 wedges. Place wedges in a single layer on a baking sheet coated with cooking spray. Spray wedges with cooking spray and sprinkle with salt or garlic powder. Bake at 350° for 12 to 15 minutes or until lightly browned. Serving size: 8 wedges *POINTS* value: 2

FRESH GREEN VEGGIE SALSA

prep: 20 minutes

Celery and cucumber aren't common ingredients in salsa, but they make this version delightfully crunchy and fresh tasting.

½   cup finely chopped tomatillos (about 2 medium)
½   medium cucumber, peeled, seeded, and chopped (about ½ cup)
⅓   cup chopped cilantro leaves
½   medium celery stalk, finely chopped (about ¼ cup)
3   tablespoons fresh lime juice (about 2)
1   green onion, thinly sliced (about 2 tablespoons)
1   tablespoon extravirgin olive oil
½   teaspoon salt
1   ripe avocado, chopped

1. Combine all ingredients in a medium bowl, tossing well. Serve immediately, or cover and chill. YIELD: 8 servings (serving size: ¼ cup).
Tip: To easily "chop" ripe avocado halves, score the flesh lengthwise, then crosswise, in ¼-inch squares with a sharp knife, cutting to, but not through, the peel. Flex the peel to push out the cubes. Add avocado last to prevent discoloration.

POINTS value: 1; **Exchanges:** 1 Vegetable, ½ Fat;
Per serving: CAL 46 (73% from fat); PRO 0.5g;
FAT 4.0g (sat 0.6g); CARB 2.8g; FIB 1.1g;
CHOL 0mg; IRON 0.3mg; SOD 154mg; CALC 7mg

ROASTED CORN SALSA

prep: 19 minutes • cook: 12 minutes

See page 18 for an easy method for cutting corn kernels from the cob.

Cooking spray
2½   cups fresh yellow corn kernels (about 5 ears)
1½   cups diced seeded plum tomato (about 4)
½   cup finely chopped green bell pepper
½   cup finely chopped red bell pepper
½   cup diced avocado
⅓   cup diced peeled jicama
⅓   cup finely chopped red onion
3   tablespoons finely chopped fresh cilantro
2   tablespoons fresh lime juice (about 1 large)
1   tablespoon olive oil
¼   teaspoon salt
3   garlic cloves, minced
1   jalapeño pepper, seeded and minced

1. Preheat oven to 475°.
2. Coat a foil-lined jelly roll pan with cooking spray. Place corn on pan in a single layer. Bake at 475° for 10 minutes; stir and bake an additional 2 minutes or until roasted. Remove from oven and cool.
3. Combine corn, tomato, and remaining ingredients in a large bowl; stir well. YIELD: 19 servings (serving size: ¼ cup).

POINTS value: 1; **Exchanges:** 1 Vegetable, ½ Fat;
Per serving: CAL 38 (34% from fat); PRO 1.0g;
FAT 1.6g (sat 0.2g); CARB 6.1g; FIB 1.3g;
CHOL 0mg; IRON 0.3mg; SOD 36mg; CALC 4mg

GINGER FRUIT SALSA

prep: 16 minutes • other: 5 minutes

1½   cups coarsely chopped cantaloupe
1   cup chopped fresh pineapple
½   cup dried cranberries (such as Craisins)
¼   cup chopped fresh mint
2   tablespoons fresh lemon juice
1   teaspoon grated peeled fresh ginger
1   jalapeño pepper, seeded and finely chopped

1. Combine all ingredients in a medium bowl, tossing gently. Let stand 5 minutes before serving. YIELD: 12 servings (serving size: ¼ cup).

POINTS value: 0; **Exchange:** ½ Fruit;
Per serving: CAL 31 (3% from fat); PRO 0.3g;
FAT 0.1g (sat 0.0g); CARB 7.9g; FIB 0.7g;
CHOL 0mg; IRON 0.2mg; SOD 2mg; CALC 6mg

AVOCADO ADVICE

Selection tips: Look for fruit that's firm, yet gives when gently squeezed. If it's still hard, it's not ready to be eaten. Two medium avocados should yield about 1 pound, or 2½ cups sliced, diced, or chopped.
Storage tips: You may refrigerate ripe avocados for 2 to 3 days. Place an apple in a paper bag with an avocado and store it at room temperature to accelerate the ripening process. Since cut and exposed avocados tend to discolor quickly, add cubed or sliced avocado to your dish as late as possible in the preparation process.

BLACK BEAN AND GOAT CHEESE SPREAD

prep: 10 minutes • cook: 30 minutes
other: 2 hours

Mirin is a syrupy, golden-colored Japanese rice wine used to add a touch of sweetness and flavor to your favorite dish. Mirin can be found in Asian markets and some supermarkets. An equal amount of white grape juice can be substituted.

2   teaspoons olive oil
1   medium onion, sliced
3   garlic cloves, crushed
¼   teaspoon salt
¼   cup mirin (sweet rice wine)
1   (15-ounce) can black beans, rinsed and drained
1   (5.3-ounce) package goat cheese
⅓   cup sliced green onions
¼   teaspoon black pepper

1. Heat oil in a medium nonstick skillet over medium-low heat. Add onion, garlic, and salt. Cook 25 to 30 minutes, stirring often, until browned. Add mirin; bring to a boil. Reduce heat, and simmer, uncovered, 5 minutes or until liquid is absorbed.
2. Place onion mixture, beans, and remaining 3 ingredients in a blender or food processor; process 1 minute or until smooth, scraping sides of bowl occasionally. Cover and chill at least 2 hours (mixture will thicken as it chills). YIELD: 12 servings (serving size: 2 tablespoons).

POINTS value: 1; **Exchanges:** ½ Starch, ½ Fat;
Per serving: CAL 64 (40% from fat); PRO 4.0g;
FAT 2.9g (sat 1.9g); CARB 5.8g; FIB 2.0g;
CHOL 6mg; IRON 0.8mg; SOD 187mg; CALC 31mg

KALAMATA-HERB CREAM CHEESE

prep: 7 minutes

Try this creamy olive spread on cucumber slices, fat-free crackers, or thin, toasted French bread slices.

1   (8-ounce) package ⅓-less-fat cream cheese, softened
½   cup finely chopped pitted kalamata olives (about 16)
¼   cup finely chopped fresh parsley
2   teaspoons minced fresh basil
1   teaspoon minced fresh oregano
1   small garlic clove, minced

1. Combine all ingredients in a bowl, stirring until blended. Cover and chill until ready to serve. YIELD: 10 servings (serving size: 2 tablespoons).

POINTS value: 2; **Exchanges:** 1 ½ Fat;
Per serving: CAL 75 (78% from fat); PRO 2.6g;
FAT 6.5g (sat 0.2g); CARB 1.6g; FIB 0.1g;
CHOL 16mg; IRON 0.1mg; SOD 299mg;
CALC 22mg

SPINACH AND SUNDRIED TOMATO CHEESE DIP

prep: 6 minutes • cook: 14 minutes

*Using a cheese sauce packet intensifies the cheese flavor without increasing the **POINTS** value.*

4   cups baby spinach
1   tablespoon light butter
½   cup chopped green onions
1   garlic clove, minced
1½   cups fat-free milk
1   (1.3-ounce) package creamy Cheddar pasta sauce mix (such as Knorr)
4   ounces light processed cheese, cubed (such as Velveeta Light)
¼   cup ready-to-use julienne-cut sun-dried tomatoes, chopped (such as Mariani)
⅛   teaspoon ground red pepper

1. Microwave spinach in a large glass bowl at HIGH 2 minutes or until spinach wilts. Drain and pat dry with paper towels; coarsely chop.
2. Melt butter in a large saucepan over medium heat. Add onions and garlic; sauté 2 minutes. Gradually add milk and cheese sauce mix, stirring well with a whisk. Bring to a boil; reduce heat, and simmer 3 minutes, stirring constantly. Add cubed cheese, tomatoes, and ground red pepper; cook 3 minutes or until cheese melts, stirring constantly. Remove from heat. Stir in spinach. Serve warm. YIELD: 12 servings (serving size: ¼ cup).

POINTS value: 1; **Exchange:** ½ High-Fat Meat;
Per serving: CAL 55 (34% from fat); PRO 3.9g;
FAT 21g (sat 1.3g); CARB 5.4g; FIB 0.5g;
CHOL 7mg; IRON 0.3mg; SOD 355mg;
CALC 111mg

CRANBERRY-SPICED PEPPER JELLY

prep: 6 minutes • cook: 4 minutes

This flavorful and versatile jelly can be paired with cream cheese, apple and pear slices, gingersnaps, or water crackers for a quick appetizer, or used as an accompaniment to turkey, chicken, or pork.

½   cup raspberry fruit spread
¼   cup dried cranberries, chopped (such as Craisins)
1   teaspoon grated orange rind
1   tablespoon fresh orange juice
¼   teaspoon ground cinnamon
⅛   teaspoon ground cloves
⅛   teaspoon crushed red pepper

1. Combine all ingredients in a small saucepan. Place over medium heat, and cook 4 minutes or until fruit spread melts, stirring often. Remove from heat; cool completely. **YIELD:** 8 servings (serving size: 1 tablespoon).

POINTS value: 2; Exchanges: 1 Starch, ½ Fruit; Per serving: CAL 109 (1% from fat); PRO 0.1g; FAT 0.1g (sat 0.0g); CARB 27.1g; FIB 0.7g; CHOL 0mg; IRON 0.1mg; SOD 0mg; CALC 3mg

CHIVE-PARMESAN POTATO CHIPS

(pictured on page 135)
prep: 9 minutes • cook: 18 minutes

Use a mandoline slicer to slice the potatoes thin enough to be "chips." Find mandoline slicers at Asian markets, specialty shops, and kitchen stores. We love these chips as a crispy side option for sandwiches.

1   (12-ounce) baking potato
1   tablespoon olive oil
3   tablespoons grated fresh Parmesan cheese
3   tablespoons minced fresh chives
¾   teaspoon salt
Cooking spray

1. Preheat oven to 400°.
2. Scrub potato with a brush. Cut potato lengthwise into very thin slices using a mandoline slicer.
3. Combine potato slices and oil in a large bowl. Add cheese, chives, and salt, and toss gently to coat.
4. Arrange potato slices in a single layer on baking sheets coated with cooking spray. Bake at 400° for 18 to 20 minutes or until golden. **YIELD:** 7 servings (serving size: 9 to 10 chips).
Note: Chips will brown at different rates. Watch chips carefully, and quickly remove individual chips from the oven as they become golden.

POINTS value: 1; Exchanges: ½ Starch, ½ Fat; Per serving: CAL 70 (33% from fat); PRO 1.8g; FAT 2.6g (sat 0.7g); CARB 10.1g; FIB 1.0g; CHOL 2mg; IRON 0.6mg; SOD 294mg; CALC 35mg

SALT AND VINEGAR PITA CHIPS

prep: 10 minutes • cook: 11 minutes

We prefer the mild flavor of malt vinegar as well as the coarse texture of kosher salt in this recipe. If you don't have kosher salt, substitute ½ teaspoon of table salt.

1   (6-ounce) package pita rounds
⅓   cup malt vinegar
1   teaspoon kosher salt

1. Preheat oven to 400°.
2. Split each pita half horizontally and cut each into 6 wedges. Place wedges, cut sides up, on an ungreased baking sheet. Brush vinegar evenly over wedges; sprinkle with kosher salt. Bake at 400° for 11 to 12 minutes or until crisp. **YIELD:** 8 servings (serving size: 9 chips).

POINTS value: 1; Exchange: ½ Starch; Per serving: CAL 62 (4% from fat); PRO 1.9g; FAT 0.3g (sat 0.0g); CARB 12.8g; FIB 0.5g; CHOL 0mg; IRON 0.6mg; SOD 352mg; CALC 19mg

KOSHER SALT

Large-grained kosher salt has long been a favorite of gourmet chefs because of its clean, pure flavor and it's becoming more popular for traditional home cooking, too. Substitute kosher salt for table salt by doubling the amount of table salt called for in a recipe.

CHARRED TOMATO BRUSCHETTA

prep: **7** minutes • cook: **21** minutes

8   plum tomatoes (about
    1¼ pounds)
Cooking spray
1½ tablespoons olive oil, divided
¼   teaspoon salt
2   tablespoons julienne-cut fresh
    basil
1   teaspoon red wine vinegar
20 (½-inch-thick) diagonally cut
    slices French bread
3   garlic cloves, halved
½   cup (2 ounces) shaved fresh
    Parmesan cheese,

1. Preheat broiler.
2. Slice tomatoes crosswise into ¼-inch-thick rounds. Place tomato on a foil-lined baking sheet coated with cooking spray. Brush tomato with 1 tablespoon oil; sprinkle with salt. Broil 19 minutes or until tomato begins to char. Place tomato in a bowl; toss with basil and vinegar, breaking up tomato slightly with a spoon (mixture should be chunky).
3. Place bread slices on a baking sheet. Brush 1 side of bread slices with 1½ teaspoons oil. Broil 1 to 2 minutes on each side or until lightly toasted. Remove from oven and rub oiled side of slices with garlic halves.
4. Spoon tomato mixture on prepared side of bread slices and top with curls of shaved Parmesan cheese. Serve immediately. YIELD: 20 servings (serving size: 1 bruschetta).

POINTS value: 1; **Exchanges:** ½ Starch, ½ Vegetable;
Per serving: CAL 52 (37% from fat); PRO 2.2g;
FAT 2.2g (sat 0.7g); CARB 6.2g; FIB 0.7g;
CHOL 2mg; IRON 0.5mg; SOD 132mg; CALC 51mg

ROASTED RED PEPPER AND ESCAROLE CROSTINI

prep: **15** minutes • cook: **14** minutes

This festive Sicilian-style topping livens up the earthy flavor of escarole with sweet raisins and savory olives and capers. The red pepper flakes add an appealing spark of heat.

24 (½-inch-thick) slices French
    bread
4   teaspoons olive oil, divided
1   pound escarole, coarsely
    chopped
18 small oil-cured ripe olives,
    pitted and coarsely chopped
½   cup sliced bottled roasted red
    bell peppers
⅓   cup golden raisins
3   large garlic cloves, minced
3   tablespoons capers
¼   teaspoon crushed red pepper

1. Preheat oven to 375°.
2. Brush 1 side of bread slices with 3 teaspoons oil; place on a baking sheet and bake at 375° for 10 minutes or until lightly toasted.
3. Heat 1 teaspoon oil in a large nonstick skillet. Add escarole, and cook 2 to 3 minutes or until escarole wilts. Add olives and next 5 ingredients; sauté 2 minutes. Drain escarole mixture.
4. Top each bread slice with about 2 tablespoons escarole mixture. Serve immediately. YIELD: 24 servings (serving size: 1 crostino).

POINTS value: 1; **Exchanges:** ½ Starch, ½ Fat;
Per serving: CAL 54 (32% from fat); PRO 1.2g;
FAT 2.1g (sat 0.4g); CARB 8.7g; FIB 1.4g;
CHOL 0mg; IRON 0.5mg; SOD 162mg; CALC 20mg

STUFFED NEW POTATOES

prep: **21** minutes • cook: **7** minutes

4   small new potatoes (about
    4 ounces each)
¼   cup evaporated fat-free milk
2   teaspoons light butter
1   large green onion, thinly
    sliced
½   teaspoon salt
⅛   teaspoon black pepper
⅛   teaspoon garlic powder
½   cup (2 ounces) shredded
    reduced-fat sharp Cheddar
    cheese

1. Pierce potatoes with a fork; arrange in a circle on paper towels in a microwave oven. Microwave at HIGH 6 minutes or until done; cool slightly. Cut each potato in half lengthwise; scoop out pulp, leaving a ¼-inch-thick shell. Transfer pulp to a medium bowl.
2. Preheat broiler.
3. Add milk and butter to potatoes; beat with a mixer at medium speed until well blended. Add onion and next 3 ingredients, beating well. Arrange shells on a baking sheet and spoon potato mixture evenly into shells. Sprinkle evenly with cheese; broil 1 to 2 minutes or until cheese melts. YIELD: 8 servings (serving size: 1 potato half).

POINTS value: 2; **Exchange:** 1 Starch;
Per serving: CAL 88 (22% from fat); PRO 3.7g;
FAT 2.1g (sat 1.4g); CARB 13.1g; FIB 1.3g;
CHOL 7mg; IRON 0.4mg; SOD 227mg; CALC 82mg

PICADILLO EMPANADAS

(pictured on page 22)
prep: 48 minutes • cook: 21 minutes

Our empanada recipe uses refrigerated pie dough rather than the traditional homemade pastry. Be sure to let the pie dough come to room temperature before rolling to ⅛-inch thickness.

1   teaspoon olive oil
½   (12-ounce) package burger-style recipe crumbles
¼   cup chopped onion
¼   cup chopped green bell pepper
1   garlic clove, minced
2   tablespoons golden raisins
2   tablespoons chopped pimiento-stuffed olives
1   tablespoon chopped sliced almonds, toasted
1   tablespoon fresh lime juice
¼   teaspoon ground cinnamon
¼   teaspoon ground cumin
⅛   teaspoon ground allspice
½   jalapeño pepper, seeded and minced
2   (15-ounce) packages refrigerated pie dough (such as Pillsbury)
Cooking spray

1. Preheat oven to 425°.
2. Heat oil in a large nonstick skillet over medium heat. Add crumbles and next 3 ingredients. Cook 3 to 4 minutes, stirring often. Add raisins and next 7 ingredients; cook 3 minutes.
3. Roll each crust to ⅛-inch thickness. Cut 9 circles out of each crust, using a 4-inch cookie cutter. Spoon 1 heaping tablespoonful mixture into center of each circle. Moisten edges of dough with water. Fold over and press edges of dough with a fork to seal. Place on a baking sheet coated with cooking spray. Lightly coat tops of empanadas with cooking spray.
4. Bake at 425° for 14 minutes or until lightly browned. Serve with chutney, salsa, or sour cream. YIELD: 36 servings (serving size: 1 empanada).

POINTS value: 3; **Exchanges:** 1 Starch, 1 Fat; **Per serving:** CAL 120 (52% from fat); PRO 1.9g; FAT 7.0g (sat 2.8g); CARB 12.4g; FIB 0.3g; CHOL 4mg; IRON 0.3mg; SOD 112mg; CALC 5mg

HOW TO MAKE EMPANADAS

1. Allow pastry to come to room temperature. If the pastry separates, press back together with your fingers. Roll each pastry to ⅛-inch thickness.

2. Cut 9 circles out of each crust, using a 4-inch cookie cutter. If you prefer, use a smaller cookie cutter. Just remember to decrease the amount of filling that you spoon onto each pastry.

3. Spoon 1 heaping tablespoon of picadillo mixture into center of each circle. We used a measuring tablespoon rather than tableware to get a more accurate measurement on the filling.

4. Moisten edges of dough using a finger dipped in warm water. Moistening the dough help the dough stick together so the filling doesn't seep out during cooking. Fold over and press edges of dough with a fork to seal.

An empanada (em-pah-NAH-dah) is a turnover or half-moon-shaped pastry. Roughly translated from Spanish, the word means "to bake in pastry" or "that which is covered in bread." Traditionally, empanadas are single-serving pastries filled with savory meat or vegetable fillings. They can be cut small for an appetizer size portion or larger for individual main dish servings. They are similar to today's calzones, pierogis, or the commercial product, "Hot Pockets."

ROASTED CORN AND CHICKEN QUESADILLAS

prep: 30 minutes • cook: 21 minutes

Queso Asadero is a mild white Mexican cheese. Monterey Jack cheese is a good substitute.

2 teaspoons olive oil, divided
½ cup fresh corn kernels or frozen whole-kernel corn, thawed
¼ teaspoon crushed red pepper
¼ cup finely chopped red bell pepper
1 cup shredded cooked chicken breast
¼ cup thinly sliced green onions
1½ tablespoons chopped fresh oregano
1½ tablespoons chopped fresh cilantro
¼ teaspoon salt
8 (6-inch) corn tortillas
¾ cup (3 ounces) shredded Queso Asadero or Monterey Jack cheese

1. Heat 1 teaspoon oil in a large nonstick skillet over medium-high heat. Stir in corn and crushed red pepper. Sauté 2 to 3 minutes or until corn is lightly browned. Add bell pepper; sauté 2 minutes. Stir in chicken and green onions; sauté 1 minute. Remove mixture from heat; stir in oregano, cilantro, and salt. Wipe pan dry with a paper towel.
2. Sprinkle each of 4 tortillas with 1½ tablespoons cheese, and top evenly with chicken mixture. Sprinkle remaining cheese evenly over chicken mixture, and top with remaining 4 tortillas.

3. Place pan over medium heat and add ¼ teaspoon oil. Carefully add 1 quesadilla, and cook 2 to 3 minutes on each side or until lightly browned. Repeat procedure with remaining oil and quesadillas. Cut each quesadilla into 4 wedges. Serve immediately. YIELD: 8 servings (serving size: 2 wedges).

POINTS value: 1; **Exchanges:** ½ Starch, ½ Fat; **Per serving:** CAL 66 (38% from fat); PRO 4.8g; FAT 2.8g (sat 1.2g); CARB 6.1g; FIB 0.7g; CHOL 12mg; IRON 0.2mg; SOD 75mg; CALC 49mg

HOW TO CUT CORN KERNELS FROM THE COB

Place the ear of corn at an angle in a large bowl. Rest the tip of the ear on the bottom of the bowl; hold the side of the ear against the top edge of the bowl. With a sharp knife, cut the corn kernels from the cob using a smooth, continuous, downward motion. Turn the cob a quarter turn; cut the kernels from the cob. Continue to turn the cob and to cut the kernels until all the corn is removed from the cob. The kernels will fall to the bottom of the bowl.

CHICKEN TENDERS SATAY WITH PEANUT DIPPING SAUCES

(pictured on page 2)
prep: 8 minutes • cook: 8 minutes
other: 2 hours

This recipe offers two dipping sauces. Red Curry Peanut Sauce has a more authentic Thai flavor. Peanut Dipping Sauce is a bit milder.

1 tablespoon sugar
2 tablespoons low-sodium soy sauce
1 tablespoon fresh lemon juice
1 tablespoon fish sauce
1 teaspoon ground coriander
1 teaspoon ground cumin
2 garlic cloves, minced
1 pound chicken tenders
Cooking spray

1. Combine sugar and next 6 ingredients in a large heavy-duty zip-top plastic bag. Cut chicken tenders in half lengthwise; add to plastic bag. Seal and marinate in refrigerator 2 hours.
2. Prepare grill.
3. Remove chicken from bag; discard marinade. Thread chicken onto 10 (6-inch) skewers. Place kabobs on grill rack coated with cooking spray; grill 4 minutes on each side or until done. Serve with Red Curry Peanut Sauce or Peanut Dipping Sauce. YIELD: 8 servings (serving size: 2 kabobs).
Note: If using wooden skewers, soak them in water 30 minutes before grilling.

(Total does *not* include dipping sauces)
POINTS value: 2; **Exchanges:** 2 Very Lean Meat; **Per serving:** CAL 75 (10% from fat); PRO 13.6g; FAT 0.8g (sat 0.2g); CARB 2.6g; FIB 0.3g; CHOL 33mg; IRON 0.6mg; SOD 345mg; CALC 13mg

RED CURRY PEANUT SAUCE

½   cup light coconut milk
1   tablespoon natural-style peanut butter (such as Smucker's)
1½   teaspoons sugar
1½   teaspoons fresh lemon juice
1½   teaspoons fish sauce
¼   teaspoon red curry paste

1. Combine all ingredients in a small saucepan over medium heat, whisking to combine. Bring to a boil; reduce heat, and simmer 1 to 2 minutes or until slightly thick. Cool to room temperature. YIELD: 8 servings (serving size: 1 tablespoon).

POINTS value: 1; **Exchange:** ½ Fat;
Per serving: CAL 24 (62% from fat); PRO 0.5g; FAT 1.7g (sat 0.6g); CARB 1.9g; FIB 0.1g; CHOL 0mg; IRON 0.1mg; SOD 100mg; CALC 2mg

PEANUT DIPPING SAUCE

¼   cup fat-free milk
¼   cup creamy peanut butter
2   teaspoons soy sauce
¼   teaspoon crushed red pepper
¼   teaspoon minced peeled fresh ginger
1   garlic clove, minced (about ½ teaspoon)

1. Combine all ingredients in a small bowl, whisking until smooth. YIELD: 8 servings (serving size: 1 tablespoon).

POINTS value: 1; **Exchange:** 1 Fat;
Per serving: CAL 52 (67% from fat); PRO 2.4g; FAT 4.1g (sat 0.8g); CARB 2.2g; FIB 0.5g; CHOL 0mg; IRON 0.2mg; SOD 86mg; CALC 13mg

TRIPLE CHOCOLATE MOCHA LATTE

prep: 5 minutes

The chocolate whipped cream gives this hot mocha-flavored drink a creamy texture—you'll never believe that it's a light recipe.

1   (0.52-ounce) envelope no sugar added hot cocoa mix (such as Nestlé)
¾   cup hot brewed coffee
¼   cup hot fat-free milk
¼   cup canned refrigerated chocolate-flavored light whipped cream (such as Redi-Whip)
½   teaspoon unsweetened cocoa

1. Empty contents of cocoa mix envelope into a large coffee mug; pour hot coffee and milk over top, stirring until cocoa is dissolved. Stir in whipped cream until melted and combined. Sprinkle with cocoa. Serve immediately. YIELD: 1 serving (serving size: 1 cup).

POINTS value: 2; **Exchanges:** 1 Starch, ½ Fat;
Per serving: CAL 101 (22% from fat); PRO 6.7g; FAT 2.7g (sat 1.3g); CARB 14.5g; FIB 1.0g; CHOL 14mg; IRON 0.6mg; SOD 175mg; CALC 201mg

ORANGE-FLAVORED HOT CHOCOLATE

prep: 5 minutes • cook: 5 minutes
other: 20 minutes

This beverage is perfect to serve on a winter evening or after a brisk walk in the cold winter air.

2   large navel oranges
4   cups 1% low-fat milk
¾   cup sweet ground chocolate and cocoa (such as Ghirardelli)
6   tablespoons frozen fat-free whipped topping, thawed
Orange curls (optional)

1. Carefully remove rind from oranges using a vegetable peeler, making sure not to get any of the white pithy part of the rind. Combine orange rind and milk in a large saucepan, reserving orange pulp for another use. Bring milk mixture to a simmer over medium-high heat, stirring constantly. Remove from heat; cover and let stand 20 minutes.
2. Strain milk mixture through a sieve into a bowl, discarding orange rind. Return milk to pan. Stir in chocolate. Bring to a simmer over medium-high heat, stirring constantly. Pour into 6 mugs; top each serving with whipped topping. Garnish with orange curls, if desired. Serve immediately. YIELD: 6 servings (serving size: ¾ cup hot chocolate and 1 tablespoon whipped topping).

POINTS value: 3; **Exchanges:** ½ Starch, ½ Fruit, 1 Skim Milk; **Per serving:** CAL 166 (15% from fat); PRO 7.3g; FAT 2.9g (sat 1.8g); CARB 30.8g; FIB 1.9g; CHOL 10mg; IRON 0.6mg; SOD 114mg; CALC 219mg

BANANA BREAKFAST SMOOTHIE

prep: 5 minutes • cook: 30 minutes
other: 8 hours

*Roast the bananas ahead of time
and store in a zip-top bag in the
freezer. Roasted ripe bananas, wheat
germ, walnuts, and bakery spices
give this smoothie the look and
flavor of speckled banana bread.
If you don't have time to roast
and freeze bananas, simply use
very ripe bananas.*

2   ripe bananas, unpeeled
¾   cup fat-free milk
½   cup plain fat-free yogurt
2   tablespoons toasted wheat
     germ
1   tablespoon chopped walnuts
3   tablespoons honey
¼   teaspoon ground cinnamon
⅛   teaspoon ground nutmeg

1. Preheat oven to 350°.
2. Place bananas on a baking sheet.
Bake at 350° for 30 minutes; cool
and peel. Place banana in a heavy-
duty zip-top plastic bag. Freeze at
least 8 hours.
3. Place frozen banana, milk, and
remaining ingredients in a blender;
process until smooth. Serve immediately. YIELD: 3 servings (serving size:
1 cup).

POINTS value: 4; **Exchanges:** 1½ Starch, 1½ Fruit;
Per serving: CAL 216 (11% from fat); PRO 7.1g;
FAT 2.7g (sat 0.5g); CARB 44.9g; FIB 2.8g;
CHOL 2mg; IRON 0.9mg; SOD 65mg; CALC 169mg

MELON AGUA FRESCA

prep: 7 minutes • other: 2 hours

*This Mexican-style fruit drink is
typically made with water and a
blend of different whole fruits. Here
we've skipped the water and opted
for an all-fruit version that is a perfect
thirst quencher for a hot summer
day. In order to get the amount of
watermelon needed for this recipe,
you need to purchase about a
3-pound watermelon.*

5½   cups cubed seeded
     watermelon
3   tablespoons fresh lime juice
2   tablespoons frozen limeade
     concentrate, thawed
2   tablespoons fresh orange juice
Lime slices (optional)

1. Combine first 4 ingredients in a
blender or food processor; process
until smooth. Strain watermelon
mixture through a sieve into a
pitcher; discard pulp. Cover and chill
2 hours or until ready to serve. Pour
melon mixture into chilled glasses.
Garnish with lime slices, if desired.
YIELD: 3 servings (serving size: 1 cup).

POINTS value: 2; **Exchanges:** 1 Starch, 1 Fruit;
Per serving: CAL 121 (9% from fat); PRO 1.9g;
FAT 1.3g (sat 0.1g); CARB 28.5g; FIB 1.5g;
CHOL 0mg; IRON 0.5mg; SOD 6mg; CALC 25mg

STRAWBERRY CHILLER

(pictured on opposite page)
prep: 4 minutes

*This recipe can also be prepared
by equally replacing the sugar
with a non-calorie, measures-like-sugar
sweetener (such as Splenda) for a treat
with a **POINTS** value of zero. Save
leftover Strawberry Chiller in the
freezer and pulse quickly in a
blender before serving.*

1   (16-ounce) package frozen
     unsweetened whole
     strawberries, partially thawed
1   (12-ounce) can diet ginger ale
⅓   cup sugar
¼   cup fresh lime juice
2   cups crushed ice

1. Combine first 4 ingredients in a
blender. Process until smooth. Add
ice; process until smooth. Serve
immediately. YIELD: 9 servings (serving
size: about ¾ cup).

POINTS value: 1; **Exchange:** ½ Starch;
Per serving: CAL 48 (1% from fat); PRO 0.3g;
FAT 0.1g (sat 0.0g); CARB 12.5g; FIB 1.2g;
CHOL 0mg; IRON 0.4mg; SOD 7mg; CALC 9mg

Strawberry
Chiller,
opposite page

Picadillo
Empanadas,
page 17

Rosemary and Kalamata
Focaccia, page 28

Overnight Caramel-Pecan
Bread,
page 28

Cornmeal Pancakes,
page 27

Breads

BUTTERY HERB BREAD

prep: 8 minutes • cook: 2 minutes

2 tablespoons yogurt-based spread (such as Brummel & Brown)
2 garlic cloves, minced
1 tablespoon chopped fresh basil
1 tablespoon chopped fresh oregano
8 (½-inch-thick) slices diagonally cut French bread
2 tablespoons shredded fresh Parmesan cheese

1. Preheat broiler.
2. Combine yogurt-based spread and next 3 ingredients in a small bowl. Spread garlic mixture evenly over each bread slice.
3. Place bread slices on a baking sheet; broil 2 minutes or until edges begin to brown. Sprinkle with cheese. Serve immediately. YIELD: 8 servings (serving size: 1 slice).

POINTS value: 1; **Exchanges:** ½ Starch, ½ Fat; **Per serving:** CAL 57 (32% from fat); PRO 1.8g; FAT 2.0g (sat 0.6g); CARB 7.7g; FIB 0.5g; CHOL 1mg; IRON 0.4mg; SOD 130mg; CALC 30mg

DIJON-CRACKED PEPPER DROP BISCUITS

prep: 2 minutes • cook: 11 minutes

Drizzling extravirgin olive oil on these savory biscuits after baking provides for an extra boost of flavor.

1 cup low-fat baking mix
½ cup low-fat buttermilk (1%)
2 teaspoons Dijon mustard
½ teaspoon cracked black pepper
Cooking spray
1 tablespoon extravirgin olive oil

1. Preheat oven to 450°.
2. Combine first 4 ingredients in a small bowl, stirring just until moist. Drop dough evenly into 6 mounds on a baking sheet coated with cooking spray.
3. Bake at 450° for 11 minutes or until lightly browned. Drizzle extravirgin olive oil evenly over biscuits. Serve immediately. YIELD: 6 servings (serving size: 1 biscuit and ½ teaspoon extravirgin olive oil).

POINTS value: 2; **Exchanges:** 1 Starch, ½ Fat; **Per serving:** CAL 106 (33% from fat); PRO 2.3g; FAT 3.9g (sat 0.7g); CARB 15.4g; FIB 0.3g; CHOL 1mg; IRON 0.8mg; SOD 296mg; CALC 47mg

TOASTED COCONUT BANANA MUFFINS

prep: 15 minutes • cook: 20 minutes

1½ cups all-purpose flour
1 cup uncooked quick-cooking oats
⅔ cup packed dark brown sugar
2 teaspoons baking powder
½ teaspoon salt
½ teaspoon ground cinnamon
¼ teaspoon baking soda
¼ teaspoon ground nutmeg
1 cup mashed ripe banana (about 2 medium)
½ cup low-fat buttermilk (1%)
2 tablespoons vegetable oil
1½ teaspoons vanilla extract
1 large egg, lightly beaten
Cooking spray
½ cup flaked sweetened coconut

1. Preheat oven to 400°.
2. Lightly spoon flour into dry measuring cups; level with a knife. Combine flour, oats, and next 6 ingredients in a large bowl; stir well with a whisk.
3. Combine banana and next 4 ingredients in a medium bowl, and stir well with a whisk. Add to flour mixture, stirring just until moist.
4. Spoon batter into 12 muffin cups coated with cooking spray; sprinkle evenly with coconut.
5. Bake at 400° for 20 minutes or until golden brown.
6. Remove muffins from pan immediately; cool on a wire rack. YIELD: 12 servings (serving size: 1 muffin).

POINTS value: 4; **Exchanges:** 2 Starch; **Per serving:** CAL 188 (21% from fat); PRO 3.4g; FAT 4.5g (sat 1.6g); CARB 34.5g; FIB 1.8g; CHOL 18mg; IRON 1.6mg; SOD 237mg; CALC 65mg

---

EXTRAVIRGIN OLIVE OIL: IT'S WELL WORTH THE PRICE

The finest of the olive oils, extravirgin olive oil has the lowest acidity and is considered the fruitiest and most flavorful. The oil is extracted from whole, unblemished olives that are cold-pressed within a day after harvest. The end result is a flavorful, high-quality olive oil. Extravirgin olive oil usually costs more than the other types, but is well worth the price. When purchasing olive oil, remember that the darker the oil, the more aromatic and the richer the flavor. Store extravirgin olive oil in a cool, dark place for up to six months.

ROSEMARY POPOVERS WITH LEMON BUTTER

prep: 10 minutes • cook: 35 minutes

Popovers are different from your average breads because they do not use baking powder, baking soda, or yeast to make them rise. Steam causes them to "pop over" the sides of the muffin tin.

3   tablespoons light butter, softened
½   teaspoon grated lemon rind
1   cup all-purpose flour
1   cup fat-free milk
½   cup egg substitute
½   teaspoon salt
½   teaspoon minced fresh rosemary
Cooking spray

1. Preheat oven to 450°.
2. Combine butter and lemon rind in a small bowl; set aside.
3. Place a 12-cup muffin pan in oven for 3 minutes.
4. While pan heats, lightly spoon flour into a dry measuring cup; level with a knife. Process flour and next 4 ingredients in a blender 1 minute.
5. Remove pan from oven; coat with cooking spray. Pour batter evenly into cups, filling about half full.
6. Bake at 450° for 15 minutes. Reduce oven temperature to 350°, and bake 20 minutes or until puffed and brown. Serve immediately with lemon butter. YIELD: 12 servings (serving size: 1 popover and ¾ teaspoon lemon butter).

POINTS value: 1; **Exchanges:** ½ Starch, ½ Fat; **Per serving:** CAL 62 (23% from fat); PRO 3.0g; FAT 1.6g (sat 1.0g); CARB 9.2g; FIB 0.3g; CHOL 5mg; IRON 0.8mg; SOD 146mg; CALC 24mg

GLAZED APRICOT SCONES

prep: 15 minutes • cook: 20 minutes

A sweet glaze and toasted almonds make these tender scones the perfect complement to a hot cup of coffee.

2   cups all-purpose flour
2   tablespoons granulated sugar
2½   teaspoons baking powder
¼   teaspoon salt
3½   tablespoons chilled butter, cut into small pieces
⅓   cup dried apricots, minced
½   cup 1% low-fat milk
1   large egg, lightly beaten
2   tablespoons honey
Cooking spray
½   cup powdered sugar
2   teaspoons 1% low-fat milk
1   tablespoon sliced almonds, toasted

1. Preheat oven to 375°.
2. Lightly spoon flour into dry measuring cups; level with a knife. Combine flour and next 3 ingredients in a large bowl. Cut in butter with a pastry blender or 2 knives until mixture resembles coarse meal. Stir in apricots.
3. Combine ½ cup milk, egg, and honey in a small bowl. Add to flour mixture, stirring just until moist.
4. Turn dough out onto a lightly floured surface; knead lightly 4 to 5 times with floured hands. Pat dough into a 7-inch circle on a baking sheet coated with cooking spray. Cut dough into 10 wedges, cutting into, but not through, dough.
5. Bake at 375° for 20 minutes or until lightly browned. Remove to a wire rack; cool 10 minutes. Combine powdered sugar and 2 teaspoons milk, stirring until smooth. Drizzle over warm scones and sprinkle with almonds. YIELD: 10 servings (serving size: 1 scone).

POINTS value: 4; **Exchanges:** 2 Starch, 1 Fat; **Per serving:** CAL 203 (23% from fat); PRO 4.0g; FAT 5.2g (sat 2.3g); CARB 35.5g; FIB 1.0g; CHOL 32mg; IRON 1.6mg; SOD 224mg; CALC 96mg

CORNMEAL PANCAKES

(pictured on page 24)
prep: 6 minutes • cook: 15 minutes

1   cup all-purpose flour
⅓   cup yellow cornmeal
1   tablespoon sugar
1½   teaspoons baking powder
¼   teaspoon baking soda
¼   teaspoon salt
1   large egg, lightly beaten
1   cup 1% low-fat milk
1   tablespoon molasses
1   tablespoon butter, melted
Cooking spray

1. Lightly spoon flour into a dry measuring cup; level with a knife. Combine flour and next 5 ingredients in a large bowl; stir with a whisk. Combine egg and next 3 ingredients in a bowl. Add egg mixture to flour mixture, stirring until well blended.
2. Spoon ¼ cup batter for each pancake onto a hot nonstick griddle or nonstick skillet coated with cooking spray. Turn pancakes when tops are covered in bubbles and edges look cooked. YIELD: 10 servings (serving size: 1 pancake).

POINTS value: 2; **Exchanges:** 1 Starch, ½ Fat; **Per serving:** CAL 99 (19% from fat); PRO 2.8g; FAT 2.0g (sat 0.9g); CARB 17.1g; FIB 0.7g; CHOL 24mg; IRON 0.8mg; SOD 173mg; CALC 75mg

...ET CORN ...ONBREAD

...es • cook: 45 minutes

2½   cups fat-free milk
1   cup yellow cornmeal
¾   teaspoon salt
¾   cup low-fat buttermilk (1%)
¼   cup pure maple syrup
2   large eggs, lightly beaten
2   large egg whites, lightly
      beaten
1   cup frozen whole-kernel
      corn, thawed
Butter-flavored cooking spray

1. Preheat oven to 400°.
2. Bring milk to a simmer in a medium saucepan over medium heat, stirring frequently with a whisk. Gradually whisk in cornmeal and salt. Simmer 3 minutes or until mixture thickens, stirring frequently with a whisk. Remove from heat. Combine buttermilk and next 3 ingredients; add to cornmeal mixture, stirring until well blended. Stir in corn.
3. Coat a 2-quart baking dish with cooking spray. Pour batter into dish.
4. Bake at 400° for 40 minutes or until puffed and golden, and a wooden pick inserted in center comes out clean. Serve warm. YIELD: 8 servings (serving size: about ⅔ cup).

POINTS value: 3; **Exchanges:** 2 Starch;
Per serving: CAL 167 (11% from fat); PRO 8.0g; FAT 2.1g (sat 0.7g); CARB 29.6g; FIB 1.8g; CHOL 56mg; IRON 1.1mg; SOD 317mg; CALC 133mg

ROSEMARY AND KALAMATA FOCACCIA

(pictured on page 23)
prep: 20 minutes • cook: 13 minutes
other: 40 minutes

Olive oil-flavored cooking spray
1   tablespoon yellow cornmeal
1   (1-pound) loaf frozen white
      bread dough, thawed
1   tablespoon olive oil
½   cup chopped pitted kalamata
      olives
2   tablespoons chopped fresh
      rosemary
1   tablespoon minced garlic
1   teaspoon sea or kosher salt
¾   teaspoon freshly ground black
      pepper

1. Coat a jelly roll pan with cooking spray and sprinkle with cornmeal.
2. Roll dough to a 15 x 10-inch rectangle. Place on prepared pan, pressing to edges with fingers. Drizzle olive oil over dough, spreading evenly with fingers; sprinkle with olives and next 4 ingredients. Cover and let rise in a warm place (85°) for 40 minutes.
3. Preheat oven to 400°.
4. Uncover dough. Make indentations in top of dough using the handle of a wooden spoon or your fingertips.
5. Bake at 400° for 13 to 14 minutes or until brown and crusty. Cut into squares and serve immediately. YIELD: 12 servings (serving size: 1 square).

POINTS value: 2; **Exchanges:** 1½ Starch;
Per serving: CAL 126 (24% from fat); PRO 4.1g; FAT 3.5g (sat 0.2g); CARB 20.8g; FIB 1.5g; CHOL 0mg; IRON 1.7mg; SOD 416mg; CALC 17mg

OVERNIGHT CARAMEL-PECAN BREAD

(pictured on page 23)
prep: 7 minutes • cook: 32 minutes
other: 8 hours and 5 minutes

Prepare these gooey caramel rolls before bed and wake up to a no-stress, no-fuss morning. Our Test Kitchens staff could not believe these rolls were light and awarded this recipe the highest possible rating.

⅓   cup chopped pecans
Cooking spray
1   (25-ounce) package frozen
      yeast rolls
¼   cup sugar-free vanilla instant
      pudding mix
1   cup packed light brown sugar
⅓   cup light butter, melted

1. Sprinkle pecans evenly in bottom of a 10-inch Bundt pan coated with cooking spray. Place rolls evenly in pan, overlapping when necessary. Sprinkle rolls with pudding mix; sprinkle with brown sugar, and drizzle evenly with butter. Cover pan with a damp towel, and place in a cold oven 8 hours.
2. Remove pan from oven.
3. Preheat oven to 350°.
4. Uncover rolls and bake at 350° for 32 to 35 minutes or until rolls are browned. Remove from oven and let stand 5 minutes. Invert rolls onto a serving platter. Serve immediately. YIELD: 24 servings (serving size: 1 roll).

POINTS value: 3; **Exchanges:** 1½ Starch, 1 Fat;
Per serving: CAL 153 (25% from fat); PRO 2.9g; FAT 4.5g (sat 1.5g); CARB 26.8g; FIB 1.2g; CHOL 5mg; IRON 1.1mg; SOD 295mg; CALC 29mg

BASIC WHITE BREAD

prep: 13 minutes • cook: 32 minutes
other: 1 hour and 20 minutes

Once you master this basic bread recipe, you can add seasonings, herbs, and even fruits to each loaf.

1   package dry yeast (about 2¼ teaspoons)
1   tablespoon sugar
1   cup warm water (100° to 110°)
2¾   cups all-purpose flour
1   tablespoon vegetable oil
1   teaspoon salt
Cooking spray

1. Dissolve yeast and sugar in warm water in a small bowl; let stand 5 minutes. Lightly spoon flour into dry measuring cups; level with a knife. Combine yeast mixture, flour, oil, and salt in a large bowl; stir until a soft dough forms.

2. Turn dough out onto a lightly floured surface and knead until smooth and elastic. Place dough in a large bowl coated with cooking spray, turning to coat top. Cover and let rise in a warm place (85°), free from drafts, 45 minutes or until dough has doubled in size. (Press two fingers into dough. If indentation remains, the dough has risen enough.)

3. Punch dough down; roll into a 13 x 6-inch rectangle on a lightly floured surface. Roll up rectangle tightly, starting with a short edge, pressing firmly to eliminate air pockets; pinch seam and ends to seal. Place roll, seam side down, in an 8 x 4-inch loaf pan coated with cooking spray. Cover and let rise 35 minutes or until doubled in size.

4. Preheat oven to 375°.

5. Bake at 375° for 32 minutes or until loaf sounds hollow when tapped. Remove from pan; cool on a wire rack. YIELD: 12 servings (serving size: 1 slice).

POINTS value: 2; **Exchanges:** 2 Starch; **Per serving:** CAL 120 (11% from fat); PRO 3.2g; FAT 1.5g (sat 0.3g); CARB 23.1g; FIB 0.9g; CHOL 0mg; IRON 1.4mg; SOD 198mg; CALC 5mg

DILL AND CHEDDAR LOAF

Add 1 cup (4 ounces) shredded reduced-fat Cheddar cheese and 1¼ teaspoons dried dill with flour. Proceed as directed. YIELD: 16 servings (serving size: 1 slice).

POINTS value: 3; **Exchanges:** 1½ Starch, ½ Fat; **Per serving:** CAL 144 (19% from fat); PRO 5.9g; FAT 3.0g (sat 1.3g); CARB 23.5g; FIB 0.9g; CHOL 5mg; IRON 1.5mg; SOD 254mg; CALC 73mg

PARMESAN TWIST

prep: 13 minutes • cook: 35 minutes
other: 1 hour and 25 minutes

1   large egg
1   teaspoon water
1   package dry yeast (about 2¼ teaspoons)
1   teaspoon sugar
1   cup warm water (100° to 110°)
2¾   cups all-purpose flour
½   cup (2 ounces) grated fresh Parmesan cheese
1   tablespoon vegetable oil
1   teaspoon dried Italian seasoning
1   teaspoon salt
Cooking spray

1. Combine egg and 1 teaspoon water in a small bowl; stir with a whisk. Reserve 1 tablespoon egg mixture; set aside.

2. Dissolve yeast and sugar in 1 cup warm water in a small bowl; let stand 5 minutes. Lightly spoon flour into dry measuring cups; level with a knife. Combine yeast mixture, flour, remaining egg mixture, and next 4 ingredients in a large bowl; stir until a soft dough forms.

3. Turn dough out onto a lightly floured surface and knead until smooth and elastic. Place dough in a large bowl coated with cooking spray, turning to coat top. Cover and let rise in a warm place (85°), free from drafts, 45 minutes or until dough has doubled in size. (Press two fingers into dough. If indentation remains, the dough has risen enough.)

4. Punch dough down; divide in half. Shape each half into a 12-inch rope. Place ropes lengthwise on a baking sheet coated with cooking spray (do not stretch); pinch ends together at one end to seal. Twist ropes, and pinch end to seal; tuck both ends slightly under. Cover dough, and let rise 35 minutes.

5. Preheat oven to 375°.

6. Brush reserved 1 tablespoon egg mixture over dough. Bake at 375° for 35 minutes or until golden. Cool on a wire rack. YIELD: 16 servings (serving size: 1 slice).

POINTS value: 3; **Exchanges:** 1½ Starch, ½ Fat; **Per serving:** CAL 140 (19% from fat); PRO 5.0g; FAT 2.9g (sat 1.0g); CARB 23.0g; FIB 0.9g; CHOL 21mg; IRON 1.6mg; SOD 254mg; CALC 46mg

CRANBERRY PECAN BUNS

prep: 13 minutes • cook: 29 minutes
other: 1 hour and 25 minutes

1   package dry yeast (about
    2¼ teaspoons)
1   tablespoon granulated sugar
1   cup warm water (100° to
    110°)
2¾ cups all-purpose flour
1   tablespoon vegetable oil
1   teaspoon salt
Cooking spray
2   tablespoons butter, melted
3   tablespoons granulated sugar
1   teaspoon ground cinnamon
½   cup dried cranberries (such as
    Craisins)
3   tablespoons finely chopped
    pecans
¾   cup powdered sugar
5   teaspoons hot water

1. Dissolve yeast and sugar in warm water in a small bowl; let stand 5 minutes. Lightly spoon flour into dry measuring cups; level with a knife. Combine yeast mixture, flour, oil, and salt in a large bowl; stir until a soft dough forms.
2. Turn dough out onto a lightly floured surface and knead until smooth and elastic. Place dough in a large bowl coated with cooking spray, turning to coat top. Cover and let rise in a warm place (85°), free from drafts, 45 minutes or until dough has doubled in size. (Press two fingers into dough. If indentation remains, the dough has risen enough.)
3. Punch dough down; roll into a 12 x 10-inch rectangle on a lightly floured surface. Brush with butter. Combine sugar and cinnamon;

sprinkle evenly over dough. Top with dried cranberries and finely chopped pecans.
4. Beginning with a long side, roll up jelly roll fashion; pinch seam to seal (do not seal ends of roll). Place a long string or dental floss under roll; slowly pull ends to cut through dough. Arrange 12 slices, cut sides down, in a 9-inch square baking pan coated with cooking spray. Cover and let rise 25 minutes or until doubled in size.
5. Preheat oven to 375°.
6. Bake at 375° for 29 minutes or until golden brown. Cool 15 minutes in pan on a wire rack. Combine ¾ cup powdered sugar and 5 teaspoons hot water in a small bowl; stir until smooth. Drizzle over buns. YIELD: 12 servings (serving size: 1 bun).

POINTS value: 4; **Exchanges:** 2 Starch, 1 Fat;
Per serving: CAL 207 (21% from fat); PRO 3.4g;
FAT 4.8g (sat 1.3g); CARB 38.3g; FIB 1.5g;
CHOL 5mg; IRON 1.5mg; SOD 211mg; CALC 9mg

CARAWAY-RAISIN WHOLE WHEAT BREAD

prep: 13 minutes • cook: 32 minutes
other: 1 hour and 20 minutes

1   package dry yeast (about
    2¼ teaspoons)
1   tablespoon molasses
1   cup warm water (100° to
    110°)
2   cups all-purpose flour
¾   cup whole wheat flour
½   cup raisins
1   teaspoon caraway seeds
1   teaspoon salt
1   tablespoon vegetable oil
Cooking spray

1. Dissolve yeast and molasses in warm water in a small bowl; let stand 5 minutes. Lightly spoon flours into dry measuring cups; level with a knife. Combine flours. Add raisins, caraway seeds, and salt to flour mixture. Combine yeast mixture, flour mixture, and oil in a large bowl; stir until a soft dough forms.
2. Turn dough out onto a lightly floured surface. Knead until smooth and elastic. Place dough in a large bowl coated with cooking spray, turning to coat top. Cover and let rise in a warm place (85°), free from drafts, 45 minutes or until doubled in size. (Press two fingers into dough. If indentation remains, the dough has risen enough.)
3. Punch dough down; roll into a 13 x 6-inch rectangle on a lightly floured surface. Roll up rectangle tightly, starting with a short edge, pressing firmly to eliminate air pockets; pinch seam and ends to seal. Place roll, seam side down, in an 8 x 4-inch loaf pan coated with cooking spray. Cover and let rise 35 minutes or until doubled in size.
4. Preheat oven to 375°.
5. Bake at 375° for 32 minutes or until loaf sounds hollow when tapped. Remove from pan; cool on a wire rack. YIELD: 12 servings (serving size: 1 slice).

POINTS value: 2; **Exchanges:** 1½ Starch;
Per serving: CAL 137 (10% from fat); PRO 3.6g;
FAT 1.6g (sat 0.3g); CARB 27.7g; FIB 2.0g;
CHOL 0mg; IRON 1.6mg; SOD 200mg; CALC 12mg

Desserts

BROWNIE OATMEAL DROPS

prep: 5 minutes • cook: 9 minutes
other: 5 minutes

*Serve these chewy, chocolate cookies
with a tall glass of fat-free milk.*

¼ cup butter
1 ounce unsweetened chocolate,
  chopped
1 cup sugar
½ cup unsweetened cocoa
2 large eggs
2 teaspoons vanilla extract
1 cup uncooked regular oats
¼ cup all-purpose flour
½ teaspoon baking powder
⅛ teaspoon salt
Cooking spray

1. Preheat oven to 350°.
2. Microwave butter and chocolate
in a small bowl at HIGH 35 seconds
or until chocolate begins to melt.
Stir chocolate mixture until smooth.
3. Beat chocolate mixture, sugar, and
next 3 ingredients in a large bowl
until smooth.
4. Combine oats, flour, baking powder, and salt; add to butter mixture,
stirring just until blended. Drop by
rounded teaspoonfuls 2 inches apart
onto baking sheets coated with
cooking spray.
5. Bake at 350° for 8 to 9 minutes or
until cookie centers are almost done.
Cool 5 minutes on pans. Remove
from pans; cool completely on wire
racks. YIELD: about 30 servings (serving
size: 1 cookie).

POINTS value: 1; **Exchanges:** ½ Starch, ½ Fat;
Per serving: CAL 67 (34% from fat); PRO 1.3g;
FAT 2.7g (sat 1.3g); CARB 10.4g; FIB 0.9g;
CHOL 18mg; IRON 0.6mg; SOD 34mg; CALC 11mg

MOCHA-DARK CHOCOLATE CHUNK BROWNIES

(pictured on page 42)
prep: 12 minutes • cook: 35 minutes

Cooking spray
1 cup sugar
½ cup unsweetened cocoa
3 tablespoons butter, melted
1½ tablespoons instant coffee
  granules
2 tablespoons water
1 teaspoon vanilla extract
½ teaspoon baking powder
1 large egg, lightly beaten
1 large egg white, lightly beaten
⅔ cup all-purpose flour
½ (3-ounce) bar dark chocolate,
  chopped (such as Ghirardelli)

1. Preheat oven to 350°.
2. Coat bottom of an 8-inch square
baking pan with cooking spray.
3. Combine sugar and next 8
ingredients in a bowl.
4. Lightly spoon flour into dry
measuring cups; level with a knife.
Add flour and dark chocolate to
cocoa mixture, stirring just until
blended. Spread batter in prepared
pan. Bake at 350° for 30 minutes.

Cool on a wire rack. YIELD: 16 servings (serving size: 1 brownie).

POINTS value: 2; **Exchanges:** 1 Starch, 1 Fat;
Per serving: CAL 113 (30% from fat); PRO 1.9g;
FAT 3.8g (sat 2.2g); CARB 19.8g; FIB 1.2g;
CHOL 19mg; IRON 0.8mg; SOD 42mg;
CALC 15mg

GINGER-LIME BARS

prep: 15 minutes • cook: 32 minutes

1¼ cups low-fat honey graham
  cracker crumbs (9 sheets)
¼ cup light butter, melted
2 tablespoons minced
  crystallized ginger
2 tablespoons granulated
  sugar
Cooking spray
3 large eggs, lightly beaten
¾ cup granulated sugar
2 teaspoons grated lime rind
⅓ cup fresh lime juice
3 tablespoons all-purpose
  flour
2 teaspoons grated peeled fresh
  ginger
½ teaspoon baking powder
⅛ teaspoon salt
2 teaspoons powdered sugar

COCOA VS. CHOCOLATE

Although unsweetened chocolate and unsweetened cocoa powder
both come from the cacao bean, they are very different ingredients
and can't be used interchangeably in recipes.

Unsweetened chocolate is made from pure chocolate. It contains
about 50 percent cocoa butter and has no sugar or flavorings
added. It is available in squares or bars.

Unsweetened cocoa is made from pure chocolate but most of the
cocoa butter is removed. The remaining product is cocoa powder.

1. Preheat oven to 350°.

2. Combine first 4 ingredients in a mixing bowl; mix well. Press into an 8-inch square baking pan coated with cooking spray.

3. Bake at 350° for 12 minutes; cool slightly on a wire rack.

4. Whisk together eggs and next 7 ingredients until smooth. Pour egg mixture over prepared crust. Bake at 350° for 20 to 22 minutes or until set. Cool completely on wire rack. Sift powdered sugar evenly over top. Cut into bars. YIELD: 12 servings (serving size: 1 bar).

POINTS value: 2; **Exchanges:** 1 Starch, ½ Fat; **Per serving:** CAL 112 (26% from fat); PRO 2.3g; FAT 3.4g (sat 1.8g); CARB 19.1g; FIB 0.2g; CHOL 60mg; IRON 0.5mg; SOD 103mg; CALC 19mg

LEMON-GLAZED SUGAR COOKIES

prep: 15 minutes • cook: 10 minutes

These delicate lemon cookies are perfect for a bridal luncheon, afternoon snack, or after-dinner treat.

⅔ cup granulated sugar
¼ cup butter, softened
1 large egg yolk
¾ teaspoon grated orange rind
¾ teaspoon vanilla extract
1¼ cups all-purpose flour
2 tablespoons 1% low-fat milk
Cooking spray
½ cup sifted powdered sugar
1¾ teaspoons water
¾ teaspoon lemon juice
2 teaspoons pastel-colored sugar
   sprinkles

1. Preheat oven to 350°.

2. Beat first 5 ingredients with a mixer at medium speed until well blended. Lightly spoon flour into dry measuring cups; level with a knife. Add flour and milk to sugar mixture, mixing well.

3. Shape dough into 21 (1-inch) balls. Place balls 2 inches apart on baking sheets coated with cooking spray. Flatten cookies with the bottom of a glass. Bake at 350° for 10 minutes. Remove from pans; cool completely on wire racks.

4. Combine powdered sugar, water, and lemon juice. Spoon glaze in center of each cookie; sprinkle with sugar sprinkles. YIELD: 21 servings (serving size: 1 cookie).

POINTS value: 2; **Exchange:** 1 Starch; **Per serving:** CAL 87 (27% from fat); PRO 1.0g; FAT 2.6g (sat 1.2g); CARB 15.0g; FIB 0.2g; CHOL 16mg; IRON 0.4mg; SOD 17mg; CALC 5mg

CHERRY-ALMOND BISCOTTI

(pictured on page 44)
prep: 11 minutes • cook: 50 minutes
other: 10 minutes

Store extra biscotti in an airtight container for up to 5 days.

2 cups all-purpose flour
1 cup sugar
1 teaspoon baking soda
1 teaspoon baking powder
¼ teaspoon salt
1 large egg
2 large egg whites
1½ teaspoons almond extract
1 teaspoon vanilla extract
½ cup dried cherries, chopped
⅓ cup slivered almonds,
   toasted
Cooking spray

1. Preheat oven to 350°.

2. Lightly spoon flour into dry measuring cups; level with a knife. Combine flour and next 4 ingredients in a large bowl. Combine egg, egg whites, almond extract, and vanilla; add to flour mixture, stirring until well blended. Stir in cherries and almonds (dough will be dry and crumbly). Turn dough out onto a lightly floured surface; knead 5 to 6 times. Divide dough in half. Shape each portion into an 8-inch-long roll. Place rolls 4 to 5 inches apart on a baking sheet coated with cooking spray; flatten each roll to 1-inch thickness.

3. Bake at 350° for 30 minutes. Remove rolls from baking sheet; cool 10 minutes on a wire rack. Reduce oven temperature to 325°. Cut each roll diagonally into ½-inch slices. Place slices, cut sides down, on baking sheets coated with cooking spray; bake 10 minutes. Turn cookies over; bake an additional 10 minutes. Remove from baking sheets, and cool completely on wire rack. YIELD: 22 servings (serving size: 1 cookie).

POINTS value: 2; **Exchanges:** 1½ Starch; **Per serving:** CAL 107 (12% from fat); PRO 2.4g; FAT 1.4g (sat 0.2g); CARB 20.7g; FIB 0.8g; CHOL 10mg; IRON 0.7mg; SOD 115mg; CALC 22mg

APPLE CIDER CRISP

(pictured on page 43)
prep: 26 minutes • cook: 40 minutes

Tart and crisp Granny Smith apples hold up best in baking and are our top choice for use in this recipe.

½   cup all-purpose flour
¼   cup granulated sugar
¼   cup packed light brown sugar
¼   cup chilled butter, cut into small pieces
7   cups sliced peeled Granny Smith apple (about 7 medium)
⅓   cup apple cider
2   tablespoons granulated sugar
1   tablespoon fresh lemon juice
1   tablespoon all-purpose flour
1   teaspoon ground cinnamon
Cooking spray

1. Preheat oven to 375°.
2. Combine first 4 ingredients in a blender or food processor; pulse 4 times or until crumbly. Set aside.
3. Combine apple and next 5 ingredients in a large bowl; toss gently to combine. Spoon apple mixture into an 8-inch square baking dish coated with cooking spray; sprinkle with crumb mixture. Bake at 375° for 40 minutes or until lightly browned. Serve warm. YIELD: 8 servings (serving size: ¾ cup).

POINTS value: 4; **Exchanges:** 1½ Starch, 1½ Fruit; **Per serving:** CAL 225 (23% from fat); PRO 1.0g; FAT 5.8g (sat 2.9g); CARB 44.8g; FIB 5.0g; CHOL 15mg; IRON 0.9mg; SOD 43mg; CALC 12mg

APPLE STRUDEL

prep: 12 minutes • cook: 35 minutes

4½   cups sliced peeled Granny Smith apple (about 5 medium)
⅓   cup sugar
½   teaspoon ground cinnamon
⅓   cup raisins
2   tablespoons sliced almonds, toasted
1   teaspoon grated lemon rind
1   tablespoon fresh lemon juice
2   teaspoons grated peeled fresh ginger
12   (14 x 9-inch) sheets frozen phyllo dough, thawed
Butter-flavored cooking spray

1. Preheat oven to 400°.
2. Place apple in a large nonstick skillet over medium-high heat; add water to cover. Bring to a boil; cover, reduce heat, and simmer 4 minutes or just until apple is tender. Drain; cool completely.
3. Combine sugar and cinnamon in a bowl; reserve ½ teaspoon sugar mixture for topping. Combine remaining sugar mixture, apple, raisins, 1 tablespoon almonds and next 3 ingredients in a bowl; toss well.
4. Place 1 phyllo dough sheet on work surface (cover remaining dough to keep from drying); lightly coat with cooking spray. Coat 5 additional phyllo sheets with cooking spray; place one on top of the other. Sprinkle with 1 tablespoon almonds.
5. Spoon half of apple mixture along 1 long edge of phyllo dough, leaving 2-inch borders along 1 long edge and 2 short edges. Fold over short edges of phyllo dough to cover 2 inches of apple mixture on each end.

6. Starting at long edge with 2-inch border, loosely roll up jelly roll fashion. Place strudel, seam side down, on a baking sheet coated with cooking spray. Cut diagonal slits into top of strudel using a sharp knife. Lightly coat top of strudel with cooking spray; sprinkle with ¼ teaspoon reserved sugar mixture. Repeat procedure with remaining ingredients.
7. Bake at 400° for 15 minutes; reduce oven temperature to 350°, and bake an additional 10 minutes or until golden brown. YIELD: 8 servings (serving size: 1 slice).

POINTS value: 3; **Exchanges:** 1½ Starch, ½ Fruit, ½ Fat; **Per serving:** CAL 180 (13% from fat); PRO 2.6g; FAT 2.7g (sat 0.5g); CARB 37.8g; FIB 2.4g; CHOL 0mg; IRON 1.1mg; SOD 140mg; CALC 13mg

BERRY AND MOUSSE PASTRIES

(pictured on page 46)
prep: 31 minutes • cook: 13 minutes

Phyllo pastry shells can be made ahead, stored in airtight containers, and filled with pudding just before serving.

2   (1-ounce) package fat-free, sugar-free white chocolate instant pudding mix
1   cup frozen reduced-calorie whipped topping, thawed
½   (16-ounce) package frozen phyllo dough
Butter-flavored cooking spray
¾   cup sugar, divided
1   cup coarsely chopped strawberries
½   cup raspberries
½   cup blueberries

1. Prepare pudding mix according to package directions. Fold in whipped topping. Cover and chill.

2. Preheat oven to 375°.

3. Unroll phyllo dough on a large cutting board or work surface. Cut phyllo dough in half lengthwise. Carefully wrap and refreeze one half of dough for use in another recipe. Using scissors, cut remaining dough half crosswise into 3 (4½ x 4-inch) rectangles.

4. Working with 1 phyllo dough section at a time (cover remaining dough with a towel to keep from drying), place 1 (4½ x 4-inch) phyllo rectangle on work surface; coat with cooking spray and sprinkle with ½ teaspoon sugar. Place second phyllo rectangle on top of sugared phyllo sheet at a 45° angle; coat with cooking spray, and sprinkle with ½ teaspoon sugar. Continue procedure until you have a 6-layer stack of phyllo dough.

5. Carefully press prepared phyllo dough stack into a 6-ounce custard cup coated with cooking spray. Repeat procedure with remaining phyllo dough.

6. Place custard cups on baking sheets. Bake at 375° for 13 minutes or until golden brown. Immediately remove phyllo shells from custard cups; cool completely on wire racks.

7. Stir berries into mousse, reserving some berries for garnish. Spoon ⅓ cup mousse evenly into each phyllo shell. Sprinkle evenly with reserved berries. YIELD: 12 servings (serving size: 1 pastry).

POINTS value: 3; **Exchanges:** 1½ Starch, ½ Fruit;
Per serving: CAL 144 (12% from fat); PRO 1.5g;
FAT 1.9g (sat 1.0g); CARB 29.9g; FIB 1.1g;
CHOL 0mg; IRON 0.7mg; SOD 286mg; CALC 6mg

HOW TO MAKE PHYLLO CUPS

1. Cut phyllo dough in half lengthwise. Carefully wrap and refreeze one half of dough for use in other recipes.

2. Using scissors, cut remaining phyllo dough half crosswise into 3 (4½ x 4-inch) rectangles.

3. Work with 1 phyllo dough section at a time. Place 1 (4½ x 4-inch) phyllo rectangle on work surface; coat with cooking spray and sprinkle with sugar. Place second phyllo rectangle on top of sugared phyllo sheet at a 45° angle; coat with cooking spray, and sprinkle with sugar. Continue procedure until you have a 6-layer stack of phyllo dough.

4. Press phyllo dough stacks into a 6-ounce custard cup coated with cooking spray. Place on baking sheets. Bake for 13 minutes.

5. Remove phyllo shell from custard cup; cool completely on wire racks. Shells can be made ahead, stored in airtight containers, and filled with pudding just before serving.

LEMONADE PUDDING PIE IN BISCOTTI CRUST

prep: 15 minutes • cook: 14 minutes
other: 8 hours and 5 minutes

1   (5.7-ounce) package biscotti
2   tablespoons butter, melted
⅔   cup sugar
3   tablespoons cornstarch
⅛   teaspoon salt
1½   cups 1% low-fat milk
1   large egg, beaten
½   cup frozen lemonade
       concentrate, thawed
1   tablespoon butter, melted
1½   cups frozen reduced-calorie
       whipped topping, thawed
1   cup raspberries

1. Preheat oven to 375°.
2. Pulse biscotti in food processor 10 times or until crumbly. Add butter through food chute; pulse 5 times or just until crumbs are moist. Set aside 2 teaspoons crumb mixture. Press remaining crumb mixture into a 9-inch pie plate.
3. Bake at 375° for 8 minutes or until edges begin to brown. Cool on a wire rack.
4. Stir together sugar, cornstarch, and salt in a medium saucepan; add milk. Bring to a boil over medium-high heat and cook 1 minute, stirring constantly with a whisk. Remove from heat. Gradually stir about one-fourth of hot mixture into egg; add mixture into remaining hot mixture, stirring constantly. Cook over low heat 3 minutes. Remove from heat; stir in lemonade concentrate and butter. Place pan in a large bowl of ice water. Cool pudding to room temperature (about 5 minutes), stirring often with a whisk.
5. Pour pudding into prepared crust. Press plastic wrap over filling. Chill 8 hours or until thoroughly chilled.
6. Before serving, spread whipped topping over filling. Sprinkle reserved crumbs over topping and garnish with raspberries. YIELD: 10 servings (serving size: 1 wedge).

*POINTS value: 5; **Exchanges:** 2 Starch, 2 Fat; **Per serving:** CAL 246 (32% from fat); PRO 3.0g; FAT 8.8g (sat 4.0g); CARB 39.0g; FIB 1.0g; CHOL 32mg; IRON 0.4mg; SOD 80mg; CALC 111mg*

QUICK PEACH AND RASPBERRY PIES

prep: 7 minutes • cook: 13 minutes
other: 15 minutes

This is a great make-ahead dessert. Prepare the fruit mixture and refrigerate in an airtight container. Bake the pastry wedges, cool, and store at room temperature in a large zip-top bag. Assemble one or more desserts just before serving.

½   (15-ounce) package
       refrigerated pie dough (such as
       Pillsbury)
¼   cup packed dark brown
       sugar
2   teaspoons cornstarch
½   teaspoon ground cinnamon
⅛   teaspoon ground allspice
       (optional)
1¾   cups frozen sliced peaches,
       thawed and diced (about
       12 ounces)
⅔   cup frozen unsweetened
       raspberries, thawed (about
       4 ounces)
½   teaspoon vanilla extract
2   cups vanilla fat-free, no sugar
       added ice cream

1. Preheat oven to 400°.
2. Unfold dough, and cut into 8 wedges; place on a baking sheet.
3. Bake at 400° for 11 minutes or until golden. Cool completely on a wire rack.
4. Combine sugar, cornstarch, cinnamon, and, if desired, allspice, in a large saucepan. Add peaches, stirring well. Bring to a boil over medium-high heat; cook 1 minute or until slightly thick and sugar dissolves, stirring constantly. Remove from heat; stir in raspberries and vanilla. Let stand 15 minutes. Top each pastry wedge with ¼ cup fruit mixture and ¼ cup ice cream. YIELD: 8 servings (serving size: 1 pastry wedge, ¼ cup fruit mixture, and ¼ cup ice cream).

*POINTS value: 5; **Exchanges:** 2 Starch, 1 Fruit, ½ Fat; **Per serving:** CAL 242 (25% from fat); PRO 3.4g; FAT 7.0g (sat 3.0g); CARB 42.8g; FIB 1.5g; CHOL 5mg; IRON 0.6mg; SOD 137mg; CALC 64mg*

REFRIGERATED PIE DOUGH

A convenient and time-saving product, refrigerated pie dough is ready to bake and adds a homemade flavor to desserts, appetizers, or main-dish meals.

Before preparing your recipe, allow the dough to stand at room temperature for about 15 minutes or microwave 30 seconds until the dough feels soft and pliable.

Follow the package directions for pie plate and tart pan sizes and for baking times and temperatures. You are sure to enjoy the tender, flaky product without the hassle of making a from-scratch crust.

PUMPKIN CHEESECAKE

prep: 24 minutes • cook: 1 hour and
20 minutes • other: 8 hours

1   cup crushed gingersnap
     cookies (about 19 cookies)
⅓   cup uncooked quick-cooking
     oats
3   tablespoons butter, melted
Cooking spray
1   (24-ounce) carton fat-free
     cottage cheese (such as
     Breakstone)
1   (8-ounce) package ⅓-less-fat
     cream cheese, softened
2   tablespoons all-purpose flour
1   teaspoon ground cinnamon
¾   teaspoon ground ginger
¼   teaspoon salt
¼   teaspoon ground nutmeg
¼   teaspoon ground allspice
1   cup canned unsweetened
     pumpkin
⅔   cup sugar
2   large eggs
2   large egg whites
1   teaspoon vanilla extract
¾   cup frozen reduced-calorie
     whipped topping, thawed

1. Preheat oven to 350°.
2. Place cookie crumbs, oats, and
butter in a food processor; process
until blended. Firmly press crumb
mixture on bottom and 1 inch up
sides of a 9-inch springform pan
coated with cooking spray.
3. Bake at 350° for 10 minutes; cool
on a wire rack. Reduce oven temperature to 325°.
4. Place cottage cheese in a blender
or food processor; process until
smooth. Beat cottage cheese and
cream cheese with a mixer at
medium speed just until smooth.

Combine flour and next 5 ingredients
in a bowl. Add flour mixture, pumpkin, and sugar to cheese mixture,
beating just until blended. Add eggs
and egg whites, 1 at a time, to cheese
mixture, beating just until blended.
Stir in vanilla. Pour pumpkin mixture
into prepared crust.
5. Bake at 325° for 1 hour and 10
minutes or until almost set. Remove
cheesecake from oven; run a knife
around outside edge. Cool to room
temperature on a wire rack. Cover
and chill 8 hours. Top each serving
with about 1 tablespoon whipped
topping. YIELD: 12 servings (serving
size: 1 slice).

POINTS value: 6; **Exchanges:** 2 Starch, 2 Fat;
Per serving: CAL 247 (36% from fat); PRO 10.8g;
FAT 9.9g (sat 5.3g); CARB 28.4g; FIB 1.2g;
CHOL 59mg; IRON 1.4mg; SOD 489mg; CALC 74mg

DARK CHOCOLATE AND
RASPBERRY LAYER CAKE

(pictured on page 46)
prep: 9 minutes • cook: 23 minutes
other: 8 hours and 10 minutes

Cooking spray
3   tablespoons unsweetened
     cocoa
1   (19.5-ounce) package
     chocolate fudge cake mix
1¼   cups water
2   (2.5-ounce) jars prune baby
     food
3   large eggs
1   (10-ounce) jar seedless
     raspberry preserves
1   tablespoon Chambord liqueur
     (raspberry-flavored liqueur) or
     water
2   tablespoons powdered sugar
Raspberries (optional)

1. Preheat oven to 350°.
2. Line a 15½ x 10½-inch jelly roll
pan with parchment paper. Coat
parchment paper with cooking
spray; dust with cocoa.
3. Combine cake mix, water, baby
food, and eggs in a large bowl;
beat with a mixer at medium speed
2 minutes. Spread cake batter into
prepared pan.
4. Bake at 350° for 23 minutes or
until cake springs back when
touched lightly in center. Cool cake
in pan 10 minutes. Loosen cake
from sides of pan, and invert onto a
wire rack. Remove parchment
paper. Cool completely. Cut cake
crosswise into 3 equal pieces to
create 3 rectangular cake layers.
5. Combine preserves and liqueur in
a small bowl; stir until smooth.
6. Place 1 cake layer on a cake
platter; spread with half of raspberry
mixture, leaving a ½-inch border.
Repeat procedure with second cake
layer and raspberry mixture. Top with
third cake layer. Cover and chill 8
hours. Sift powdered sugar evenly
over cake before serving.
7. To slice the finished cake into triangles, slice cake lengthwise down
the center. Cut widthwise into 4
equal squares and cut each square
diagonally. Garnish with raspberries,
if desired. YIELD: 16 servings (serving
size: 1 triangle slice).

POINTS value: 5; **Exchanges:** 3 Starch;
Per serving: CAL 235 (16% from fat); PRO 3.2g;
FAT 4.3g (sat 1.6g); CARB 46.6g; FIB 0.6g;
CHOL 40mg; IRON 1.1mg; SOD 248mg; CALC 41mg

CARROT CAKE WITH CREAM CHEESE FROSTING

prep: 16 minutes • cook: 30 minutes
other: 10 minutes

Cooking spray
1 cup all-purpose flour
1 teaspoon baking soda
1 teaspoon ground cinnamon
¼ teaspoon ground nutmeg
⅛ teaspoon salt
1 (8-ounce) can crushed
  pineapple in juice
¾ cup granulated sugar
⅓ cup vegetable oil
2 large egg whites
1 large egg
1 teaspoon grated orange rind
1 teaspoon vanilla extract
1½ cups grated carrot
⅓ cup raisins
½ cup (4 ounces) ⅓-less-fat
  cream cheese
2 cups sifted powdered sugar
2 teaspoons finely chopped
  pecans

1. Preheat oven to 350°.
2. Coat bottom of a 9-inch square baking pan with cooking spray; line bottom with wax paper. Coat wax paper with cooking spray.
3. Lightly spoon flour into a dry measuring cup; level with a knife. Combine flour and next 4 ingredients.
4. Combine pineapple and next 6 ingredients in a large bowl. Beat with a mixer at medium speed until well blended. Add flour mixture; beat just until blended. Stir in carrot and raisins. Pour batter into prepared pan. Bake at 350° for 30 minutes or until a wooden pick inserted in center comes out clean. Cool in pan 10 minutes on a wire rack; remove from pan. Remove wax paper. Cool completely on wire rack.
5. Beat cream cheese with a mixer at medium speed until smooth. Gradually add powdered sugar; beat at low speed just until blended.
6. Place cake layer on a plate; spread top and sides with cream cheese mixture. Sprinkle top with pecans. Store cake loosely covered in refrigerator.
YIELD: 12 servings (serving size: 1 piece).

POINTS value: 6; **Exchanges:** 2½ Starch, 1½ Fat;
Per serving: CAL 272 (30% from fat); PRO 3.6g;
FAT 9.1g (sat 0.6g); CARB 45.1g; FIB 1.4g;
CHOL 24mg; IRON 0.8mg; SOD 190mg;
CALC 22mg

PEAR UPSIDE-DOWN CAKE WITH PECANS

(pictured on page 47)
prep: 18 minutes • cook: 32 minutes

1 tablespoon butter
¼ cup packed light brown sugar
1 cup thinly sliced peeled pear
  (about 1 large)
8 pecan halves
1 cup all-purpose flour
1 teaspoon baking powder
¼ teaspoon baking soda
⅛ teaspoon salt
⅔ cup granulated sugar
¼ cup butter, softened
1 large egg
1 teaspoon vanilla extract
¼ teaspoon almond extract
⅓ cup low-fat sour cream
½ cup 1% low-fat milk

1. Preheat oven to 350°.
2. Place butter in a 9-inch round cake pan; place in oven 2 minutes or until butter melts. Remove pan from oven.
3. Sprinkle brown sugar evenly over bottom of pan. Arrange pear slices and pecan halves spokelike over sugar; set aside.
4. Lightly spoon flour into a dry measuring cup; level with a knife. Combine flour, baking powder, baking soda, and salt in a medium bowl. Beat sugar, butter, egg, and extracts with a mixer at medium speed until well blended. Add sour cream and half of flour mixture; beat well. Add remaining flour mixture and milk; beat well. Pour batter over pear slices, spreading gently. Bake at 350° for 30 to 33 minutes or until a wooden pick inserted in center comes out clean. Cool on a wire rack 5 minutes.
5. Run a sharp knife around edge of pan to loosen cake. Place a serving plate upside-down over pan; invert cake onto serving plate. Serve warm or cool completely. YIELD: 10 servings (serving size: 1 wedge).

POINTS value: 4; **Exchanges:** 1½ Starch, 1½ Fat;
Per serving: CAL 194 (32% from fat); PRO 2.2g;
FAT 7.1g (sat 3.1g); CARB 31.0g; FIB 1.0g;
CHOL 36mg; IRON 0.9mg; SOD 160mg; CALC 40mg

BAKING SODA BASICS

Baking soda, a natural leavener for cakes and quick breads, reacts when combined with an acid like lemon juice, buttermilk, cream of tartar, or yogurt. The reaction releases carbon dioxide and causes the batter or dough to rise and become light and tender. This reaction begins immediately upon moistening, and, if allowed to stand too long, will lose its leavening power so mix baking soda with dry ingredients first.

PEACH PRESERVES POUND CAKE

prep: 20 minutes • cook: 55 minutes
other: 10 minutes

Choose your favorite fruit spread to flavor this versatile pound cake.

Cooking spray
2   tablespoons flour
⅔   cup butter, softened
1   cup packed light brown sugar
¼   cup granulated sugar
1¼   cups peach spread (such as Polaner All Fruit)
2   tablespoons finely chopped crystallized ginger
3   large eggs
1   large egg white
3   cups all-purpose flour
¼   teaspoon salt
1   cup low-fat buttermilk (1%)
1   teaspoon baking soda
1   teaspoon vanilla extract
½   teaspoon almond extract
Powdered sugar

1. Preheat oven to 350°.
2. Coat a 10-inch Bundt pan with cooking spray; dust with 2 tablespoons flour.
3. Beat butter with a mixer at medium speed until fluffy. Gradually add brown sugar and granulated sugar, beating at medium speed until light and fluffy. Beat in peach spread and ginger. Add eggs and egg white, 1 at a time, beating after each addition.
4. Lightly spoon 3 cups flour into dry measuring cups; level with a knife. Combine flour and salt. Combine buttermilk and baking soda. Add flour mixture and buttermilk mixture alternately to sugar mixture, beginning and ending with flour mixture. Stir in extracts.
5. Spoon batter into prepared pan.
6. Bake at 350° for 55 minutes or until a long wooden pick inserted in center of cake comes out clean. Cool in pan 10 minutes; remove from pan, and cool completely on a wire rack. Dust with powdered sugar. YIELD: 16 servings (serving size: 1 slice).

POINTS value: 6; **Exchanges:** 3 Starch, 1 Fat; **Per serving:** CAL 290 (27% from fat); PRO 4.5g; FAT 8.8g (sat 4.2g); CARB 48.2g; FIB 0.6; CHOL 60mg; IRON 1.5mg; SOD 208mg; CALC 39mg

CHOCOLATE-TOFFEE PUDDING CAKE

prep: 11 minutes • cook: 35 minutes
other: 15 minutes

This decadent chocolate dessert forms two layers as it bakes: a rich, creamy pudding on the bottom and a tender cake layer on the top.

1   cup all-purpose flour
⅔   cup granulated sugar
¼   cup unsweetened cocoa
1   tablespoon instant coffee granules
2   teaspoons baking powder
¼   teaspoon salt
½   cup 1% low-fat milk
2   tablespoons vegetable oil
1   teaspoon vanilla extract
Cooking spray
⅔   cup packed light brown sugar
2   tablespoons unsweetened cocoa
1   cup hot water
½   cup almond toffee bits

1. Preheat oven to 350°.
2. Lightly spoon flour into a dry measuring cup; level with a knife. Combine flour and next 5 ingredients in a bowl. Add milk, oil, and vanilla, stirring just until combined.
3. Pour batter into an 8-inch square baking pan coated with cooking spray. Combine brown sugar and 2 tablespoons cocoa in a small bowl; sprinkle evenly over batter. Pour hot water over batter (do not stir).
4. Bake at 350° for 35 minutes. Remove from oven; sprinkle with toffee bits. Let stand 15 minutes. Serve warm. YIELD: 9 servings (serving size: ⅑ of pudding cake).

POINTS value: 6; **Exchanges:** 3 Starch, 1 Fat; **Per serving:** CAL 283 (26% from fat); PRO 2.8g; FAT 8.3g (sat 3.2g); CARB 51.6g; FIB 1.6g; CHOL 11mg; IRON 1.6mg; SOD 248mg; CALC 102mg

MEASURING FLOUR

1. Lightly spoon flour into a dry measuring cup. Do not pack.

2. Level off using the straight edge of a knife.

TIRAMISU

(pictured on page 4)
prep: 13 minutes • chill: 8 hours

Strong coffee can be made using 2 teaspoons instant coffee granules and ¾ cup hot water. For additional coffee flavor, beat 2 tablespoons Kahlua into cheese mixture. Since this tiramisu is soft, we prefer to prepare it in a bowl.

1   (8-ounce) package fat-free cream cheese, softened
½   cup (4 ounces) mascarpone cheese
½   cup sugar
2   tablespoons Kahlúa (coffee-flavored liqueur) (optional)
1   cup frozen reduced-calorie whipped topping, thawed
¾   cup cold strong brewed coffee
1   (3-ounce) package cake-style ladyfingers (12 ladyfingers)
½   teaspoon unsweetened cocoa

1. Combine first 3 ingredients and, if desired, Kahlúa, in a large bowl; beat with a mixer at medium speed until smooth. Fold in whipped topping.
2. Pour coffee into a shallow dish. Split ladyfingers in half lengthwise. Quickly dip ladyfingers, flat sides down, into coffee; arrange half of ladyfingers, dipped sides up, in bottom of a medium bowl.
3. Gently spread half of cream cheese mixture evenly over ladyfingers. Repeat procedure with remaining ladyfingers and cream cheese mixture. Sift cocoa over top. Cover and chill 8 hours. Spoon into dessert

glasses or small bowls to serve. Lightly dust with cocoa, if desired.
YIELD: 9 servings (serving size: ½ cup).

POINTS value: 4; **Exchanges:** 1½ Starch, 1 Fat; **Per serving:** CAL 182 (33% from fat); PRO 6.1g; FAT 6.6g (sat 3.8g); CARB 22.2g; FIB 0.1g; CHOL 33mg; IRON 0.6mg; SOD 196mg; CALC 113mg

CREAMY RICE PUDDING WITH DRIED CHERRIES

prep: 14 minutes • cook: 46 minutes

Light coconut milk adds a subtle coconut flavor and gives this pudding its rich and creamy texture. Store leftover coconut milk in an airtight container in the refrigerator for 2 to 3 days. Use leftover coconut milk in Pan-Fried Tofu with Coconut Rice, page 80.

1½   cups water
¾   cup uncooked jasmine rice
¼   teaspoon salt
½   cup dried cherries
½   cup orange juice
3¼   cups 2% reduced-fat milk
¾   cup light coconut milk
⅓   cup sugar
2   tablespoons honey
1   teaspoon grated orange rind
1   (3-inch) piece vanilla bean, split lengthwise, or 1 teaspoon vanilla extract

1. Combine first 3 ingredients in a heavy saucepan. Bring to a boil; cover, reduce heat, and simmer 13 minutes or until liquid is absorbed.
2. Meanwhile, combine cherries and orange juice in a small microwave-safe bowl. Microwave at HIGH 2 minutes or until hot. Let stand.

3. Stir reduced-fat milk and next 4 ingredients into rice. Scrape seeds from vanilla bean; stir seeds and vanilla bean into milk mixture.
4. Cook over medium heat, stirring frequently, 30 minutes or until mixture is thick and creamy (mixture will look like cooked oatmeal or cream of wheat). Remove and discard vanilla bean. Drain cherries, if needed. Stir into pudding. Serve warm or chilled. **YIELD:** 10 servings (serving size: ½ cup).
Note: Overcooking the pudding will cause it to become thick and solidify. Cook pudding to a cooked cereal (oatmeal, cream of wheat) consistency.

POINTS value: 3; **Exchanges:** 1 Starch, ½ Reduced-Fat Milk; **Per serving:** CAL 146 (15% from fat); PRO 3.4g; FAT 2.5g (sat 1.6g); CARB 27.4g; FIB 0.9g; CHOL 6mg; IRON 0.4mg; SOD 104mg; CALC 106mg

VANILLA BEANS

Vanilla beans, at $2 to $3 per bean, are more expensive than vanilla extract, but add a rich flavor to any dish. They are better than extract for foods that are lightly cooked, such as syrups and sauces, and are also great for flavoring coffee or as a flavoring substitute in a recipe that uses a small amount of alcohol. You can find vanilla beans in the spice section of most supermarkets. Freeze extra beans in an airtight container and when ready to use, microwave for 15 seconds to thaw.

Substitute 1 tablespoon vanilla extract for 1 (6-inch) vanilla bean.

The Challenge

KAY ALEXANDER • **HEIGHT** 5'6" • **BEFORE** 218 LBS. • **AFTER** 145 LBS.

Tip: "Focus on losing weight one step at a time. Don't think about the total number of pounds you need to lose, just concentrate on 5 pounds at a time."

The Christmas holidays had once again come and gone and Kay Alexander had "feasted as usual" on her favorites—her mom's pound cake, homemade butter cookies, and sweet potato pie. "I did notice that my work clothes were a bit snug," she says. "But I wondered if it was just my imagination."

Kay quickly realized that it was not a figment of her imagination. Once back at work, one of Kay's coworkers challenged her to a diet. "We were huffing and puffing in an attempt to keep up with our special needs children in adaptive physical education," she says. "My friend proposed that we go on a 'diet' and see who could lose the most weight before Valentine's Day. Well, being just a bit competitive, I eagerly agreed!"

> *"Knowing I was going to have to step on that scale every week really helped me stick with it."*

Another coworker suggested that they start a *Weight Watchers* at Work program. However, Kay was too excited to wait for that to be established, and, instead, attended a traditional *Weight Watchers* meeting at a local center.

"I found myself looking forward to the weekly meetings," she says. "The leader was so upbeat, the members were so inspirational, and we all shared so much great information. Also, knowing I was going to have to step on that scale every week really helped me stick with it."

Kay also began walking. "I could only walk the quarter-mile track twice," she says. "But I persisted and after a few weeks I was walking twice as far in the same amount of time.

"As I continued to drop pounds, I became more confident that I would win the challenge. And I did!" But the challenge didn't stop on Valentine's Day. Kay continued to challenge herself for the next year and finally achieved her goal—losing 59 pounds. Even then Kay believed she could lose more and pressed ahead until she lost a total of 80 pounds.

Today—two years since she lost the weight—Kay finds maintaining her figure a piece of cake. "I've been surprised that it hasn't been very hard to keep off," she says. "I guess it's because *Weight Watchers* really isn't a diet. *Weight Watchers* just teaches you the proper way of eating.

"That little friendly competition between friends introduced me to *Weight Watchers* where I learned not to 'diet.' I know now that I can make healthy choices, yet not be deprived. I carry a photo of the 'old' me everywhere I go, to remind the 'new' me that I can live up to the challenges necessary to remain the woman that I now am—mentally and physically."

Weight-loss results not typical.

Mocha-Dark Chocolate
Chunk Brownies,
page 32

Banana Pudding Ice Cream Cupcake, page 50

Apple Cider Crisp, page 34

Cherry-Almond Biscotti,
page 33

Dark Chocolate Crème
Brûlée,
page 49

Berry and
Mousse Pastries,
page 34

Dark Chocolate and
Raspberry Layer Cake,
page 37

Pear Upside-Down Cake
with Pecans,
page 38

It's All About Health

TAMMY MOORE • **HEIGHT** 5'6½" • **BEFORE** 190 LBS. • **AFTER** 122 LBS.

Motto: "It's not about clothing size or about pounds coming off; it's about feeling healthy and being the best you can!"

Tammy Moore, a stay-at-home mother of two, says she never knew the severity of her weight problem. "I thought I could hide everything, until one day I caught my reflection in a store window. I barely recognized myself!"

Realizing that the mirror wasn't lying, Tammy decided to give *Weight Watchers* a try. "My sister-in-law had been having success with *Weight Watchers* and I liked the idea that you could eat what you wanted—as long as you stayed within your **POINTS** value total," Tammy says. So on May 6, 2003, Tammy embarked on her weight-loss voyage.

When she began her journey, Tammy was sure of one thing: She didn't want to feel deprived in any way. "When you are trying to lose weight, you are already different from the people around you," she says. "I didn't want the added stress of having to eat a frozen dinner instead of partaking in the family meal. Overall, I just didn't want to feel alienated from my family."

Tammy found *Weight Watchers* to be a good fit for her family and her lifestyle. Tammy discovered that mealtime could be enjoyable for her and for the entire family.

"I quickly learned portion control," she says. "I never understood that when I went to a restaurant, I was really getting three portions of pasta instead of one. I had been so oblivious!"

Portion control is one of the habits that Tammy credits for her success. But Tammy is also quick to tout the benefits of accountability, journaling, and exercise.

"Accountability and journaling helped so much in achieving my success," Tammy says. "But exercise played a huge factor in my losing 68 pounds in less than one year."

Once she began exercising regularly, Tammy discovered that she actually enjoyed running. "I would never have run before," Tammy says. "I just

"It's about being healthy, being fit, and living longer."

never thought I could do it!" And that's just one of the many lessons that Tammy learned.

The most important lesson, however, was about health. "Sure, the weight will come off if you stick to the plan, but the weight isn't necessarily the biggest issue," she says. "It's about being healthy, being fit, and living longer.

"I'm lucky—I'm not even 30 years old and I've made this positive change in my life. It's not about clothing size or about pounds coming off; it's about feeling healthy and being the best you can!"

DARK CHOCOLATE CRÈME BRÛLÉE

(pictured on page 45)
prep: 15 minutes • cook: 48 minutes
other: 4 hours

Give yourself a break and make these truly decadent desserts the day before your guests arrive. Before serving, sprinkle each custard with sugar and caramelize the top for a delicious combination of warm, crunchy topping and cool, rich custard. Or simply top with a dollop of reduced-calorie whipped topping.

2   cups 1% low-fat chocolate milk
1   (3.5-ounce) bar bittersweet chocolate, chopped
1   teaspoon vanilla extract
½   teaspoon almond extract
4   large egg yolks, lightly beaten
⅛   teaspoon salt
6   teaspoons sugar
6   tablespoons frozen reduced-calorie whipped topping, thawed

1. Preheat oven to 300°.
2. Heat milk in a heavy saucepan over medium heat to 180° or until tiny bubbles form around edge (do not boil), stirring occasionally. Remove from heat; add chocolate, stirring occasionally, until chocolate melts. Stir in extracts.
3. Combine egg yolk and salt in a small bowl; stir well with a whisk. Gradually add milk mixture to egg mixture, stirring constantly with a whisk. Divide mixture evenly among 6 (4-ounce) ramekins, custard cups, or shallow baking dishes. Place ramekins in a 13 x 9-inch baking pan, and add hot water to pan to a depth of 1 inch.
4. Bake at 300° for 40 minutes or until center barely moves when ramekin is touched. Remove ramekins from pan, and cool completely on a wire rack. Cover ramekins, and chill at least 4 hours or overnight.
5. Sift 1 teaspoon sugar evenly over each custard. Holding a kitchen torch about 2 inches from top of each custard, heat sugar, moving torch back and forth, until sugar is completely melted and caramelized. Top with 1 tablespoon whipped topping. Serve custards immediately. YIELD: 6 servings (serving size: 1 crème brûlée).

POINTS value: 5; **Exchanges:** 1 Starch, 2½ Fat; **Per serving:** CAL 200 (59% from fat); PRO 5.5g; FAT 13.0g (sat 6.1g); CARB 18.7g; FIB 1.2g; CHOL 235mg; IRON 0.9mg; SOD 94mg; CALC 74mg

PUMPKIN-CRANBERRY CUSTARD WITH MAPLE CREAM

prep: 14 minutes • cook: 40 minutes
other: 5 minutes

1   cup canned pumpkin
⅔   cup sugar
2   teaspoons pumpkin-pie spice
¼   teaspoon salt
2   large eggs, lightly beaten
1   large egg white, lightly beaten
2   cups 2% reduced-fat milk
2   tablespoons maple syrup
1   teaspoon vanilla extract
6   cups (1-inch) cubed day-old French bread
½   cup dried cranberries
Cooking spray
Maple Cream

1. Preheat oven to 325°.
2. Combine first 6 ingredients. Stir with a whisk. Gradually stir in milk, maple syrup, and vanilla. Add bread cubes and cranberries; stir until bread is well coated. Pour into an 11 x 7-inch baking dish coated with cooking spray. Bake at 325° for 40 to 45 minutes or until custard is set. Cool 5 minutes on a wire rack. Serve warm with Maple Cream. YIELD: 12 servings (serving size: ¹⁄₁₂ of custard and 1 tablespoon Maple Cream).

(Total includes Maple Cream) *POINTS value: 5;* **Exchanges:** 3 Starch, ½ Fat; **Per serving:** CAL 248 (16% from fat); PRO 7.0g; FAT 4.3g (sat 1.7g); CARB 45.7g; FIB 2.4g; CHOL 100mg; IRON 1.3mg; SOD 250mg; CALC 131mg

MAPLE CREAM

½   cup 2% reduced-fat milk
¼   cup maple syrup
2   large egg yolks, lightly beaten

1. Combine milk and syrup in a saucepan. Cook over medium heat until milk begins to steam.
2. Gradually add one-fourth of hot milk mixture to egg yolk. Add egg yolk mixture to pan. Cook over medium heat, stirring constantly, until mixture begins to thicken. Pour into a bowl. Cover and chill (mixture will thicken as it cools). YIELD: 12 servings (serving size: 1 tablespoon).

POINTS value: 1; **Exchange:** ½ Starch; **Per serving:** CAL 32 (29% from fat); PRO 0.8g; FAT 1.1g (sat 0.4g); CARB 5.0g; FIB 0.0g; CHOL 36mg; IRON 0.2mg; SOD 7mg; CALC 21mg

RASPBERRY LEMONADE SORBET

prep: 3 minutes • other: 8 hours

Sugar is a critical ingredient when making sorbets because it helps prevent sorbet from freezing rock solid. Frozen raspberries in syrup and frozen lemonade concentrate provide enough sugar to give a refreshing taste and smooth, not icy, texture.

1   (10-ounce) package frozen raspberries in syrup, thawed
1   (12-ounce) can frozen lemonade concentrate, thawed
1½   cups water

1. Process raspberries in a blender until smooth. Strain berries through a sieve into a bowl. Discard solids. Add lemonade concentrate and water; stir well.
2. Pour mixture into an 8-inch square baking pan. Cover and freeze at least 8 hours. Scrape surface of sorbet with a spoon or ice cream scoop to serve. YIELD: 8 servings (serving size: ½ cup).

POINTS value: 2; **Exchanges:** 1 Starch, ½ Fruit; **Per serving:** CAL 113 (1% from fat); PRO 0.4g; FAT 0.1g (sat 0.0g); CARB 29.3g; FIB 1.6g; CHOL 0mg; IRON 0.5mg; SOD 2mg; CALC 8mg

BANANA PUDDING ICE CREAM CUPCAKES

(pictured on page 43)
prep: 26 minutes

24   vanilla wafers
4   ripe bananas
1   tablespoon lemon juice
3¼   cups vanilla low-fat ice cream
1   (12-ounce) container frozen reduced-calorie whipped topping, thawed and divided
1½   cups vanilla wafer crumbs, divided (about 30 cookies)

1. Place 1 vanilla wafer in the bottom of 24 foil-lined muffin cups.
2. Process bananas and lemon juice in a blender or food processor until smooth. Add ice cream; pulse 4 to 5 times or just until blended. Add 1¼ cups whipped topping and 1 cup wafer crumbs; pulse 2 to 3 times or just until blended.
3. Divide ice cream mixture evenly among muffin cups; cover with plastic wrap and freeze.
4. Top each ice cream cup evenly with remaining whipped topping; sprinkle with ½ cup wafer crumbs before serving. Serve immediately. YIELD: 24 servings (serving size: 1 cupcake).

POINTS value: 3; **Exchanges:** 1 Starch, ½ Fruit; **Per serving:** CAL 126 (33% from fat); PRO 1.5g; FAT 4.5g (sat 3.1g); CARB 19.2g; FIB 0.9g; CHOL 6mg; IRON 0.4mg; SOD 42mg; CALC 27mg

MINT BROWNIE ICE CREAM BARS

(pictured on cover)
prep: 11 minutes • cook: 34 minutes
other: 8 hours

1   (13.7-ounce) package fat-free fudge brownie mix (such as No Pudge!)
⅔   cup vanilla low-fat yogurt
Cooking spray
3   cups vanilla low-fat ice cream, softened
1   teaspoon peppermint extract
18   chocolate thin mints, chopped (such as Andes)
2   tablespoons chocolate syrup

1. Preheat oven to 350°.
2. Prepare brownie mix according to package directions, using ⅔ cup yogurt. Pour batter into a foil-lined 8-inch square baking pan coated with cooking spray. Bake at 350° for 34 minutes. Cool completely in pan on a wire rack.
3. Combine ice cream and peppermint extract in a large bowl; stir well. Spread evenly over brownie. Cover and freeze 8 hours or until firm.
4. Sprinkle chopped mints over ice cream. Cut into squares; drizzle with chocolate syrup before serving. YIELD: 12 servings (serving size: 1 ice cream square).

POINTS value: 4; **Exchanges:** 2 Starch, ½ Skim Milk; **Per serving:** CAL 210 (11% from fat); PRO 5.3g; FAT 2.5g (sat 1.6g); CARB 42.2g; FIB 0.4g; CHOL 9mg; IRON 1.5mg; SOD 151mg; CALC 114mg

Fish & Shellfish

TERIYAKI AMBERJACK SKEWERS

prep: 20 minutes • cook: 14 minutes
other: 1 hour

We created a teriyaki-style marinade that is less sweet and more flavorful than commercial teriyaki sauces.

⅓   cup packed brown sugar
¼   cup low-sodium soy sauce
¼   cup fresh orange juice
¼   cup fresh lemon juice
¼   cup rice wine vinegar
3   garlic cloves, minced
1   tablespoon minced peeled
     fresh ginger
1   pound amberjack fillets, cut
     into 1-inch pieces
1   small red bell pepper, cut into
     1-inch pieces
1   small green bell pepper, cut
     into 1-inch pieces
1½   cups (1-inch) cubed fresh
     pineapple
     Cooking spray

1. Combine first 7 ingredients in a small saucepan; cook over medium heat 2 to 3 minutes or until sugar dissolves. Pour half of soy sauce mixture (about ½ cup) into a small bowl; set aside to cool.
2. Bring remaining soy sauce mixture to a boil over medium heat; reduce heat, and simmer 9 to 11 minutes or until mixture is reduced by half and forms a thin syrup (about ¼ cup). Remove from heat, pour into a small bowl, and refrigerate until ready to serve.
3. Pour reserved ½ cup soy sauce mixture into a zip-top plastic bag. Add fish and bell peppers; seal bag

and marinate in refrigerator 1 hour, turning occasionally.
4. Prepare grill.
5. Remove fish and bell peppers from marinade; discard marinade. Thread fish, bell pepper, and pineapple alternately onto 6 (12-inch) skewers.
6. Place on grill rack coated with cooking spray; grill 3 to 4 minutes on each side or until fish is opaque. Remove from heat; brush with reserved soy sauce mixture. YIELD: 3 servings (serving size: 2 kabobs).
Note: If you use wooden skewers, be sure to soak them in water for 30 minutes to prevent the wood from burning on the grill.

POINTS value: 5; **Exchanges:** 1 Starch, ½ Fruit, 1 Vegetable, 4 Very Lean Meat; **Per serving:** CAL 280 (6% from fat); PRO 31.3g; FAT 1.8g (sat 0.4g); CARB 35.5g; FIB 1.8g; CHOL 56mg; IRON 2.5mg; SOD 623mg; CALC 80mg

SEARED FISH WITH TOMATO-TARRAGON SALSA

prep: 12 minutes • cook: 6 minutes

1   cup chopped cherry tomatoes
2   tablespoons finely chopped
     green onions
2   tablespoons chopped fresh
     parsley
2   tablespoons capers
1   tablespoon olive oil
1   tablespoon balsamic vinegar
¼   teaspoon dried tarragon
¼   teaspoon salt
4   (6-ounce) firm white fish
     fillets (such as cod, grouper,
     or mahimahi)
2   teaspoons blackened seasoning
     Cooking spray
     Lemon wedges

1. Combine first 8 ingredients in a small bowl. Stir to blend and set aside.
2. Sprinkle both sides of fillets with blackened seasoning.
3. Place a large nonstick skillet over medium-high heat until hot. Coat pan with cooking spray; add fillets, and cook 3 to 4 minutes on each side or until fish flakes easily when tested with a fork.
4. Remove from heat; place 1 fillet on each of 4 dinner plates. Spoon salsa evenly over fillets. Serve with lemon wedges. YIELD: 4 servings (serving size: 1 fillet and ¼ cup salsa).

POINTS value: 4; **Exchanges:** 1 Vegetable, 4½ Very Lean Meat, ½ Fat; **Per serving:** CAL 200 (25% from fat); PRO 33.5g; FAT 5.3g (sat 0.9g); CARB 2.9g; FIB 0.7g; CHOL 63mg; IRON 2.0mg; SOD 561mg; CALC 55mg

STRIPED BASS EN PAPILLOTE

(pictured on page 66)

prep: 20 minutes • cook: 10 minutes

½   cup diced yellow tomato
¼   cup zucchini strips
¼   cup sliced red onion
¼   cup red bell pepper strips
1   tablespoon olive oil
1   tablespoon chopped fresh
     parsley
2   teaspoons chopped fresh
     oregano
½   teaspoon salt, divided
¼   teaspoon freshly ground black
     pepper, divided
4   (6-ounce) striped bass fillets
2   tablespoons crumbled feta
     cheese
4   teaspoons fresh lemon
     juice

1. Preheat oven to 500°.

2. Combine first 7 ingredients, ¼ teaspoon salt, and ⅛ teaspoon black pepper in a small bowl. Toss gently.

3. Cut 4 (24-inch) lengths of parchment paper. Fold each in half; open each. Place 1 fillet near fold on each. Sprinkle fillets with ¼ teaspoon salt and ⅛ teaspoon pepper. Top each evenly with vegetable mixture, feta cheese, and lemon juice.

4. Fold paper; seal edges with narrow folds. Place packets on baking sheets. Bake at 500° for 10 minutes or until puffed and lightly browned. Place on plates; cut open. Serve immediately. YIELD: 4 servings (serving size: 1 packet).

Note: You may use aluminum foil in place of parchment paper.

POINTS value: 5; **Exchanges:** ½ Vegetable, 4½ Very Lean Meat, 1 Fat; **Per serving:** CAL 217 (35% from fat); PRO 31.3g; FAT 8.4g (sat 2.0g); CARB 2.4g; FIB 0.5g; CHOL 140mg; IRON 1.7mg; SOD 468mg; CALC 59mg

---

EN PAPILLOTE

The French technique of cooking fish *en papillote*—in a package made of parchment paper—is a simple way to steam fish and vegetables for a complete meal. The flavor of various seasonings and vegetables permeates the fish, and the steam keeps it moist and flavorful. If you can't find parchment paper, foil makes a fine substitute, although it doesn't puff up as much with steam during cooking as parchment.

CORNMEAL- AND PECAN-CRUSTED CATFISH

prep: 6 minutes • cook: 8 minutes

Double-dredging the fish creates a nice thick crust that may remind you of batter-fried catfish.

6 tablespoons yellow cornmeal
¼ cup all-purpose flour
3 tablespoons finely chopped pecans
1½ teaspoons salt
1 teaspoon garlic powder
1 teaspoon paprika
¼ teaspoon ground red pepper
1 large egg, lightly beaten
1 tablespoon water
4 (6-ounce) farm-raised catfish fillets
1 teaspoon vegetable oil
Cooking spray
4 lemon wedges

1. Combine first 7 ingredients; divide evenly into 2 shallow dishes.

2. Place egg in another shallow dish; whisk in water. Dredge each fillet in cornmeal mixture; dip in egg mixture and dredge in second cornmeal mixture.

3. Heat oil in a large nonstick skillet coated with cooking spray over medium heat. Add fillets; cook 4 minutes on each side or until golden and fish flakes easily when tested with a fork. Serve with lemon wedges. YIELD: 4 servings (serving size: 1 fillet).

POINTS value: 7; **Exchanges:** 1 Starch, 3½ Lean Meat, 1 Fat; **Per serving:** CAL 309 (34% from fat); PRO 32.1g; FAT 11.6g (sat 2.1g); CARB 17.8g; FIB 2.0g; CHOL 152mg; IRON 1.9mg; SOD 377mg; CALC 38mg

---

PAN-FRIED FLOUNDER

prep: 11 minutes • cook: 8 minutes

Serve this crusty flounder with baked potato fries and malt vinegar for a lower-fat version of English fish and chips.

4 (6-ounce) flounder fillets
¾ teaspoon salt, divided
½ teaspoon freshly ground black pepper, divided
2 large eggs, lightly beaten
1 large egg white, lightly beaten
¼ cup chopped chives
1 teaspoon hot sauce
½ cup all-purpose flour
1 tablespoon olive oil
Lemon wedges

1. Sprinkle fillets with ½ teaspoon salt and ¼ teaspoon pepper.

2. Combine ¼ teaspoon salt, ¼ teaspoon pepper, egg, egg white, chives, and hot sauce in a shallow dish. Place flour in a separate shallow dish.

3. Heat 1½ teaspoons oil in a large nonstick skillet over medium-high heat. Dredge 2 fillets in flour, shaking off any excess; dip into egg mixture, coating both sides. Immediately place fillets in pan; cook 2 minutes on each side or until golden and fish flakes easily when tested with a fork. Repeat with remaining oil, fillets, flour, and egg mixture. Serve immediately with lemon wedges. YIELD: 4 servings (serving size: 1 fillet).

POINTS value: 6; **Exchanges:** ½ Starch, 5 Very Lean Meat, 1 Fat; **Per serving:** CAL 271 (28% from fat); PRO 37.4g; FAT 8.1g (sat 1.7g); CARB 9.6g; FIB 0.5g; CHOL 187mg; IRON 1.8mg; SOD 630mg; CALC 51mg

LEMON GROUPER WITH TOMATO-DILL SAUCE

prep: 10 minutes • cook: 13 minutes

4	(6-ounce) grouper fillets
2	tablespoons all-purpose flour
Cooking spray	
1	tablespoon olive oil
¾	cup dry white wine
3	tablespoons thinly sliced green onions (about 2)
2	tablespoons chopped fresh dill
1	plum tomato, seeded and diced
2	teaspoons grated lemon rind
1	tablespoon fresh lemon juice
2	tablespoons light butter, cut into small pieces
¼	teaspoon salt

1. Rinse fillets in cold water; pat dry with paper towels.

2. Sprinkle flour evenly over fish; shake off any excess.

3. Heat a large nonstick skillet coated with cooking spray over medium-high heat; add oil. Add fish; cook 4 minutes on each side or until fish flakes easily when tested with a fork. Remove fish; set aside and keep warm.

4. Add wine to pan, scraping pan to loosen browned bits. Add onions and dill; cook 3 minutes, stirring frequently, or until liquid is reduced to about ⅓ cup. Add tomato, lemon rind, and lemon juice; cook 1 minute or until slightly thick. Remove pan from heat; add butter and salt, stirring until butter melts. Spoon sauce over fish. YIELD: 4 servings (serving size: 1 fillet and about 3 tablespoons sauce).

POINTS value: 5; **Exchanges:** 1 Vegetable, 4 Very Lean Meat, 1½ Fat; **Per serving:** CAL 235 (32% from fat); PRO 34.1g; FAT 8.2g (sat 2.9g); CARB 5.2g; FIB 0.6g; CHOL 73mg; IRON 2.0mg; SOD 279mg; CALC 53mg

GRILLED GROUPER TACOS

(pictured on page 71)

prep: 20 minutes • cook: 20 minutes

Save steps at dinnertime by making the sour cream mixture and the corn salsa ahead of time.

¼	cup low-fat sour cream
3½	tablespoons fresh lime juice, divided
¾	cup fresh corn kernels or frozen corn kernels, thawed
2	small plum tomatoes, seeded and diced
¼	cup thinly sliced green onions (about 3)
2½	tablespoons olive oil, divided
2	tablespoons chopped fresh cilantro
1	teaspoon minced seeded jalapeño pepper
¾	teaspoon salt, divided
¼	teaspoon freshly ground black pepper, divided
1½	cups thinly sliced onion
½	red bell pepper, seeded and cut into thin strips
8	(6-inch) tostada shells
1	pound grouper or other firm white fish fillets
½	teaspoon chili powder
¼	teaspoon ground cumin
Cooking spray	
2	cups shredded romaine or leaf lettuce

1. Combine sour cream and 2 tablespoons lime juice. Cover and chill.

2. Place a large nonstick skillet over medium heat. Add corn; sauté 3 to 4 minutes or until corn is lightly browned. Combine corn, tomato, green onions, 1 tablespoon lime juice, 1 tablespoon oil, cilantro, jalapeño pepper, ¼ teaspoon salt, and ⅛ teaspoon black pepper in a bowl. Toss gently. Cover and chill.

3. Add 1 tablespoon oil to pan. Place over medium heat. Add sliced onion; sauté 3 to 4 minutes or until onion is crisp-tender. Add bell pepper; cook 2 to 3 minutes or until pepper softens. Stir in ¼ teaspoon salt; transfer to a bowl.

4. Heat tostada shells according to package directions; keep warm.

5. Prepare grill.

6. Combine fish, 1½ teaspoons oil, 1½ teaspoons lime juice, chili powder, cumin, ¼ teaspoon salt, and ⅛ teaspoon black pepper in a large zip-top plastic bag. Toss gently. Place fish on grill rack coated with cooking spray; grill 6 to 7 minutes on each side or until fish flakes easily when tested with a fork. Flake fish.

7. Top each tostado shell with ¼ cup shredded lettuce. Spoon onion and bell pepper mixture evenly over lettuce; divide fish evenly over onion and bell pepper mixture. Top fish with corn salsa; drizzle with the sour cream mixture. YIELD: 8 servings (serving size: 1 taco).

POINTS value: 4; **Exchanges:** 1 Starch, 2 Very Lean Meat, 1 Fat; **Per serving:** CAL 202 (38% from fat); PRO 13.7g; FAT 8.6g (sat 1.8g); CARB 18.2g; FIB 2.7g; CHOL 25mg; IRON 1.2mg; SOD 356mg; CALC 44mg

MUSTARD-GLAZED HALIBUT WITH WARM SCALLIONS

prep: 6 minutes • cook: 20 minutes

¼ cup mirin (sweet rice wine)
1 tablespoon honey
2 teaspoons low-sodium soy sauce
2 teaspoons stone-ground mustard
¼ teaspoon chili garlic sauce
2 teaspoons canola oil, divided
12 green onions, diagonally cut into 4-inch pieces
4 (6-ounce) halibut fillets
¼ teaspoon salt

1. Combine first 5 ingredients in a small saucepan. Cook over medium-high heat 4 minutes or until sauce thickens, stirring constantly. Remove from heat; keep warm.

2. Heat 1 teaspoon oil in a large nonstick skillet over medium-high heat. Add onions; sauté 3 minutes or until tender. Remove from pan; keep warm.

3. Heat 1 teaspoon oil in pan over medium-high heat. Sprinkle fish with salt. Add fish to pan, skin side down. Cook 6 minutes on each side or until lightly browned and fish flakes easily when tested with a fork. Divide onions evenly among 4 plates. Place fish over onions; drizzle with mustard glaze. YIELD: 4 servings (serving size: 1 fillet, ¼ cup onions, and 1 tablespoon glaze).

POINTS value: 5; **Exchanges:** 1 Vegetable, 5 Very Lean Meat, 1 Fat; **Per serving:** CAL 243 (23% from fat); PRO 36.5g; FAT 6.3g (sat 1.0g); CARB 8.5g; FIB 1.5g; CHOL 54mg; IRON 2.3mg; SOD 383mg; CALC 116mg

OVEN-ROASTED HALIBUT

prep: 8 minutes • cook: 8 minutes

This simple oven-roasting method can be used for any type of firm white fish. Serve this recipe with Barley and Brussels Sprouts, page 149, for a meal with a **POINTS** *value of 7.*

4 (6-ounce) halibut fillets
Cooking spray
¼ teaspoon salt
⅛ teaspoon freshly ground black pepper
1 (1-ounce) slice white bread
1 tablespoon chopped fresh parsley
1½ teaspoons chopped fresh chives
1 tablespoon butter, melted
Lemon wedges

1. Preheat oven to 425°.

2. Coat fillets with cooking spray; sprinkle with salt and pepper. Place fillets on a foil-lined baking sheet.

3. Place bread in a blender or food processor; pulse 5 times or until coarse crumbs measure ½ cup.

4. Combine breadcrumbs, parsley, chives, and 1½ teaspoons butter in a small bowl; toss well. Spoon breadcrumb mixture on top of fillets, pressing down gently. Drizzle remaining butter over breadcrumb mixture.

5. Bake at 425° for 8 to 10 minutes or until fish flakes easily when tested with a fork. Serve with lemon wedges. YIELD: 4 servings (serving size: 1 fillet).

POINTS value: 5; **Exchanges:** 5 Very Lean Meat, 1 Fat; **Per serving:** CAL 230 (30% from fat); PRO 36.1g; FAT 7.7g (sat 1.9g); CARB 2.5g; FIB 0.7g; CHOL 60mg; IRON 1.9mg; SOD 282mg; CALC 90mg

---

FIRE UP THE COALS

Grilling seafood is easy if you know which kinds work best. You want fish that has a thick, firm, meaty texture so that it won't fall apart while cooking. The seafood listed below is particularly suitable for the grill.

Grouper: This white-meat fish is sold in fillets and steaks. If you can't find grouper, use sea bass, orange roughy, or mahimahi.

Halibut: The meat of halibut is white and mild-flavored, and comes in steaks and fillets. Although it's a firm fish, it's a little more delicate than others—so be gentle when turning it on the grill.

Salmon: With a range of flavor from rich to mild, salmon can take on a char and still keep its distinctive taste. Salmon comes in steaks and fillets.

Scallops: This bivalve is usually classified into two groups: bay scallops and sea scallops. The larger sea scallops are best for grilling because, like shrimp, they have a meaty texture and can be easily skewered. They cook fast, though, so keep a close eye on them.

Shrimp: Large shrimp are best for grilling. They can be easily skewered, and they cook quickly.

Swordfish: This mild fish has a firm, meaty texture. Its natural oil content keeps it moist while grilling. You can usually find it sold as steaks.

Tuna: Start with fresh tuna if you're new to grilling fish. It cooks like a beef steak, and its deep-red meat almost never sticks to the grill.

MAHIMAHI FINGERS WITH CREAMY DILL TARTAR SAUCE

prep: 15 minutes • cook: 17 minutes

⅓	cup low-fat sour cream
3	tablespoons sweet pickle relish
2	tablespoons light mayonnaise
1	tablespoon finely chopped shallots
1	tablespoon chopped fresh dill
2	teaspoons capers, drained and minced
1	teaspoon grated lemon rind
1	large egg white
1	tablespoon fresh lemon juice
1	tablespoon water
⅓	cup all-purpose flour
1	tablespoon sesame seeds
½	teaspoon salt
½	teaspoon garlic powder
½	teaspoon paprika
1	tablespoon canola oil, divided
1½	pounds mahimahi fillets, cut lengthwise into ½-inch-thick strips

1. Combine first 7 ingredients in a small bowl; stir with a whisk. Cover and chill.
2. Combine egg white, lemon juice, and water in a shallow bowl; stir with a whisk.
3. Combine flour and next 4 ingredients in another shallow dish; stir with a whisk.
4. Pat fish strips dry with paper towels; dip in egg white mixture, and dredge in flour mixture.
5. Heat a large nonstick skillet over medium-high heat. Add 1½ teaspoons oil and half of fish; cook 4 minutes on each side or until browned. Repeat procedure with remaining oil and fish. Serve with tartar sauce. YIELD: 4 servings (serving size: 4 fish strips and 2 tablespoons tartar sauce).

POINTS value: 6; **Exchanges:** 1 Starch, 4 Very Lean Meat, 1½ Fat; Per serving: CAL 285 (34% from fat); PRO 29.8g; FAT 10.7g (sat 2.5g); CARB 15.8g; FIB 0.7g; CHOL 116mg; IRON 5.6mg; SOD 640mg; CALC 61mg

BAKED SALMON WITH CREAMY ONION SAUCE

prep: 8 minutes • cook: 12 minutes

Serve this simple baked salmon over fresh field greens and top with onion sauce. The creamy onion sauce doubles as a dressing and can be made ahead and stored in the refrigerator for up to 3 days.

4	(6-ounce) salmon fillets (about 1 inch thick)
¼	teaspoon freshly ground black pepper
⅛	teaspoon salt
⅓	cup plain fat-free yogurt
2	tablespoons light mayonnaise
1	tablespoon chopped onion
1	tablespoon capers
¼	teaspoon salt
4	lemon wedges

1. Preheat oven to 400°.
2. Line a jelly roll pan with nonstick foil. Arrange fillets, skin sides down, on foil; sprinkle with pepper and ⅛ teaspoon salt.
3. Bake at 400° for 12 minutes or until fish flakes easily when tested with a fork.
4. While fish bakes, process yogurt and next 4 ingredients in a blender until smooth.
5. Place fillets on a serving platter. Serve with sauce and lemon wedges. YIELD: 4 servings (serving size: 1 fillet and about 2 tablespoons sauce).

POINTS value: 5; **Exchanges:** 4 Lean Meat; Per serving: CAL 235 (33% from fat); PRO 35.0g; FAT 8.4g (sat 1.3g); CARB 3.3g; FIB 0.3g; CHOL 91mg; IRON 1.4mg; SOD 470mg; CALC 51mg

PAN-SEARED SALMON WITH HONEY-BALSAMIC SAUCE

(pictured on page 67)
prep: 5 minutes • cook: 12 minutes

To clean leeks, remove roots, outer leaves, and tops. Rinse with cold water; cut into 2-inch julienne strips. Onions may be substituted for leeks.

	Cooking spray
¼	teaspoon olive oil
½	cup julienne-cut leeks (about 1 small)
4	(6-ounce) salmon fillets (about 1 inch thick)
½	teaspoon salt, divided
¼	teaspoon pepper, divided
½	cup balsamic vinegar
1	tablespoon honey

1. Coat a large nonstick skillet with cooking spray; add oil. Place over medium-high heat; add leeks, and sauté 3 to 4 minutes or until soft. Remove from pan and set aside.
2. Sprinkle fish with ¼ teaspoon salt and ⅛ teaspoon pepper. Add fish to pan; cook 3 to 4 minutes on each side or until lightly browned and fish flakes easily when tested with a fork. Remove from pan; set aside, and keep warm.

3. Add vinegar, honey, ¼ teaspoon salt, and ⅛ teaspoon pepper to pan. Cook over medium-high heat 3 to 4 minutes or until reduced by half. Divide leeks evenly over fish; drizzle with sauce. YIELD: 4 servings (serving size: 1 fillet and 1 tablespoon sauce).

POINTS value: 5; **Exchanges:** ½ Starch, 3½ Lean Meat; **Per serving:** CAL 243 (23% from fat); PRO 34.2g; FAT 6.3g (sat 1.0g); CARB 10.7g; FIB 0.3g; CHOL 88mg; IRON 1.8mg; SOD 417mg; CALC 39mg

POACHED SALMON WITH SPRING VEGETABLES

prep: 15 minutes • cook: 40 minutes

This recipe uses a court-bouillon (coor bwee-YAWN), a poaching liquid flavored with vegetables and herbs. This French cooking method is frequently used with fish because of the subtle flavor it imparts to seafood.

4   cups water
½   cup dry white wine
1   cup julienne-cut leek, white and green parts (about 1 large)
1   cup julienne-cut carrot
1   bay leaf
1   teaspoon freshly ground black peppercorns
1   teaspoon freshly ground pink peppercorns
2   parsley sprigs
4   (6-ounce) salmon steaks (about 1 inch thick)
1   teaspoon salt

1. Combine water, wine, and next 6 ingredients in a large Dutch oven. Bring mixture to a boil. Simmer, uncovered, over medium heat 20 minutes. Remove bay leaf and parsley; discard. Keep mixture at a low simmer.
2. Carefully lower fish into pan. Simmer 10 minutes or until fish flakes easily when tested with a fork.
3. Remove fish from poaching liquid and place in shallow individual pasta bowls. Stir salt into poaching liquid and spoon mixture evenly over fish. YIELD: 4 servings (serving size: 1 steak).

POINTS value: 5; **Exchanges:** 1 Vegetable, 3½ Lean Meat; **Per serving:** CAL 230 (24% from fat); PRO 34.7g; FAT 6.0g (sat 1.0g); CARB 7.5g; FIB 1.6g; CHOL 88mg; IRON 2.2mg; SOD 719mg; CALC 51mg

SALMON

In addition to being a great source of protein, salmon is also a good source of omega-3 fatty acids, which have been shown to help lower cholesterol and triglycerides, work against inflammation, and possibly help to prevent cancer. Omega-3 fatty acids have also been in the spotlight recently concerning their ability to promote brain, eye, and nerve tissue development during pregnancy.

Smoked and canned salmon have been readily available for years. Today, fresh or frozen salmon can be found at supermarkets for a reasonable price.

PAN-SEARED SNAPPER WITH GARLIC-HERB VINAIGRETTE

prep: 11 minutes • cook: 10 minutes

This quick recipe received the highest rating from our tasting panel.

2   tablespoons fresh lemon juice
1   tablespoon water
1   garlic clove, minced
½   teaspoon salt, divided
½   teaspoon freshly ground black pepper, divided
1½   tablespoons olive oil, divided
1   tablespoon minced fresh parsley
1   tablespoon minced fresh oregano
4   (6-ounce) snapper fillets
Cooking spray

1. Combine lemon juice, water, garlic, ¼ teaspoon salt, and ¼ teaspoon pepper in a small bowl; stir with a whisk. Gradually whisk in 1 tablespoon oil. Stir in parsley and oregano; set aside.
2. Sprinkle fillets with ¼ teaspoon salt and ¼ teaspoon pepper.
3. Heat 1½ teaspoons oil in a large nonstick skillet coated with cooking spray over medium-high heat. Add fillets; cook 5 to 6 minutes on each side or until fish flakes easily when tested with a fork. Transfer fish to serving plates; drizzle with vinaigrette. YIELD: 4 servings (serving size: 1 fillet and 1 tablespoon garlic-herb vinaigrette).

POINTS value: 5; **Exchanges:** 5 Very Lean Meat, 1 Fat; **Per serving:** CAL 220 (30% from fat); PRO 35.1g; FAT 7.4g (sat 1.2g); CARB 1.3g; FIB 0.1g; CHOL 63mg; IRON 0.4mg; SOD 403mg; CALC 64mg

SOUTHWESTERN TILAPIA

prep: 4 minutes • cook: 7 minutes

Tilapia has a sweet, mild flavor and firm texture, and is suitable for almost any cooking method.

4   (6-ounce) tilapia fillets
½   teaspoon salt
½   teaspoon pepper
Cooking spray
3   tablespoons light butter, divided
1   cup finely chopped onion (about 1 medium)
1   teaspoon chili powder
½   teaspoon ground cumin
2   tablespoons water
1   tablespoon fresh lime juice

1. Preheat broiler.
2. Sprinkle both sides of fish with salt and pepper. Place on a broiler pan coated with cooking spray. Spray fish with cooking spray. Broil 6 to 8 minutes or until fish flakes easily when tested with a fork.
3. Meanwhile, melt 1 tablespoon butter in a large nonstick skillet over medium heat. Add onion; cook 4 minutes or until tender, stirring constantly. Stir in chili powder and cumin; cook 30 seconds, stirring constantly. Remove from heat; stir in 2 tablespoons butter, water, and lime juice until well blended. Spoon onion mixture evenly over fish. YIELD: 4 servings (serving size: 1 fillet and 2 tablespoons onion mixture).

POINTS value: 5; **Exchanges:** 4½ Very Lean Meat, 1 Fat; **Per serving:** CAL 214 (27% from fat); PRO 34.4g; FAT 6.5g (sat 3.4g); CARB 4.4g; FIB 1.1g; CHOL 78mg; IRON 1.9mg; SOD 444mg; CALC 60mg

MIXED SEAFOOD GRILL WITH LEMON BUTTER

prep: 18 minutes • cook: 6 minutes

¾   pound unpeeled large shrimp (about 22 to 24)
¾   pound sea scallops (about 16 to 18)
Cooking spray
1   tablespoon butter, melted
1   tablespoon minced shallots
1   tablespoon minced fresh parsley
⅛   teaspoon grated lemon rind
2   teaspoons fresh lemon juice
¼   teaspoon salt
¼   teaspoon freshly ground black pepper

1. Prepare grill.
2. Peel and devein shrimp, leaving tails intact. Thread shrimp onto 4 (10-inch) skewers.
3. Thread scallops onto 3 (10-inch) skewers.
4. Place shrimp and scallops on grill rack coated with cooking spray. Grill shrimp, uncovered, 2 minutes on each side or until done; grill scallops, uncovered, 3 to 4 minutes on each side or until done.
5. Remove seafood from skewers, and place in a large bowl. Add butter and remaining ingredients; toss. Serve immediately. YIELD: 4 servings (serving size: about 5 shrimp and about 4 scallops).
Note: If using wooden skewers, soak them in water for 30 minutes to prevent the wood from burning on the grill.

POINTS value: 4; **Exchanges:** 4½ Very Lean Meat, 1 Fat; **Per serving:** CAL 206 (29% from fat); PRO 31.7g; FAT 6.4g (sat 2.5g); CARB 3.6g; FIB 0.1g; CHOL 169mg; IRON 2.4mg; SOD 441mg; CALC 69mg

ASIAN-STYLE CRAB CAKES

(pictured on page 68)
prep: 26 minutes • cook: 28 minutes

½   cup light mayonnaise
¼   cup chopped green onions
1   tablespoon fresh lemon juice
¾   teaspoon salt
½   teaspoon pepper
1   large egg, lightly beaten
1   (2-ounce) jar diced pimiento, drained
1   pound lump crabmeat, drained and shell pieces removed
2½   cups Japanese breadcrumbs (panko), divided
Cooking spray
2   tablespoons olive oil

1. Combine first 7 ingredients in a large bowl. Fold in crabmeat and 1 cup breadcrumbs.
2. Divide crab mixture into 12 equal portions, shaping each into a 2-inch-round patty. Place 1½ cups breadcrumbs in a shallow dish; dredge crab cakes in breadcrumbs. Coat crab cakes with cooking spray.
3. Heat 1 tablespoon oil in a large nonstick skillet over medium heat. Add 6 crab cakes; cook 7 to 8 minutes on each side or until browned. Remove crab cakes from pan; keep warm. Repeat procedure with remaining oil and patties. Serve with tartar or cocktail sauce. YIELD: 12 servings (serving size: 1 crab cake).
Note: Cover and place crab cakes in the freezer for 10 minutes before frying to help retain their shape.

POINTS value: 4; **Exchanges:** ½ Starch, 1 Very Lean Meat, 2 Fat; **Per serving:** CAL 170 (49% from fat); PRO 9.3g; FAT 9.2g (sat 1.3g); CARB 11.9g; FIB 0.5g; CHOL 61mg; IRON 0.6mg; SOD 587mg; CALC 47mg

CURRIED MUSSELS

(pictured on page 67)

prep: 20 minutes • cook: 10 minutes

Steam mussels over a bath of flavorful liquids—the shells open up and the mussels become tender in about 5 minutes.

1½ teaspoons butter
2   tablespoons minced shallots
3   garlic cloves, minced
1½ pounds mussels, scrubbed and debearded (about 40)
¼   cup dry white wine
½   cup light coconut milk
½   teaspoon curry powder
¼   teaspoon salt
2   tablespoons chopped fresh cilantro

1. Melt butter in a large nonstick skillet over medium-high heat. Add shallots and garlic; sauté 1 minute or until tender. Add mussels and wine. Bring to a boil; cover, reduce heat, and simmer 5 minutes or until shells open. Discard any unopened shells. Remove mussels with a slotted spoon. Divide mussels evenly among 4 bowls. Keep warm.
2. Increase heat to medium-high. Add coconut milk, curry powder, and salt to pan; cook 3 minutes, stirring constantly. Ladle sauce evenly over each serving; sprinkle with cilantro. YIELD: 4 servings (serving size: 10 mussels, about ¼ cup sauce, and 1½ teaspoons cilantro).

POINTS value: 4; **Exchanges:** 4 Very Lean Meat, 1 Fat; **Per serving:** CAL 180 (34% from fat); PRO 20.2g; FAT 6.7g (sat 2.6g); CARB 8.4g; FIB 0.1g; CHOL 51mg; IRON 7.0mg; SOD 651mg; CALC 49mg

SCALLOP VERMICELLI WITH SPINACH

prep: 7 minutes • cook: 15 minutes

6   ounces uncooked vermicelli, broken in thirds
¾   teaspoon salt, divided
½   teaspoon paprika
½   teaspoon coarsely ground black pepper
⅛   teaspoon garlic powder
1   pound sea scallops, rinsed and patted dry (about 24)
1   tablespoon butter, divided
Cooking spray
¼   cup water
1½ cups thinly sliced spinach leaves (about 1½ ounces)
1   teaspoon grated lemon rind
2   tablespoons fresh lemon juice
4   lemon wedges

1. Cook pasta according to package directions, omitting salt and fat.
2. Meanwhile, sprinkle ¼ teaspoon salt, paprika, pepper, and garlic powder evenly over scallops.
3. Heat 1½ teaspoons butter in a large nonstick skillet coated with cooking spray over medium-high heat. Add 12 scallops to pan; cook 4 to 5 minutes or until done, turning once. Remove scallops; set aside and keep warm. Repeat with remaining butter and scallops.
4. Add water to pan; bring to a boil, scraping pan to loosen browned bits. Remove from heat; add pasta, spinach, lemon rind, lemon juice, and ½ teaspoon salt. Toss gently. Divide evenly among 4 serving plates. Top with scallops; serve immediately with lemon wedges.

YIELD: 4 servings (serving size: 1 cup pasta mixture and 6 scallops).

POINTS value: 6; **Exchanges:** 2 Starch, 3 Very Lean Meat, ½ Fat; **Per serving:** CAL 284 (15% from fat); PRO 25.1g; FAT 4.8g (sat 1.7g); CARB 35.1g; FIB 1.9g; CHOL 45mg; IRON 2.0mg; SOD 661mg; CALC 50mg

SCALLOPS WITH MILD CREAMY GINGER SAUCE

prep: 6 minutes • cook: 8 minutes

1½ pounds sea scallops (about 36 scallops)
Cooking spray
½   teaspoon salt, divided
¼   teaspoon paprika
⅔   cup light coconut milk
2   tablespoons grated peeled fresh ginger
2   tablespoons butter
¼   teaspoon black pepper

1. Rinse scallops and blot dry on paper towels.
2. Heat a large nonstick skillet coated with cooking spray over medium heat. Add scallops; sprinkle lightly with ¼ teaspoon salt and paprika. Cook 3 minutes on each side or until opaque in center. Remove scallops with a slotted spoon. Set aside; keep warm.
3. Add coconut milk and ginger to pan drippings. Cook 1 minute, scraping pan to loosen browned bits. Remove from heat. Stir in butter and ¼ teaspoon salt; stir until butter melts. Pour sauce over scallops. Sprinkle with black pepper. YIELD: 5 servings (serving size: about 7 scallops).

POINTS value: 4; **Exchanges:** 4 Lean Meat, 1 Fat; **Per serving:** CAL 181 (37% from fat); PRO 23g; FAT 7.2g (sat 3.5g); CARB 4.8g; FIB 0.1g; CHOL 57mg; IRON 0.6mg; SOD 378mg; CALC 35mg

CREAMY COCONUT SHRIMP

prep: 13 minutes • cook: 10 minutes

In a hurry? Use instant rice or new ready-cook varieties.

1½   cups uncooked long-grain rice
Cooking spray
1   cup chopped red bell pepper
1   cup chopped green onions
1   tablespoon grated peeled fresh
       ginger
1   teaspoon curry powder
¼   teaspoon crushed red pepper
1   (13.5-ounce) can light
       coconut milk
1¼   pounds medium shrimp,
       peeled and deveined
½   teaspoon salt
1   lime, quartered
¼   cup chopped fresh cilantro

1. Cook rice according to package directions, omitting salt and fat.
2. Heat a large nonstick skillet coated with cooking spray over medium-high heat; add bell pepper and next 4 ingredients. Sauté 2 minutes. Add coconut milk, shrimp, and salt; cook over medium heat 7 to 8 minutes or until shrimp are done (do not boil), stirring occasionally.
3. Place ¾ cup rice on each of 4 serving plates; spoon shrimp mixture evenly over rice. Squeeze 1 lime quarter over each serving and sprinkle with chopped cilantro. YIELD: 4 servings (serving size: 1 cup shrimp mixture and ¾ cup rice).

POINTS value: 4; **Exchanges:** 1 Vegetable, 3½ Very Lean Meat, 1 Fat; **Per serving:** CAL 197 (32% from fat); PRO 24.0g; FAT 7.0g (sat 3.6g); CARB 8.9g; FIB 0.9g; CHOL 172mg; IRON 4.0mg; SOD 197mg; CALC 82mg

THAI CURRY SHRIMP

prep: 15 minutes • cook: 10 minutes
other: 1 hour and 30 minutes

Red curry paste, found on the Asian-ingredient aisle in the supermarket, makes these shrimp wonderfully spicy.

2   tablespoons chopped peeled
       fresh lemon grass
2   tablespoons brown sugar
2   tablespoons fresh lime juice
1   tablespoon olive oil
2   teaspoons fish sauce
1½   teaspoons red curry paste
1   pound jumbo shrimp, peeled
       and deveined
¾   cup uncooked rice
Cooking spray
½   cup light coconut milk
1   tablespoon chopped fresh
       cilantro

1. Combine first 6 ingredients in a shallow dish or heavy-duty zip-top plastic bag; add shrimp. Seal and marinate in refrigerator up to 1½ hours, stirring occasionally.
2. Cook rice according to package directions, omitting salt and fat.
3. Heat a large nonstick skillet coated with cooking spray over medium-high heat; add shrimp. Cook 3 to 4 minutes or until shrimp are done, stirring occasionally. Stir in coconut milk, and cook 1 minute. Stir in cilantro. Serve over rice. YIELD: 3 servings (serving size: about 1 cup shrimp mixture and ½ cup rice).

POINTS value: 4; **Exchanges:** ½ Starch, 1 Vegetable, 4 Very Lean Meat; **Per serving:** CAL 198 (31% from fat); PRO 23.3g; FAT 6.9g (sat 1.8g); CARB 10.4g; FIB 0.0g; CHOL 172mg; IRON 3.3mg; SOD 475mg; CALC 68mg

RISOTTO WITH SPINACH AND SHRIMP

prep: 8 minutes • cook: 37 minutes

2¾   cups fat-free, less-sodium
       chicken broth
2   teaspoons olive oil
1   large Vidalia onion, chopped
4   garlic cloves, minced
1   cup uncooked Arborio rice
½   teaspoon salt
½   teaspoon saffron threads,
       crushed
⅛   teaspoon crushed red pepper
¼   cup dry white wine
1   pound peeled and deveined
       large fresh shrimp
3   cups firmly packed fresh baby
       spinach
¼   cup (1 ounce) shredded fresh
       Parmesan cheese

1. Bring broth to a simmer in a medium saucepan (do not boil). Keep warm over low heat.
2. Heat oil in a large saucepan over medium heat. Add onion; sauté 5 minutes. Add garlic; sauté 1 minute. Add rice and next 3 ingredients; cook 1 minute, stirring constantly. Add wine; cook until liquid is nearly absorbed, stirring constantly. Add warm broth, ½ cup at a time, stirring constantly, until each portion of broth is absorbed before adding the next (about 25 minutes total). Stir in shrimp and spinach; cook 5 to 7 minutes or until shrimp turn pink. Stir in Parmesan cheese. YIELD: 6 servings (serving size: about ¾ cup).

POINTS value: 5; **Exchanges:** 1½ Starch, 4 Very Lean Meat, ½ Fat; **Per serving:** CAL 238 (16% from fat); PRO 24.1g; FAT 4.2g (sat 1.3g); CARB 25.4g; FIB 1.6g; CHOL 134mg; IRON 3.1mg; SOD 944mg; CALC 139mg

Meatless Main Dishes

GRILLED PROVOLONE AND VEGETABLE PIZZA

prep: 10 minutes • cook: 14 minutes

1	(1-pound) loaf frozen bread dough, thawed
	Olive oil-flavored cooking spray
1	(8-ounce) can tomato sauce with roasted garlic
1	cup (4 ounces) shredded provolone cheese
1	cup sliced mushrooms
⅓	cup thinly sliced onion
¼	cup chopped pitted kalamata olives

1. Prepare grill.

2. Divide dough into 2 equal portions; roll out each portion into an 11-inch circle (about ¼ inch thick) on work surface coated with cooking spray. Let dough rest while preparing sauce and toppings.

3. Cook tomato sauce, uncovered, in a saucepan over medium-high heat 2 to 3 minutes or until slightly thick.

4. Coat grill racks with cooking spray; grill 1 portion of dough over medium-low heat 2 to 3 minutes or until browned. Turn dough. Spread half of tomato sauce over cooked side of dough. Top with half each of cheese, mushrooms, onion, and olives. Close grill lid; grill 4 minutes or until cheese melts and bottom of crust is browned. Remove from heat; repeat procedure with remaining ingredients. Cut each pizza into 4 slices. YIELD: 8 servings (serving size: 1 slice).

POINTS value: 4; **Exchanges:** 2 Starch, ½ Vegetable, 1 Lean Meat; **Per serving:** CAL 223 (27% from fat); PRO 10.4g; FAT 6.9g (sat 2.5g); CARB 32.2g; FIB 2.6g; CHOL 10mg; IRON 2.5mg; SOD 656mg; CALC 126mg

MARGHERITA PIZZA

prep: 20 minutes • cook: 20 minutes
other: 1 hour and 15 minutes

1	package dry yeast (about 2¼ teaspoons)
2	teaspoons sugar
1	cup warm water (100° to 110°)
3	cups all-purpose flour, divided
2	tablespoons cornmeal, divided
1	tablespoon olive oil
½	teaspoon salt, divided
	Cooking spray
¾	cup (3 ounces) shredded part-skim mozzarella cheese
½	cup (2 ounces) grated fresh Parmesan cheese
½	cup chopped fresh flat-leaf parsley
4	garlic cloves, minced
1	teaspoon olive oil
2	large tomatoes, sliced
¼	teaspoon freshly ground black pepper
1	tablespoon chopped fresh basil

1. Dissolve yeast and sugar in water in a large bowl; let stand 5 minutes. Lightly spoon flour into dry measuring cups; level with a knife. Add 2½ cups flour, 1 tablespoon cornmeal, 1 tablespoon olive oil, and ¼ teaspoon salt to yeast mixture. Turn dough out onto a floured surface. Knead until smooth and elastic (about 10 minutes). Add enough of remaining flour, 1 tablespoon at a time, to prevent dough from sticking to hands (dough will feel tacky).

2. Place dough in a large bowl coated with cooking spray, turning to coat top. Cover and let rise in a warm place (85°), free from drafts, 50 minutes or until doubled in size. (Press two fingers into dough. If indentation remains, the dough has risen enough.) Punch dough down; cover and let rest 5 minutes.

3. Preheat oven to 400°.

4. Roll dough into a 13-inch circle on a floured surface. Place dough on a baking sheet sprinkled with 1 tablespoon cornmeal. Crimp edges of dough with fingers to form a rim. Cover and let dough rise 15 minutes or until puffy. Combine cheeses; set aside. Combine parsley, garlic, and 1 teaspoon olive oil. Brush garlic mixture over dough. Top with 1 cup cheese mixture and tomato slices. Sprinkle with remaining cheese mixture, ¼ teaspoon salt, and pepper.

5. Bake at 400° for 20 minutes or until cheese melts. Sprinkle with basil. Let pizza stand 5 minutes. Cut into 8 slices. YIELD: 8 servings (serving size: 1 slice).

POINTS value: 5; **Exchanges:** 2 Starch, 1 Medium-Fat Meat; **Per serving:** CAL 238 (18% from fat); PRO 9.8g; FAT 5.9g (sat 2.3g); CARB 36.4g; FIB 2.1g; CHOL 10mg; IRON 2.7mg; SOD 279mg; CALC 157mg

---

COOKING WITH FRESH HERBS

Unlike dried herbs, fresh herbs are usually added toward the end of cooking to preserve their flavor. Herbs like dill, oregano, rosemary, and thyme can be added during the last 20 minutes of cooking. However, more delicate herbs like basil, cilantro, dill leaves, and mint should be added in the last few minutes or sprinkled over the food just before serving.

VEGETARIAN TORTILLA PIZZA

prep: 10 minutes • cook: 9 minutes

Flour tortillas give this vegetable-packed pizza a delicious, thin-crust crunch.

1   (16-ounce) can pinto beans, rinsed and drained
3   tablespoons fresh lime juice, divided
1   teaspoon ground cumin
1   garlic clove, minced
1½ cups halved grape tomatoes
¼   cup chopped fresh cilantro
1   tablespoon cider vinegar
1   jalapeño pepper, minced
¼   teaspoon salt
Cooking spray
1   green bell pepper, thinly sliced
1   small yellow onion, cut into ½-inch wedges
4   (8-inch) 97%-fat-free flour tortillas
1   cup (4 ounces) shredded pepper Jack cheese

1. Preheat oven to 350°.
2. Place beans, 2 tablespoons lime juice, cumin, and garlic in a blender; process until smooth, scraping bottom and sides frequently.
3. Combine tomatoes, cilantro, vinegar, jalapeño, 1 tablespoon lime juice, and salt. Toss and set aside.
4. Place a large nonstick skillet coated with cooking spray over medium-high heat. Add bell pepper and onion; coat with cooking spray and cook 4 minutes or until onion is crisp-tender.
5. Place tortillas on ungreased baking sheets. Spread equal amounts of bean mixture on each tortilla. Add onion and pepper mixture evenly to each; top with cheese, and bake at 350° for

5 minutes or until cheese melts. Remove from oven; sprinkle evenly with tomato mixture. YIELD: 4 servings (serving size: 1 tortilla pizza).

POINTS value: 6; **Exchanges:** 2 Starch, 2 Vegetable, 2 Medium-Fat Meat; **Per serving:** CAL 328 (27% from fat); PRO 15.4g; FAT 9.9g (sat 5.0g); CARB 44.3g; FIB 7.0g; CHOL 30mg; IRON 3.0mg; SOD 772mg; CALC 283mg

MEDITERRANEAN PIZZA WITH WHOLE WHEAT CRUST

(pictured on page 69)

prep: 18 minutes • cook: 20 minutes
other: 1 hour and 5 minutes

2   tablespoons honey
1½ teaspoons dry yeast
2   tablespoons warm water (100° to 110°)
1   tablespoon olive oil
1   cup all-purpose flour
¼   cup whole wheat flour
¾   teaspoon salt, divided
⅓   cup cold water
Cooking spray
2   teaspoons cornmeal
1   plum tomato, thinly sliced
1   teaspoon olive oil
½   cup chopped red onion
1   small zucchini, thinly sliced
4   garlic cloves, minced
1   (14-ounce) can quartered artichoke hearts, drained
2   tablespoons chopped fresh basil, divided
2   tablespoons chopped fresh oregano, divided
¼   teaspoon black pepper
¾   cup (3 ounces) preshredded part-skim mozzarella and provolone cheese blend
½   cup crumbled feta cheese with basil and sun-dried tomatoes

1. Combine first 3 ingredients in a large bowl; let stand 5 minutes. Stir in 1 tablespoon oil. Lightly spoon flours into dry measuring cups; level with a knife. Stir flours and ½ teaspoon salt into yeast mixture. Gradually add ⅓ cup cold water, stirring until dough forms a ball.
2. Turn dough out onto a lightly floured surface. Knead until smooth and elastic (about 2 minutes). Roll dough into a 9-inch circle on a lightly floured surface. Place dough on a 12-inch pizza pan coated with cooking spray and sprinkled with cornmeal.
3. Cover and let rise in a warm place (85°), free from drafts, 1 hour or until doubled in size.
4. Place tomato slices on paper towels; let stand 5 minutes.
5. Preheat oven to 400°.
6. Heat 1 teaspoon oil in a large nonstick skillet. Add onion, zucchini, and garlic; sauté 4 minutes or until tender. Add artichokes and 1½ tablespoons each of basil and oregano; sauté 30 seconds. Drain. Stir in ¼ teaspoon salt and pepper. Set aside.
7. Crimp edges of dough with fingers to form a rim; coat with cooking spray. Bake at 400° for 9 to 10 minutes or until lightly browned. Sprinkle crust with ½ cup cheese blend. Top with vegetable mixture. Sprinkle with ¼ cup cheese blend. Place tomato slices on top of cheese. Sprinkle with feta cheese and remaining basil and oregano. Bake an additional 6 to 7 minutes or until crust is golden. Serve immediately. YIELD: 8 servings (serving size: 1 slice).

POINTS value: 4; **Exchanges:** 1 Starch, 1 Vegetable, 1 Medium-Fat Meat, ½ Fat; **Per serving:** CAL 189 (28% from fat); PRO 8.1g; FAT 6.2g (sat 2.6g); CARB 27.3g; FIB 3.8g; CHOL 11mg; IRON 2.1mg; SOD 394mg; CALC 127mg

BEAN AND ROASTED VEGETABLE BURRITOS

prep: 25 minutes • cook: 45 minutes
other: 5 minutes

*For a simple make-ahead lunch,
prepare burritos the night before,
and chill in the refrigerator. When
ready to serve, bake as directed.*

2   cups diced zucchini
     (about 2 small)
1¾   cups diced yellow squash
     (about 2 small)
1¼   cups diced red onion
     (about 1 large)
1¼   cups diced red bell pepper
     (about 1 large)
2   tablespoons olive oil
2   teaspoons dried oregano
1½   teaspoons ground cumin
½   teaspoon black pepper
¼   teaspoon salt
¼   teaspoon sugar
Cooking spray
½   cup chopped fresh cilantro
2   tablespoons fresh lime juice
1   (16-ounce) can fat-free refried
     beans
3   tablespoons bottled salsa
1   to 2 chipotle chiles in adobo
     sauce, chopped
¼   teaspoon ground cumin
7   (8-inch) 97%-fat-free flour
     tortillas
½   cup low-fat sour cream

1. Preheat oven to 500°.
2. Combine zucchini and next 3
ingredients in a large zip-top plastic
bag. Add oil and next 5 ingredients;
shake well to coat.
3. Spoon vegetable mixture onto a
15 x 10-inch jelly roll pan coated
with cooking spray.

4. Bake at 500° for 30 minutes or
until browned, stirring occasionally.
Let stand 5 minutes. Sprinkle with
cilantro and lime juice.
5. Combine refried beans, salsa,
chipotle chile, and cumin in a
medium bowl. Spoon ¼ cup bean
mixture down center of each tortilla. Top each tortilla with ½ cup
roasted vegetable mixture, and roll
up; wrap in foil.
6. Reduce oven temperature to
350° and bake for 15 minutes or
until thoroughly heated. Top each
burrito evenly with sour cream.
YIELD: 7 servings (serving size: 1
burrito).

POINTS value: 5; **Exchanges:** 2 Starch, 1 Vegetable,
1 Very Lean Meat, 1 Fat; **Per serving:** CAL 277
(19% from fat); PRO 10.7g; FAT 6.0g (sat 1.3g);
CARB 46.1g; FIB 7.6g; CHOL 4mg; IRON 3.9mg;
SOD 640mg; CALC 123mg

MUSHROOM AND ONION QUESADILLAS

prep: 6 minutes • cook: 15 minutes

*Make quick quesadillas with presliced
mushrooms and bottled salsa. Use an
expandable spatula to easily flip your
quesadillas without any mess.*

Cooking spray
1   cup sliced mushrooms
1   cup chopped onion
8   (8-inch) 97%-fat-free flour
     tortillas
½   cup (2 ounces) preshredded
     reduced-fat Mexican blend or
     Cheddar cheese
¼   cup salsa
4   teaspoons chopped fresh
     cilantro
¼   cup low-fat sour cream

1. Place a large nonstick skillet
coated with cooking spray over
medium-high heat. Add mushrooms
and onion; cook 3 minutes or until
tender. Remove from heat.
2. Wipe pan with paper towels;
recoat with cooking spray. Coat 1
side of a tortilla with cooking spray.
Place tortilla, coated side down, in
pan, and top with ½ cup mushroom
mixture, 2 tablespoons cheese, and a
tortilla; cook 2 minutes or until
browned. Coat top of quesadilla with
cooking spray. Turn quesadilla using a
wide spatula; cook 1 minute or until
browned, pressing down on quesadilla
to flatten as it cooks. Set aside and
keep warm. Repeat procedure with
remaining tortillas, mushroom mixture, and cheese. Cut each quesadilla
into 4 wedges. Serve immediately
with salsa, cilantro, and sour cream.
YIELD: 4 servings (serving size: 4
wedges, 1 tablespoon salsa, and 1
tablespoon sour cream).

POINTS value: 4; **Exchanges:** 2 Starch, 1 Vegetable,
1 Very Lean Meat; **Per serving:** CAL 222 (20% from fat);
PRO 11.0g; FAT 5.1g (sat 2.7g); CARB 34.2g;
FIB 2.8g; CHOL 13mg; IRON 2.2mg; SOD 561mg;
CALC 176mg

EXPANDABLE SPATULAS

A unique kitchen utensil, an
expandable spatula looks like
an ordinary spatula, but with
the flip of a small lever, the
spatula opens to reveal two
spatulas underneath. This three-
in-one tool lets you easily flip
tricky foods like omelets, quesadillas, fish fillets, and pancakes. Find expandable spatulas in specialty kitchen stores or
at retail supercenters.

A Friend For Life

KERRY CLACK • **HEIGHT** 5'4" • **BEFORE** 239 LBS. • **AFTER** 145 LBS.

Thankful: "I'm thankful that I'm going to live longer and spend more time with my husband because I've lost weight for the right reason: good health."

"Would I pick up something that weighs 93 pounds? No way," Kerry Clack exclaims. "But that was the excess amount of weight that I carried around every day." That was, of course, every day until Kerry joined *Weight Watchers.*

"I have been overweight since I was around 10 years old," she says. "Over the years I tried all kinds of diets and only managed to be at a comfortable weight in my twenties—and that was only for a short time. I was getting nowhere with yo-yo dieting. But it wasn't until my health became an issue that I finally got serious about losing the weight."

With high blood pressure and chronic back problems—in addition to the extra pounds—Kerry knew she needed help. And the first person willing to help was her husband, Tim. "Tim was quick to suggest *Weight Watchers,*" Kerry says. "And he was right. *Weight Watchers* is an awesome program. It is very flexible, very nutritious, and is something that I was easily able to work into my schedule."

From the beginning, Kerry decided to set small, reachable goals that would ultimately help her get to her final destination a year and a half later. "I didn't get large overnight and so I knew the weight wouldn't come off overnight," she says. "I just broke it all down into small goals that I thought I could achieve.

"It was my philosophy that if I was going to set a goal, I should set a reasonable one. Too many people fail when trying to lose weight because they want fast results. I found that if you look at things on a smaller scale, you are more likely to succeed." With Tim's support and the changes she made in her eating habits, Kerry was able to change her lifestyle. "It became second nature," she says. "I discovered that I could actually eat healthy food and feel full. I don't have to eat junk food to be happy."

> *"I discovered that I could actually eat healthy food and feel full. I don't have to eat junk food to be happy."*

Kerry discovered something else that makes her happy...exercise. "I now do some form of activity six days a week for 30 or 40 minutes," she says. "Never before in my life had I done any exercise. Now I actually look forward to it!"

Kerry's favorite form of activity is walking, but she also likes to find time for yoga and an occasional run. "I'm not very good at the running yet," she says. "But it's like anything else; you just have to get used to it and build up your stamina.

"People now say that they see a difference in my life by how my face lights up when I talk about *Weight Watchers,*" she says. "Good things have come from my sticking with the program. It's been a definite plus in my life. Thank you, *Weight Watchers,* for the knowledge and support you have shown me. You will be my friend for life!"

Striped Bass en Papillote,
page 52

Curried Mussels,
page 59

Pan-Seared Salmon with
Honey-Balsamic Sauce,
page 56

Asian-Style Crab Cakes,
page 58

White Beans Oreganata,
page 79

Mediterranean Pizza with
Whole Wheat Crust,
page 63

Pan-Fried Tofu with
Coconut Rice,
page 80

70

Tofu and Chickpea
Patties with Cucumber
Mint Relish,
page 79

Grilled Grouper Tacos,
page 54

Success Speaks Volumes

GARY COX • **HEIGHT** 6'2" • **BEFORE** 272 LBS. • **AFTER** 202 LBS.

Proudest Moment: "It sure was nice not to have to go to the big boys' store anymore. Had I not lost the weight, my next size up from the XXL would have been a Z!"

Gary Cox will tell you he's from the "old school." Raised in a small Mississippi River town in Illinois, Gary has always boasted of his mother's down-home cooking—pork chops and fried chicken, among other things. "She could fry water," he says with a chuckle.

But it wasn't just consuming large amounts of greasy, fat-laden foods during his formative years that helped Gary become overweight and unhealthy. His adult lifestyle was a factor as well. It was a fateful visit to a cardiologist in November 2002 that steered him in a new direction.

"The heart specialist said I needed to quit smoking, lose some weight, and start exercising. I was scared I was going to have a heart attack, and I knew I needed to do something."

"Success speaks volumes. Weight Watchers worked for me and that says something."

So Gary and his wife, Peggy, joined *Weight Watchers*. Gary had tried *Weight Watchers* 14 years earlier and had succeeded, but once he reached his goal he quit—regaining the weight he'd lost, and then some. Gary knew *Weight Watchers* could work; he just needed to stick with it this time.

And he did! After one year of counting the **POINTS**

values of his meals and snacks, drinking lots of water, and making exercise a part of his daily routine, Gary lost 70 pounds. And what's even more impressive is that Gary has maintained his goal weight for the past year, too.

So what was the key to Gary's success? Gary says the most important factor was the program itself. "It's just a healthy way to eat and lose weight," he says. "It has worked for me by emphasizing that it really is a lifestyle change, not a diet."

Another key was his leader. "It's important to have a leader you like," he says. "Finding a leader is like finding a doctor: There needs to be a good rapport."

Since reaching his goal, Gary has had many friends and coworkers tell him how thin he looks. But the comment he likes best is this: You not only look thinner, you look healthier. "I just feel better all around," he says. "It is a win-win situation."

Now, instead of boasting of his mother's high-calorie cooking, Gary boasts solely about *Weight Watchers*. "There are tons of ways to lose weight," he says. "But I don't think there's any other program that's all-around healthier or better-suited for keeping the weight off.

"Success speaks volumes," he says. "*Weight Watchers* worked for me and that says something."

CLASSIC MUSHROOM AND CHEESE OMELETS

prep: 8 minutes • cook: 16 minutes

*Combining regular eggs and egg substitute increases the volume of the omelet without significantly increasing the **POINTS** value.*

1   tablespoon light butter
1   (8-ounce) package presliced mushrooms
2   tablespoons minced shallot (about 1 small)
½   teaspoon salt, divided
½   teaspoon freshly ground black pepper, divided
4   large eggs, beaten
1   cup egg substitute
Cooking spray
½   cup (2 ounces) shredded light Havarti cheese

1. Melt butter in a small nonstick omelet pan over medium-high heat; add mushrooms and shallot. Cook 5 minutes or until mushrooms are tender; stir in ¼ teaspoon salt and ¼ teaspoon pepper. Remove from heat; keep warm.
2. Combine egg, egg substitute, ¼ teaspoon salt, and ¼ teaspoon pepper in a bowl; stir with a whisk.
3. Wipe pan with paper towels; coat with cooking spray, and place over medium heat. Pour half of egg mixture into pan. As mixture starts to cook, gently lift edges of omelet with a spatula, and tilt pan so uncooked portion flows underneath. Spoon half of mushroom mixture over omelet; top with ¼ cup cheese. Loosen omelet with spatula; fold in half. Slide omelet onto a plate; keep warm. Repeat procedure with remaining egg mixture, mushroom mixture, and cheese. YIELD: 4 servings (serving size: ½ omelet).

POINTS value: 4; **Exchanges:** ½ Vegetable, 3 Medium-Fat Meat; **Per serving:** CAL 173 (48% from fat); PRO 18.5g; FAT 9.2g (sat 2.6g); CARB 4.2g; FIB 0.8g; CHOL 222mg; IRON 2.4mg; SOD 591mg; CALC 152mg

FRITTATA WITH WHOLE WHEAT SPAGHETTI AND SPINACH

prep: 10 minutes • cook: 25 minutes

Feta is traditionally made from sheep's milk, which gives it a strong, tangy flavor. Today, pasteurized cow's milk is often used for a much milder flavor. We prefer the flavor of traditional feta in this recipe.

4   ounces uncooked whole wheat thin spaghetti, broken in half
1   teaspoon butter, divided
1   cup vertically sliced onion
2   large garlic cloves, minced
3   large eggs
3   large egg whites
½   cup fat-free milk
¼   teaspoon salt
⅛   teaspoon pepper
1   (10-ounce) package frozen chopped spinach, thawed, drained, and squeezed dry
⅔   cup tomato and basil pasta sauce (such as Classico)
⅓   cup (1⅓ ounces) crumbled feta cheese

1. Cook pasta according to package directions, omitting salt and fat.
2. Meanwhile, melt ½ teaspoon butter in a large nonstick skillet over medium heat. Add onion, and sauté 7 minutes or until lightly browned. Add garlic; sauté 30 seconds. Remove from heat.
3. Combine eggs, egg whites, and next 3 ingredients in a large bowl; stir well with a whisk. Stir in pasta, onion mixture, and spinach.
4. Melt ½ teaspoon butter in same pan; add egg mixture. Cover and cook 12 minutes or until top is almost set.
5. Preheat broiler.
6. Spread pasta sauce to within 1½ inches of edges of frittata; sprinkle with cheese.
7. Wrap handle of pan with foil. Broil 5 minutes or until golden. Cut into 4 wedges. YIELD: 4 servings (serving size: 1 wedge).

POINTS value: 5; **Exchanges:** 1½ Starch, 1 Very Lean Meat, 1½ Medium-Fat Meat; **Per serving:** CAL 271 (27% from fat); PRO 18.2g; FAT 8.7g (sat 3.8g); CARB 33.3g; FIB 6.9g; CHOL 173mg; IRON 3.7mg; SOD 584mg; CALC 268mg

---

OMELETS AND FRITTATAS

Omelets and frittatas vary in their preparation as well as their origin. Omelets (French) begin by cooking the eggs; once cooked, eggs are topped with meats, cheeses, and vegetables. They are then folded over to form a semi-circle shape. Frittatas (Italian) combine raw eggs and toppings before cooking and then are cooked on the stove top and finished in the oven. Because they are not folded, frittatas retain their round shape.

GREEK FRITTATA

prep: 15 minutes • cook: 31 minutes

Save prep time by using prediced potatoes and onion. Pair this with a green salad or Fresh Fruit Salad with Ginger-Lime Syrup, page 118.

1½	teaspoons olive oil
3	cups diced peeled eggplant
1½	cups diced potato with onion (such as Simply Potatoes)
2	garlic cloves, chopped
⅔	cup chopped red bell pepper
¼	cup chopped pitted kalamata olives
4	large eggs
4	large egg whites
1	tablespoon chopped fresh oregano
½	teaspoon salt
¼	teaspoon freshly ground black pepper
½	cup (2 ounces) crumbled feta cheese

1. Preheat oven to 425°.
2. Heat oil in a medium nonstick skillet over medium-high heat. Add eggplant and next 3 ingredients; cook 10 minutes or until vegetables are tender. Stir in olives.
3. Combine eggs, egg whites, and next 3 ingredients in a small bowl, stirring with a whisk. Pour over vegetable mixture. Sprinkle with feta cheese. Wrap handle of pan with foil. Bake at 425° for 20 minutes or until set. Cut into 4 wedges. YIELD: 4 servings (serving size: 1 wedge).

POINTS value: 5; Exchanges: ½ Starch, 1 Vegetable, 2 Medium-Fat Meat, ½ Fat; Per serving: CAL 237 (45% from fat); PRO 14.6g; FAT 11.8g (sat 4.7g); CARB 18.4g; FIB 3.5g; CHOL 229mg; IRON 1.7mg; SOD 792mg; CALC 141mg

CREAMY SPINACH AND MUSHROOM ALFREDO

prep: 8 minutes • cook: 11 minutes

8	ounces uncooked no-yolk dumplings
1	teaspoon olive oil
1	cup coarsely chopped mushrooms
2	large garlic cloves, minced
1	(10-ounce) container light Alfredo sauce (such as Buitoni)
½	cup fat-free milk
¼	teaspoon salt
⅛	teaspoon ground nutmeg
2	cups firmly packed fresh baby spinach, coarsely chopped
¼	cup (1 ounce) shredded Parmesan cheese
¼	teaspoon freshly ground black pepper

1. Cook dumplings according to package directions, omitting salt and fat.
2. Meanwhile, heat olive oil in a large nonstick skillet over medium heat. Sauté mushrooms 2 minutes or until soft. Add garlic; sauté 1 minute. Reduce heat to low; stir in Alfredo sauce and next 3 ingredients. Stir in spinach. Cook 3 minutes or until thoroughly heated and spinach wilts.
3. In a large bowl, combine dumplings and sauce. Sprinkle with cheese and black pepper; toss well. Serve immediately. YIELD: 4 servings (serving size: about 1½ cups).

POINTS value: 5; Exchanges: 1½ Starch, 1 Vegetable, 1½ Fat; Per serving: CAL 222 (43% from fat); PRO 11.3g; FAT 10.8g (sat 5.3g); CARB 20.7g; FIB 1.0g; CHOL 30mg; IRON 1.5mg; SOD 788mg; CALC 329mg

BOW TIE PASTA AND KALAMATA OLIVE TOSS

prep: 3 minutes • cook: 16 minutes

While pasta cooks, prepare remaining ingredients. Toss and serve warm, or chill and serve as a cold pasta salad.

2½	cups uncooked bow tie pasta
1½	cups halved grape tomatoes
1	cup (4 ounces) diced part-skim mozzarella cheese
16	kalamata olives, pitted and coarsely chopped
½	cup thinly sliced fresh basil
2	tablespoons red wine vinegar
2	tablespoons extravirgin olive oil
2	garlic cloves, minced
¾	teaspoon salt
¼	teaspoon crushed red pepper

1. Cook pasta according to package directions, omitting salt and fat.
2. In a large bowl, combine pasta and remaining ingredients. Toss well. YIELD: 6 servings (serving size: 1¼ cups).

POINTS value: 5; Exchanges: 1½ Starch, 1 Medium-Fat Meat, 1 Fat; Per serving: CAL 242 (42% from fat); PRO 10.5g; FAT 11.4g (sat 3.7g); CARB 25.1g; FIB 1.6g; CHOL 11mg; IRON 1.3mg; SOD 614mg; CALC 168mg

BAKED SHELLS WITH THREE CHEESES

prep: 6 minutes • cook: 42 minutes
other: 10 minutes

Baked mac-and-cheese fans will find it hard to believe this cheesy, full-flavored dish is actually light.

3   cups uncooked sea shell pasta
⅓   cup fresh breadcrumbs
¼   cup (1 ounce) shredded Asiago cheese, divided
2½   cups 1% low-fat milk
2   tablespoons all-purpose flour
1½   teaspoons butter
½   teaspoon salt
¼   teaspoon pepper
4   ounces light processed cheese, cubed (such as Velveeta Light)
¾   cup (3 ounces) shredded light Havarti cheese
Cooking spray

1. Cook pasta in a Dutch oven according to package directions, omitting salt and fat.
2. Preheat oven to 375°.
3. Combine breadcrumbs and 1 tablespoon Asiago cheese. Set aside.
4. Gradually whisk milk into flour in a medium saucepan until smooth; add butter, salt, and pepper. Bring to a boil over medium heat, whisking constantly. Add processed cheese, whisking until cheese melts. Remove from heat.
5. Stir cheese sauce, Havarti cheese, and 3 tablespoons Asiago cheese into pasta until blended. Pour into a 2-quart oval casserole coated with cooking spray. Sprinkle with bread-crumb mixture.

6. Bake at 375° for 30 minutes or until bubbly and golden. Let stand 10 minutes before serving. YIELD: 6 servings (serving size: ⅙ of casserole).

POINTS value: 6; **Exchanges:** 2 Starch, 1½ Medium-Fat Meat, ½ Fat; **Per serving:** CAL 291 (23% from fat); PRO 17.4g; FAT 7.3g (sat 4.4g); CARB 38.7g; FIB 1.4g; CHOL 24mg; IRON 1.5mg; SOD 602mg; CALC 392mg

BAKED VEGETABLE PENNE

prep: 10 minutes • cook: 1 hour and 4 minutes

3   cups uncooked penne pasta
1   tablespoon olive oil
1   pound asparagus spears, trimmed and cut into 1-inch pieces
1   (8-ounce) package cremini mushrooms, sliced
1   cup chopped red bell pepper
1   cup chopped sweet onion
1   garlic clove, minced
1   (14-ounce) can quartered artichoke hearts, drained and coarsely chopped
½   cup dry sherry
2   tablespoons chopped fresh basil
½   teaspoon salt, divided
¼   teaspoon freshly ground black pepper
2½   cups 2% reduced-fat milk, divided
¼   cup all-purpose flour
1   tablespoon butter
½   cup (2 ounces) preshredded fresh Parmesan cheese
⅛   teaspoon black pepper
Cooking spray
1½   cups (6 ounces) shredded mozzarella and provolone cheese blend

1. Cook pasta according to package directions, omitting salt and fat.
2. While pasta cooks, heat oil in a large nonstick skillet over medium-high heat. Add asparagus, mushrooms, bell pepper, and onion; sauté 4 minutes. Add garlic; sauté 1 minute. Add artichokes and sherry. Cook, stirring frequently, 3 minutes or until most of liquid evaporates. Stir in basil, ¼ teaspoon salt, and ¼ teaspoon black pepper.
3. Combine ½ cup milk and flour; whisk until smooth. Combine flour mixture, 2 cups milk, and butter in a medium saucepan. Cook over medium heat, whisking constantly, 20 minutes or until thick and bubbly. Stir in Parmesan cheese, ¼ teaspoon salt, and ⅛ teaspoon black pepper.
4. Preheat oven to 350°.
5. Combine pasta, vegetables, and white sauce. Spoon into a 13 x 9-inch baking dish coated with cooking spray. Cover and bake at 350° for 30 minutes. Uncover, sprinkle with cheese blend, and bake 7 minutes or until cheese melts. YIELD: 12 servings (serving size: 1¼ cups).

POINTS value: 5; **Exchanges:** 1½ Starch, 1 Vegetable, 1 Medium-Fat Meat, 1 Fat; **Per serving:** CAL 266 (29% from fat); PRO 13.4g; FAT 8.8g (sat 4.7g); CARB 32.8g; FIB 2.9g; CHOL 22mg; IRON 1.5mg; SOD 446mg; CALC 221mg

STUFFED PASTA SHELLS WITH TOFU MUSHROOM SAUCE

prep: 10 minutes • cook: 50 minutes
other: 5 minutes

Sneak a little soy protein into your diet by blending tofu into the tomato and garlic sauce. If you want to use the entire package of tofu, the sauce can easily be doubled and refrigerated for later use.

12   uncooked jumbo pasta shells
2   teaspoons olive oil
1   (8-ounce) package presliced mushrooms
1   garlic clove, minced
1   (14.5 ounce) can diced tomatoes with basil, garlic, and oregano
½   (12-ounce) package soft tofu, drained
⅓   cup chopped fresh basil
¼   teaspoon salt
¼   teaspoon crushed red pepper
Cooking spray
¾   cup (3 ounces) grated fresh Parmesan cheese
¼   cup chopped fresh flat-leaf parsley

1. Cook pasta shells according to package directions, omitting salt and fat.
2. While pasta cooks, heat a large nonstick skillet over medium-high heat; add oil. Add mushrooms and garlic; cook 4 minutes or until tender.
3. Stir in tomatoes and next 4 ingredients; bring to a boil. Reduce heat; simmer, stirring occasionally, 20 minutes or until slightly thick. Remove from heat. Let stand 5 minutes.

4. Preheat oven to 350°.
5. Spoon ¼ cup sauce into an 11 x 7-inch baking dish coated with cooking spray.
6. Spoon sauce evenly into cooked shells. Arrange shells in baking dish. Sprinkle with cheese and parsley.
7. Cover and bake at 350° for 20 minutes or until bubbly and cheese melts. YIELD: 6 servings (serving size: 2 stuffed shells).

POINTS value: 5; **Exchanges:** 1½ Starch, 1 Vegetable, 1 Medium-Fat Meat, ½ Fat; **Per serving:** CAL 252 (30% from fat); PRO 13.7g; FAT 8.4g (sat 3.1g); CARB 30.8g; FIB 2.7g; CHOL 13mg; IRON 2.5mg; SOD 853mg; CALC 244mg

RISOTTO WITH SPINACH AND MUSHROOMS

prep: 3 minutes • cook: 30 minutes

A combination of vegetable broth and water are used in this risotto to create a rich, full-flavored dish that has less sodium than traditional risottos.

2   (14-ounce) cans vegetable broth
2   cups water
2   teaspoons olive oil
Cooking spray
1   (8-ounce) package presliced mushrooms
½   cup chopped onion
1½   cups uncooked Arborio rice or other short-grain rice
¼   cup dry vermouth
1   (10-ounce) package frozen chopped spinach, thawed, drained, and squeezed dry
½   cup (2 ounces) grated fresh Parmesan cheese
¼   teaspoon black pepper
⅛   teaspoon ground nutmeg

1. Bring broth and water to a simmer in a medium saucepan (do not boil). Keep warm over low heat.
2. Heat oil in a large nonstick skillet coated with cooking spray over medium-high heat. Add mushrooms and onion; sauté 4 minutes. Remove from heat; set aside and keep warm.
3. Place rice in a Dutch oven over medium-high heat; cook 1 minute. Stir in vermouth; cook, stirring constantly, 1 minute or until liquid is nearly absorbed. Reduce heat to medium-low; add broth, ½ cup at a time, stirring constantly, until each portion of broth is absorbed before adding the next (about 20 minutes total). Remove from heat; stir in reserved mushroom mixture, spinach, and remaining ingredients. Serve immediately. YIELD: 5 servings (serving size: 1¼ cups).

POINTS value: 4; **Exchanges:** 1½ Starch, 1 Lean Meat, ½ Fat; **Per serving:** CAL 218 (26% from fat); PRO 12.2g; FAT 6.8g (sat 2.4g); CARB 31.2g; FIB 2.9g; CHOL 10mg; IRON 1.8mg; SOD 818mg; CALC 220mg

SPINACH

Your mother was right—spinach IS good for you! Not only is this veggie rich in vitamins and minerals such as folate, vitamin K, magnesium, and manganese, it also serves as a powerful antioxidant. Enjoy spinach raw in sandwiches or salads or cooked in casseroles, entrées, or side dishes. Spinach is one vegetable that provides more nutrition once it's cooked because cooking makes it easier for the body to absorb the antioxidant carotenoids that are responsible for much of spinach's nutritional power.

CHEDDAR AND BLUE CHEESE TWICE-BAKED POTATOES

prep: 15 minutes • cook: 32 minutes

4   (8-ounce) baking potatoes
Cooking spray
1   cup chopped onion (about
     1 medium)
1   (8-ounce) package presliced
     mushrooms
1   teaspoon dried oregano
¼   cup chopped fresh parsley
½   cup fat-free milk
2   tablespoons crumbled blue
     cheese
2   tablespoons light butter
¾   teaspoon salt
¼   teaspoon pepper
¾   cup (3 ounces) shredded
     reduced-fat sharp Cheddar
     cheese

1. Pierce potatoes with a fork, and arrange in a circle on paper towels in microwave oven. Cover potatoes with damp paper towels. Microwave at HIGH 12 minutes or until done.
2. Heat a large nonstick skillet coated with cooking spray over medium-high heat. Add onion, mushrooms, and oregano; coat with cooking spray. Cook 6 minutes or until tender. Remove from heat; stir in parsley.
3. Preheat oven to 350°.
4. Cut potatoes in half lengthwise, and scoop out pulp, leaving a ¼-inch-thick shell. Arrange shells on a baking sheet. Set aside.
5. Beat potato pulp, milk, and next 4 ingredients in a large bowl with a mixer at medium speed until smooth. Stuff shells evenly with potato mixture. Top with mushroom mixture. Sprinkle evenly with Cheddar cheese.

6. Bake at 350° for 20 minutes or until cheese melts. YIELD: 4 servings (serving size: 2 potato halves).

POINTS value: 6; **Exchanges:** 2½ Starch, 1 Vegetable, 1½ Medium-Fat Meat; **Per serving:** CAL 317 (26% from fat); PRO 14.3g; FAT 8.6g (sat 5.5g); CARB 47.8g; FIB 4.5g; CHOL 28mg; IRON 2.9mg; SOD 802mg; CALC 225mg

BUTTERNUT SQUASH STUFFED WITH ORANGE COUSCOUS

prep: 15 minutes • cook: 1 hour
other: 5 minutes

The pulp of winter squash is rich in vitamins A and C, iron, and riboflavin.

2   (1½- to 2-pound) butternut
     squash, halved lengthwise
½   teaspoon olive oil
½   cup chopped onion
½   cup chopped carrot
¾   cup vegetable broth
½   cup water
3   tablespoons orange juice
1   teaspoon butter
½   teaspoon salt
¾   cup uncooked couscous
2   tablespoons sweetened dried
     cranberries
1   teaspoon curry powder
½   teaspoon ground cinnamon
¼   teaspoon grated orange rind
¼   teaspoon black pepper
¾   cup canned chickpeas
     (garbanzo beans), rinsed and
     drained
2   tablespoons slivered almonds,
     toasted
1   cup orange juice
2   tablespoons honey
⅛   teaspoon curry powder
⅛   teaspoon ground cinnamon

1. Preheat oven to 350°.
2. Place butternut squash, cut sides down, in a 13 x 9-inch baking pan. Add hot water to pan to a depth of ½ inch. Bake at 350° for 40 minutes or until tender.
3. While squash bakes, heat a large nonstick skillet over medium-high heat; add oil. Add onion and carrot. Reduce heat to medium-low, and cook 20 minutes or until onion is golden and carrot is tender, stirring frequently. Set aside.
4. Bring broth and next 4 ingredients to a boil. Stir in couscous and next 5 ingredients. Remove from heat. Cover and let stand 5 minutes.
5. Remove and discard seeds from squash; scoop out pulp, leaving ¼-inch-thick shells. Coarsely chop 1 cup pulp, reserving remaining pulp for another use.
6. Combine reserved onion mixture, squash pulp, couscous mixture, chickpeas, and almonds; toss gently. Spoon mixture evenly into squash shells. Place shells in a 13 x 9-inch baking pan. Bake at 350° for 20 minutes or until thoroughly heated.
7. While shells bake, bring 1 cup orange juice and honey to a boil in a small saucepan. Reduce heat; simmer, uncovered, 10 to 15 minutes or until mixture reduces to ⅓ cup, stirring occasionally. Stir in curry powder and cinnamon. Drizzle juice mixture evenly over couscous mixture. YIELD: 4 servings (serving size: 1 stuffed squash shell).

POINTS value: 6; **Exchanges:** 3 Starch, 2 Vegetable, 1 Fat; **Per serving:** CAL 331 (14% from fat); PRO 9.6g; FAT 5.2g (sat 0.9g); CARB 64.0g; FIB 7.3g; CHOL 3mg; IRON 2.2mg; SOD 510mg; CALC 79mg

FRIED RICE WITH ASPARAGUS AND EGGS

prep: 10 minutes • cook: 8 minutes

Save leftover rice for this quick, meatless dish. If you choose to make fresh rice, chill it quickly by spreading it on a jelly roll pan and refrigerating it for 20 minutes.

⅓ cup vegetable broth
3 tablespoons low-sodium soy sauce
1 teaspoon grated peeled fresh ginger
1 teaspoon dark sesame oil
¼ teaspoon salt
1½ cups (1-inch) diagonally cut asparagus
½ cup preshredded carrot
2 teaspoons vegetable oil, divided
Cooking spray
4 large eggs, lightly beaten
3 cups cooked long-grain rice, chilled
½ cup frozen green peas, thawed
¼ cup thinly sliced green onions

1. Combine first 5 ingredients in a medium bowl; stir with a whisk.
2. Steam asparagus and carrot, covered, 2 minutes or until crisp-tender. Rinse with cold water; drain.
3. Heat 1 teaspoon vegetable oil in a large nonstick skillet coated with cooking spray over medium-high heat. Add egg; cook 1 minute or until scrambled, stirring constantly. Remove egg from pan.
4. Heat 1 teaspoon oil in pan. Add rice; cook 3 minutes or until hot, stirring occasionally. Add asparagus, carrot, scrambled egg, peas, onions, and broth mixture; cook 2 minutes

or until thoroughly heated. YIELD: 5 servings (serving size: 1 cup).

POINTS value: 4; **Exchanges:** 1½ Starch, 1 Lean Meat, 1 Fat; **Per serving:** CAL 216 (30% from fat); PRO 9.6g; FAT 7.2g (sat 1.6g); CARB 28.3g; FIB 2.8g; CHOL 170mg; IRON 2.2mg; SOD 579mg; CALC 51mg

PAN-SEARED POLENTA WITH MEDITERRANEAN VEGETABLES

prep: 18 minutes • cook: 23 minutes
other: 30 minutes

Salting the sliced eggplant in this recipe helps to draw out the bitter-tasting liquid inside the vegetable. Rinse and dry the eggplant thoroughly after 30 minutes.

4 cups cubed peeled eggplant (about 1 small)
½ teaspoon salt
1 (12-ounce) jar roasted red bell peppers
2 teaspoons olive oil
2 small zucchini, sliced in half lengthwise, then cut into ½-inch-thick slices (about 3 cups)
1 cup chopped onion
3 garlic cloves, minced
1 (14.5-ounce) can diced tomatoes with basil, garlic, and oregano, undrained
2 tablespoons red wine vinegar
¼ teaspoon freshly ground black pepper
1 (17-ounce) tube polenta, cut into 8 slices
Olive oil-flavored cooking spray
¼ cup thinly sliced fresh basil
¼ cup toasted pine nuts
¼ cup grated Parmesan cheese

1. Sprinkle eggplant with ½ teaspoon salt in a colander; let stand 30 minutes. Rinse well; pat dry with paper towels.
2. Drain roasted bell peppers; cut peppers into 1-inch pieces. Set aside.
3. Heat oil in a large nonstick skillet over medium-high heat. Add eggplant, zucchini, and onion; sauté 8 minutes. Add garlic and roasted bell pepper; cook 1 minute. Add tomatoes, vinegar, and pepper; cook over medium heat, stirring occasionally, 8 minutes or until vegetables are tender. Set aside and keep warm.
4. Wipe pan with paper towels, and heat over medium-high heat. Coat polenta with cooking spray; add to pan. Sear on each side 3 to 4 minutes or until browned.
5. Place 2 slices of polenta on each of 4 plates; top evenly with eggplant mixture, basil, pine nuts, and cheese. YIELD: 4 servings (serving size: 2 slices polenta, 1½ cups eggplant mixture, 1 tablespoon basil, 1 tablespoon pine nuts, and 1 tablespoon cheese).

POINTS value: 6; **Exchanges:** 1½ Starch, 4 Vegetable, 1½ Fat; **Per serving:** CAL 295 (31% from fat); PRO 9.4g; FAT 10.3g (sat 1.8g); CARB 42.3g; FIB 5.4g; CHOL 4mg; IRON 3.0mg; SOD 972mg; CALC 154mg

TOASTING NUTS

Toasting nuts before you use them in a recipe will enhance the flavor of the dish. Simply place the nuts in an ungreased skillet and cook over medium heat, stirring often until the nuts are lightly browned and release a fragrant, toasted aroma.

WHITE BEANS OREGANATA

(pictured on page 69)
prep: 23 minutes • cook: 1 hour and
15 minutes • other: 8 hours

1	(16-ounce) package dried Great Northern beans
6	cups water
2	cups chopped onion (about 1 large)
½	cup thinly sliced celery
4	garlic cloves, minced
1	bay leaf
1	(6-ounce) package fresh baby spinach
¼	cup chopped fresh oregano
¼	cup chopped fresh parsley
2	teaspoons salt, divided
½	teaspoon freshly ground black pepper
2	tablespoons olive oil, divided
4	garlic cloves, minced
6	plum tomatoes, seeded and chopped

1. Sort and wash beans; place in a large Dutch oven. Cover with water to 2 inches above beans; cover and let stand 8 hours. Drain beans.
2. Combine beans, 6 cups water, and next 4 ingredients in Dutch oven. Bring to a boil; cover, reduce heat, and simmer 70 to 80 minutes or until beans are tender. Discard bay leaf. Stir in spinach, oregano, parsley, 1½ teaspoons salt, and pepper; cook 2 minutes or until spinach wilts.
3. Heat 1 tablespoon oil in a large nonstick skillet over medium heat. Add garlic; sauté 1 minute or until lightly browned. Stir in tomato and ½ teaspoon salt; sauté 2 minutes or until thoroughly heated. Gently stir tomato mixture into bean mixture.

4. Ladle oreganata into bowls; drizzle servings evenly with 1 tablespoon oil. YIELD: 8 servings (serving size: 1⅓ cups).

POINTS value: 5; Exchanges: 2½ Starch, 1 Vegetable, 1 Very Lean Meat; **Per serving:** CAL 260 (15% from fat); PRO 14.3g; FAT 4.4g (sat 0.7g); CARB 43.5g; FIB 13.6g; CHOL 0mg; IRON 4.2mg; SOD 625mg; CALC 152mg

TOFU AND CHICKPEA PATTIES WITH CUCUMBER MINT RELISH

(pictured on page 71)
prep: 20 minutes • cook: 10 minutes
other: 30 minutes

½	(14-ounce) package firm tofu, drained
2	garlic cloves
½	cup chopped onion
½	cup loosely packed fresh flat-leaf parsley leaves
1	(16-ounce) can chickpeas, rinsed and drained
1	large egg
⅓	cup dry breadcrumbs
1	teaspoon ground coriander
¾	teaspoon ground cumin
½	teaspoon salt
½	teaspoon black pepper
1	tablespoon olive oil
	Cucumber Mint Relish

1. Wrap tofu blocks in several layers of heavy-duty paper towels. Press with a heavy object for about 30 minutes to remove excess water. Remove paper towels, pat tofu dry, and cut into 1-inch cubes; set aside.
2. With food processor running, drop garlic through food chute; process until minced. Add onion and parsley; pulse 3 times. Add chickpeas and tofu;

pulse twice. Scrape down sides. Add egg and next 5 ingredients; pulse 4 times or just until beans are chopped (mixture should be chunky; do not overprocess). Shape mixture into 8 (3-inch) patties, using ⅓ cup for each patty.
3. Heat olive oil in a large nonstick skillet over medium heat. Add patties, and cook 5 minutes on each side or until browned. Serve immediately with Cucumber Mint Relish. YIELD: 4 servings (serving size: 2 patties and about ½ cup relish).

(Total includes Cucumber Mint Relish) *POINTS* value: 6; Exchanges: 1 Starch, 1 Medium-Fat Meat, 2 Fat; **Per serving:** CAL 287 (41% from fat); PRO 11.8g; FAT 13.5g (sat 2.1g); CARB 31.2g; FIB 5.6g; CHOL 58mg; IRON 3.7mg; SOD 650mg; CALC 177mg

CUCUMBER MINT RELISH

3	cups finely diced seeded peeled cucumber (about 2 large)
¼	cup light mayonnaise
2	tablespoons finely chopped fresh mint
2	tablespoons finely chopped fresh flat-leaf parsley
1	teaspoon grated lemon rind
1	tablespoon fresh lemon juice
¼	teaspoon salt
¼	teaspoon freshly ground black pepper

1. Stir together all ingredients in a bowl; cover and chill 30 minutes. YIELD: 4 servings (serving size: about ½ cup).

POINTS value: 2; **Exchanges:** 1 Vegetable, 1 Fat; **Per serving:** CAL 65 (69% from fat); PRO 0.9g; FAT 5.1g (sat 0.8g); CARB 4.2g; FIB 0.9g; CHOL 5mg; IRON 0.5mg; SOD 270mg; CALC 26mg

RED CURRY TOFU STIR-FRY

prep: 28 minutes • cook: 13 minutes
other: 1 hour and 30 minutes

1	(14-ounce) package extrafirm tofu, drained
1	(13.5-ounce) can light coconut milk
2	tablespoons light brown sugar
2	tablespoons fish sauce
1	tablespoon dry sherry
1½	teaspoons Thai red curry paste
1	teaspoon grated peeled fresh ginger
⅔	cup uncooked basmati rice
8	ounces asparagus spears
2	teaspoons peanut oil
8	ounces shiitake mushrooms, stemmed and sliced
½	cup chopped onion

1. Wrap tofu blocks in several layers of heavy-duty paper towels. Press with a heavy object for about 30 minutes to remove excess water. Remove paper towels, pat tofu dry, and cut into 1-inch cubes; set aside.
2. Combine coconut milk and next 5 ingredients in a bowl; stir well with a whisk. Add tofu to coconut milk mixture. Cover and chill 1 hour.
3. Cook rice according to package directions, omitting salt and fat.
4. Drain tofu well, reserving marinade. Snap off tough ends of asparagus. Cut asparagus into 2-inch pieces.
5. Heat a large nonstick skillet over medium-high heat. Add peanut oil and tofu; cook 5 minutes, turning cubes until lightly browned on all sides. Transfer tofu to a serving bowl.
6. Add asparagus, mushrooms, and onion to pan; stir-fry 3 minutes. Add reserved marinade to pan;

cook, stirring constantly, 5 minutes or until thick. Pour vegetable mixture over tofu, tossing gently. Serve immediately over hot cooked basmati rice. YIELD: 5 servings (serving size: ¾ cup tofu mixture and ½ cup rice).

POINTS value: 5; **Exchanges:** 1½ Starch, 1 Medium-Fat Meat, 2 Fat; **Per serving:** CAL 247 (38% from fat); PRO 10.8g; FAT 10.4g (sat 3.8g); CARB 27.0g; FIB 1.8g; CHOL 0mg; IRON 2.7mg; SOD 627mg; CALC 77mg

PAN-FRIED TOFU WITH COCONUT RICE

(pictured on page 70)
prep: 2 minutes • cook: 15 minutes
other: 40 minutes

1	(14-ounce) package extrafirm tofu, drained
½	teaspoon ground cumin
½	teaspoon curry powder
½	teaspoon ground allspice
½	teaspoon ground ginger
½	teaspoon salt
½	teaspoon black pepper
2	teaspoons olive oil, divided
1	teaspoon chili oil
8	cups fresh baby spinach
2	garlic cloves, minced
1	tablespoon chopped cashews
	Coconut Rice

1. Wrap tofu blocks in several layers of heavy-duty paper towels. Press with a heavy object for about 30 minutes to remove excess water. Remove paper towels, pat tofu dry, and cut into 1-inch cubes; set aside.
2. Combine cumin and next 5 ingredients in a large zip-top plastic bag; add tofu. Seal bag; shake to coat.

3. Heat 1 teaspoon olive oil and chili oil in a nonstick skillet over medium-high heat. Add tofu; sauté 8 minutes or until golden. Remove tofu from pan; cover and keep warm.
4. Heat 1 teaspoon olive oil in pan; add spinach and garlic. Cook, stirring constantly, 4 minutes or just until spinach wilts. Add tofu; cook, stirring until thoroughly heated. Sprinkle with cashews; serve with Coconut Rice. YIELD: 6 servings (serving size: ⅙ of tofu mixture and ⅔ cup rice).

(Total includes Coconut Rice) *POINTS* value: 5; **Exchanges:** 1½ Starch, 1 Lean Meat, 1½ Fat; **Per serving:** CAL 240 (38% from fat); PRO 8.3g; FAT 10.5g (sat 3.9g); CARB 30.7g; FIB 2.0g; CHOL 0mg; IRON 3.3mg; SOD 358mg; CALC 87mg

COCONUT RICE

¾	cup uncooked basmati rice
1	(13.5-ounce) can light coconut milk
¼	teaspoon salt
3	tablespoons flaked sweetened coconut

1. Combine rice, coconut milk, and salt in a saucepan. Bring to a boil; cover, reduce heat, and simmer 15 minutes. Remove from heat; let stand, covered, 10 minutes. Add coconut; fluff with a fork. YIELD: 6 servings (serving size: ⅔ cup).

POINTS value: 3; **Exchanges:** 1½ Starch, ½ Fat; **Per serving:** CAL 138 (24% from fat); PRO 1.4g; FAT 3.9g (sat 2.8g); CARB 25.9g; FIB 0.8g; CHOL 0mg; IRON 1.1mg; SOD 120mg; CALC 0mg

Meats

PASTITSIO

(pictured on page 90)
prep: 15 minutes • cook: 59 minutes
other: 20 minutes

Another option for preparing this Greek-inspired dish is to cook it in individual gratin dishes. Simply layer ⅓ cup noodles, ⅔ cup meat sauce, another ⅓ cup noodles, ¼ cup white sauce, and 2 tablespoons cheese in each of 6 gratin dishes and bake for 12 minutes. Individual dishes can be frozen for up to 2 weeks and hold 2 servings each.

1	pound ground round
1	cup chopped onion
½	cup chopped carrot
1	(28-ounce) can diced tomatoes
1	teaspoon salt, divided
½	teaspoon black pepper, divided
1	(10-ounce) package frozen chopped spinach, thawed, drained, and squeezed dry
1	teaspoon dried oregano
½	teaspoon ground nutmeg
¼	teaspoon ground cinnamon
2	cups uncooked penne pasta
4½	cups 1% low-fat milk
14	black peppercorns
1	small onion, thinly sliced
1	bay leaf
3	tablespoons light butter
⅓	cup all-purpose flour
¼	teaspoon ground nutmeg
¾	cup (3 ounces) grated fresh Parmesan cheese, divided

Cooking spray

1. Cook beef, onion, and carrot in a large nonstick skillet over medium-high heat until browned, stirring to crumble. Drain well; return meat mixture to pan. Add tomatoes, ½ teaspoon salt, ¼ teaspoon pepper, and next 4 ingredients; bring to a boil. Reduce heat, and simmer, uncovered, 28 minutes or until liquid evaporates, stirring occasionally.

2. Cook pasta according to package directions, omitting salt and fat.

3. Combine milk and next 3 ingredients in a large, heavy saucepan. Cook over medium-high heat to 180° or until tiny bubbles form around edge (do not boil). Remove from heat. Cover; let stand 10 minutes. Strain mixture through a sieve into a bowl; discard solids. Set milk mixture aside.

4. Preheat oven to 375°.

5. Melt butter in a large saucepan over medium-low heat. Add flour, stirring well with a whisk. Cook 1 minute, stirring constantly. Gradually add milk mixture, stirring well with a whisk; cook over medium heat until thick (about 10 minutes). Stir in ½ teaspoon salt, ¼ teaspoon pepper, and nutmeg. Remove from heat; stir in ½ cup cheese. Reserve 1½ cups sauce.

6. Combine pasta and remaining cheese sauce. Spoon half of pasta mixture into a 13 x 9-inch baking dish coated with cooking spray. Spoon meat mixture over pasta. Top with remaining pasta mixture. Pour reserved cheese sauce evenly over pasta layer. Sprinkle with ¼ cup cheese.

7. Bake at 375° for 25 minutes or until bubbly. Let stand 10 minutes before serving. YIELD: 12 servings (serving size: 1/12 of casserole).

POINTS value: 5; **Exchanges:** 1½ Starch, 1 Vegetable, 2 Lean Meat, ½ Fat; **Per serving:** CAL 230.7 (22% from fat); PRO 18g; FAT 5.9g (sat 3.2g); CARB 28.4g; FIB 2.8g; CHOL 33.1mg; IRON 2.9mg; SOD 466.4mg; CALC 241.6mg

HOW TO MAKE A WHITE SAUCE

1. Steep peppercorns, onion, and bay leaf in milk over medium-high heat for about 5 minutes. Strain through a sieve into a bowl; discard solids.

2. Gradually whisk flour into melted butter, and cook 1 minute, stirring constantly.

3. Slowly but vigorously whisk the milk into the butter-flour mixture.

4. Cook over medium heat until thick (about 10 minutes), stirring constantly.

SPAGHETTI WITH FRESH BASIL MEAT SAUCE

prep: 5 minutes • cook: 36 minutes
other: 5 minutes

Use Fresh Basil Meat Sauce on Open-Faced Eggplant-Olive Sandwiches, page 126, or Artichoke, Mushroom, or Prosciutto Calzones, page 130.

8	ounces uncooked spaghetti
¾	pound ground round
1	cup finely chopped onion
3	garlic cloves, minced
1	(14.5-ounce) can diced tomatoes, undrained
¼	cup dry red wine
3	tablespoons tomato paste
¾	teaspoon sugar
⅛	teaspoon crushed red pepper
½	cup chopped fresh basil
1	tablespoon olive oil
½	teaspoon salt

1. Cook pasta according to package directions, omitting salt and fat.
2. Combine beef, onion, and garlic in a large saucepan, and cook over medium-high heat until browned, stirring to crumble. Drain well. Wipe drippings from pan with a paper towel; return meat mixture to pan.
3. Stir in tomatoes and next 4 ingredients. Bring to a boil; cover, reduce heat, and simmer 25 minutes. Remove from heat; stir in basil, olive oil, and salt. Cover and let stand 5 minutes before serving. Serve over pasta. YIELD: 6 servings (serving size: ⅔ cup pasta and ½ cup meat sauce).

POINTS value: 5; Exchanges: 2 Starch, 1 Vegetable, 2 Very Lean Meat; Per serving: CAL 255 (17% from fat); PRO 17.7g; FAT 4.9g (sat 1.2g); CARB 35.5g; FIB 3.7g; CHOL 30mg; IRON 2.7mg; SOD 325mg; CALC 32mg

CINNAMON BEEF OVER COUSCOUS

prep: 4 minutes • cook: 19 minutes
other: 5 minutes

1¼	cups uncooked couscous
1	pound ground round
1½	teaspoons ground cinnamon, divided
1	(14.5-ounce) can diced tomatoes with roasted garlic
½	cup raisins
¼	cup water
1	teaspoon ground cumin
½	teaspoon ground allspice
10	pimiento-stuffed olives, coarsely chopped
3	tablespoons slivered almonds, toasted

1. Cook couscous according to package directions, omitting salt and fat.
2. Cook beef in a large nonstick skillet over medium-high heat 3 minutes or until browned, stirring to crumble. Stir in 1 teaspoon cinnamon, tomatoes, and next 5 ingredients.
3. Bring to a boil; cover, reduce heat, and simmer 10 minutes. Remove from heat; stir in almonds and ½ teaspoon cinnamon. Cover and let stand 5 minutes.
Serve over couscous. YIELD: 6 servings (serving size: ½ cup couscous and ⅔ cup meat mixture).

POINTS value: 5; Exchanges: 2 Starch, 3 Very Lean Meat; Per serving: CAL 269 (17% from fat); PRO 20.8g; FAT 5.2g (sat 1.3g); CARB 36.1g; FIB 3.0g; CHOL 40mg; IRON 2.4mg; SOD 502mg; CALC 68mg

LIME-MARINATED FLANK STEAK

prep: 8 minutes • cook: 12 minutes
other: 8 hours and 5 minutes

Cut the meat across the grain to create thin, tender, juicy slices of steak.

¼	cup white wine vinegar
2	tablespoons chopped fresh cilantro
1	tablespoon vegetable oil
2	teaspoons coarsely chopped jalapeño pepper
1½	teaspoons fresh lime juice
2	garlic cloves, pressed
½	teaspoon salt
¼	teaspoon black pepper
1½	pounds flank steak
	Cooking spray

1. Combine vinegar and next 7 ingredients in a large zip-top plastic bag; shake to combine. Add steak to bag and marinate in refrigerator at least 8 hours, turning bag occasionally.
2. Prepare grill.
3. Remove steak from bag; discard marinade. Place steak on grill rack coated with cooking spray; grill 6 to 8 minutes on each side or to desired degree of doneness. Let stand 5 minutes. Cut steak diagonally across grain into thin slices. YIELD: 6 servings (serving size: about 3 ounces).

POINTS value: 4; Exchanges: 3 Lean Meat; Per serving: CAL 173 (45% from fat); PRO 22.6g; FAT 8.3g (sat 2.9g); CARB 0.6g; FIB 0.1g; CHOL 45mg; IRON 1.6mg; SOD 243mg; CALC 15mg

KOREAN BEEF WITH SPICY CABBAGE

prep: 26 minutes • cook: 14 minutes
other: 8 hours and 5 minutes

Use a mortar and pestle to crush small seeds, like sesame seeds. Or place seeds in a plastic bag and crush with a rolling pin.

⅓   cup low-sodium soy sauce
¼   cup chopped green onions
2   tablespoons brown sugar
1½   tablespoons sesame seeds, toasted and coarsely crushed
1   tablespoon minced peeled fresh ginger
2   tablespoons mirin (sweet rice wine)
2   teaspoons dark sesame oil
½   teaspoon minced garlic
½   teaspoon crushed red pepper
1   pound flank steak, trimmed
Cooking spray
Spicy Cabbage

1. Combine first 9 ingredients in a bowl, stirring until sugar dissolves. Reserve ⅓ cup marinade. Pour remaining marinade into a large zip-top plastic bag. Add meat, and marinate in refrigerator 8 hours, turning bag occasionally.
2. Preheat broiler.
3. Remove meat from bag; discard marinade from bag. Place meat on a broiler pan coated with cooking spray. Broil 6 to 8 minutes per side. Let stand 5 minutes.
4. Place reserved ⅓ cup marinade in a small saucepan. Cook over medium heat 2 to 3 minutes or until hot.
5. Cut steak diagonally across grain into thin slices. Serve over Spicy Cabbage; drizzle with reserved marinade. YIELD: 6 servings (serving size: 3 ounces beef and 1½ cups Spicy Cabbage).

(Total includes Spicy Cabbage) *POINTS* value: 3;
Exchanges: 2 Vegetable, 2 Lean Meat, 1 Fat;
Per serving: CAL 240 (36% from fat); PRO 19.3g;
FAT 9.5g (sat 2.3g); CARB 17.4g; FIB 2.9g;
CHOL 25mg; IRON 2.1mg; SOD 643mg;
CALC 103mg

SPICY CABBAGE

2   teaspoons dark sesame oil
1   teaspoon chili oil
½   cup vertically sliced onion
1   tablespoon minced peeled fresh ginger
1   teaspoon minced garlic
1   red bell pepper, thinly sliced
1   green bell pepper, thinly sliced
½   cup julienne-cut snow peas
1   medium head napa (Chinese) cabbage, cored and cut crosswise into thin strips (about 6 cups)
¼   cup apple juice
¼   teaspoon salt
¼   teaspoon ground red pepper
1   cup shredded carrot
2   teaspoons rice vinegar

1. Heat oils in a nonstick skillet over medium-high heat. Add onion and next 5 ingredients; stir-fry 1 minute. Add cabbage, apple juice, salt, and ground red pepper. Cook 3 to 5 minutes or until cabbage is crisp-tender. Stir in carrot and vinegar. Serve immediately. YIELD: 6 servings (serving size: 1½ cups).

POINTS value: 1; **Exchanges:** 2 Vegetable, ½ Fat;
Per serving: CAL 66 (33% from fat); PRO 1.8g;
FAT 2.5g (sat 0.4g); CARB 9.8g; FIB 2.2g;
CHOL 0mg; IRON 0.3mg; SOD 124mg; CALC 75mg

BEEF TENDERLOIN STEAK WITH CHERRY-PORT SAUCE

prep: 6 minutes • cook: 22 minutes
other: 30 minutes

¼   cup dried cherries
1   cup port or other sweet red wine, divided
¼   cup black cherry juice
4   (4-ounce) beef tenderloin steaks, trimmed (about 1 inch thick)
Butter-flavored cooking spray
¼   teaspoon salt
¼   teaspoon black pepper
1   teaspoon olive oil
2   tablespoons minced shallot (about 1 medium)
1   large garlic clove, minced
½   cup low-salt beef broth
½   teaspoon dried thyme

1. Combine cherries, ¼ cup port, and juice in a small bowl. Let stand 30 minutes for cherries to absorb most of the liquid.
2. Coat steaks with cooking spray; sprinkle with salt and pepper. Cook steaks in a large nonstick skillet over medium heat 5 minutes on each side or until desired degree of doneness. Remove steaks; keep warm.
3. Heat oil in pan over medium-high heat. Add shallot and garlic; sauté 1½ minutes. Stir in cherry mixture, ¾ cup port, broth, and thyme. Bring to a boil; cook 10 minutes or until reduced to ½ cup. Pour sauce over steaks. Serve immediately. YIELD: 4 servings (serving size: 1 steak and 2 tablespoons sauce).

POINTS value: 5; **Exchanges:** ½ Starch, 3 Lean Meat;
Per serving: CAL 209 (36% from fat); PRO 20.1g;
FAT 8.0g (sat 2.7g); CARB 12.4g; FIB 1.2g;
CHOL 57mg; IRON 3.2mg; SOD 253mg; CALC 26mg

DIJON STEAK WITH ORANGE-BALSAMIC SAUCE

prep: 5 minutes • cook: 20 minutes

Quickly searing the steak in a cast iron skillet allows the meat to retain much of its moisture, making it more tender and flavorful.

⅔ cup orange juice
½ cup minced green onions (about 3)
⅓ cup balsamic vinegar
1 teaspoon sugar
½ teaspoon coarsely ground black pepper
⅛ teaspoon salt
4 (4-ounce) beef tenderloin steaks (1 inch thick)
2 garlic cloves, halved
2 teaspoons Dijon mustard
2 teaspoons Creole seasoning

1. Combine first 6 ingredients in a small saucepan; bring to a boil. Reduce heat to medium. Cook, uncovered, 10 minutes. Set aside.
2. Place a 12-inch cast iron skillet over medium-high heat until very hot.
3. Rub both sides of steaks with garlic halves. Spread mustard evenly over both sides of steaks. Sprinkle with Creole seasoning.
4. Cook steaks 3 to 5 minutes on each side or to desired degree of doneness.
5. Spoon sauce over steaks. YIELD: 4 servings (serving size: 1 steak and 3 tablespoons sauce).
Tip: We prefer a cast iron skillet but a nonstick skillet can also be used.

POINTS value: 4; Exchanges: ½ Fruit, 3 Lean Meat; Per serving: CAL 189 (35% from fat); PRO 20.1g; FAT 7.2g (sat 2.6g); CARB 10.3g; FIB 0.5g; CHOL 57mg; IRON 3.0mg; SOD 488mg; CALC 32mg

FILET MIGNON WITH ROSEMARY-PORT SAUCE

prep: 5 minutes • cook: 14 minutes
other: 15 minutes

Port adds a rich, spicy flavor to the sauce in this recipe. However, you may use any sweet red wine in its place.

2 large garlic cloves, halved
4 (4-ounce) beef tenderloin steaks, trimmed (about 1 inch thick)
½ teaspoon salt, divided
½ teaspoon coarsely ground black pepper
½ cup port or other sweet red wine
½ cup low-salt beef broth
1 teaspoon chopped fresh rosemary
Cooking spray
2 teaspoons light butter

1. Rub cut sides of garlic over each side of steaks; sprinkle with ¼ teaspoon salt and ½ teaspoon pepper. Let stand 15 minutes.
2. Combine port, broth, and rosemary in a large nonstick skillet over medium-high heat; bring to a boil. Reduce heat; simmer, uncovered, 5 minutes or until mixture measures ⅓ cup. Stir ¼ teaspoon salt into sauce. Pour into a small bowl; set aside. Wipe pan clean with a paper towel.
3. Coat pan with cooking spray; place over medium-high heat. Add beef; cook 4 minutes on each side or until desired degree of doneness. Set beef aside. Add reserved port mixture to hot pan. Simmer 30 seconds, scraping pan to loosen browned bits, until mixture reduces to ¼ cup.

Remove from heat and stir in butter. Spoon sauce over steaks. YIELD: 4 servings (serving size: 1 steak and about 1 tablespoon sauce).

POINTS value: 4; Exchanges: 3 Lean Meat; Per serving: CAL 158 (46% from fat); PRO 19.8g; FAT 7.8g (sat 3.2g); CARB 1.1g; FIB 0.1g; CHOL 61mg; IRON 2.7mg; SOD 405mg; CALC 12mg

---

SAFE COOKING TEMPERATURES

One of the major causes of foodborne illness is eating undercooked meat and poultry—something that is almost 100% preventable for food prepared in your own kitchen. Heating food to the correct temperature destroys harmful microorganisms. The most reliable way to test the doneness of meat is to use a meat thermometer.

According to the USDA, meat should be cooked until a thermometer inserted into the thickest part of the meat reads as follows:

Beef, Veal, Lamb, Pork:
    Medium: 160°
    Well Done: 170°
Ground Meat: 160°-165°
Chicken and Turkey:
    Ground: 165°
    Breasts: 170°
    Legs, Thighs, Wings: 180°
    Whole Bird: 180°
Eggs (fried, poached, hard-cooked): cook until yolk and white are firm
Eggs (casseroles, custards, sauces): 160°

FILET MIGNON WITH SHERRY-MUSHROOM SAUCE

(pictured on page 90)
prep: 5 minutes • cook: 16 minutes

Asparagus and mashed potatoes are perfect accompaniments to this tender, juicy filet. Serve Asparagus Spears with Lemon-Tarragon Butter, page 142, and Gorgonzola and Chive Mashed Potatoes, page 147, with the filet for a delicious and impressive meal with a ***POINTS*** *value of 9.*

1	cup dry sherry
¼	cup Worcestershire sauce
1½	teaspoons sugar
1	teaspoon dried oregano
¾	teaspoon salt
4	(4-ounce) beef tenderloin steaks, trimmed (about 1 inch thick)

Cooking spray

1	tablespoon olive oil
1	(8-ounce) package presliced mushrooms
¼	cup (1 ounce) crumbled blue cheese
¼	cup chopped fresh parsley

1. Stir together first 5 ingredients in a small bowl. Set aside.
2. Coat steaks with cooking spray. Cook steaks in a large nonstick skillet over medium-high heat 10 minutes or until desired degree of doneness. Remove steaks to a serving platter. Keep warm.
3. Heat oil in same pan over medium-high heat. Add mushrooms; sauté 2 minutes. Stir in ¼ cup sherry mixture. Cook, stirring constantly, 2 minutes or until liquid is reduced to about 2 tablespoons. Spoon mushrooms around steaks.

4. Pour remaining sherry mixture into pan. Bring to a boil; cook 2 minutes or until mixture is reduced to about 6 tablespoons. Pour sherry mixture over steak and mushrooms; sprinkle with cheese and parsley. Serve immediately. YIELD: 4 servings (serving size: 1 steak, ½ cup mushrooms, about 1½ tablespoons sauce, and 1 tablespoon blue cheese).

POINTS value: 6; **Exchanges:** 1 Vegetable, 3½ Lean Meat, 1 Fat; **Per serving:** CAL 254 (45% from fat); PRO 23.4g; FAT 12.8g (sat 4.6g); CARB 10.3g; FIB 1.6g; CHOL 64mg; IRON 4.6mg; SOD 779mg; CALC 90mg

VEAL CUTLETS WITH WINE-BRAISED MUSHROOMS

prep: 10 minutes • cook: 12 minutes

1	pound veal scaloppine
¼	cup all-purpose flour
2	teaspoons olive oil, divided
1	(8-ounce) package presliced mushrooms
¼	cup sliced green onions
⅓	cup low-salt beef broth
¼	cup dry Marsala wine
¼	cup water
½	cup chopped seeded tomato
½	teaspoon salt
¼	teaspoon freshly ground black pepper
2	tablespoons chopped fresh parsley

1. Place veal between 2 sheets of heavy-duty plastic wrap and flatten to ⅛-inch thickness, using a meat mallet or rolling pin. Cut into serving sized pieces; dredge pieces in flour.
2. Heat 1 teaspoon oil a large non-stick skillet over medium-high heat.

Add half of veal, and cook 1 to 1½ minutes on each side. Transfer veal to a serving platter; cover and keep warm. Repeat procedure with remaining oil and veal.
3. Add mushrooms and onions to pan, and sauté 1½ minutes until tender. Combine beef broth, Marsala, and water. Add to pan, scraping pan to loosen browned bits. Remove from heat. Stir in tomato, salt, and pepper. Pour mushroom sauce over veal. Sprinkle with parsley, and serve immediately. YIELD: 4 servings (serving size: 3 ounces veal and about 2 tablespoons sauce).

POINTS value: 4; **Exchanges:** ½ Starch, 3 Lean Meat; **Per serving:** CAL 201 (29% from fat); PRO 25.2g; FAT 6.3g (sat 1.5g); CARB 9.6g; FIB 0.8g; CHOL 91mg; IRON 1.8mg; SOD 443mg; CALC 34mg

CUMIN LAMB CHOPS WITH PEAR CHUTNEY

(pictured on page 91)
prep: 15 minutes • cook: 30 minutes other: 1 hour

Serve these lamb chops over a bed of couscous or rice. The Pear Chutney is also delicious over chicken, turkey, or pork tenderloin.

1	tablespoon lemon juice
2	teaspoons olive oil
1	teaspoon ground cumin
1	teaspoon minced garlic
¼	teaspoon salt
¼	teaspoon pepper
6	(6-ounce) lean lamb loin chops

Cooking spray
Pear Chutney

1. Combine first 6 ingredients in a small bowl. Place lamb chops in a shallow dish. Spoon cumin mixture evenly over both sides of chops. Cover and chill 1 hour.

2. Heat a large nonstick skillet coated with cooking spray over medium-high heat. Add chops; cook 8 minutes on each side or to desired degree of doneness. Serve with Pear Chutney. YIELD: 6 servings (serving size: 1 chop and ¼ cup chutney).

(Total includes Pear Chutney) *POINTS* value: 5;
Exchanges: ½ Starch, 1½ Fruit, 2½ Lean Meat;
Per serving: CAL 266 (25% from fat); PRO 19.8g;
FAT 7.5g (sat 2.2g); CARB 30.1g; FIB 2.7g;
CHOL 61mg; IRON 2.2mg; SOD 259mg; CALC 26mg

PEAR CHUTNEY

3	cups chopped pear (about 2)
⅓	cup dried cranberries
⅓	cup sugar
¼	cup orange juice
2	tablespoons minced peeled fresh ginger
2	tablespoons white vinegar
¼	teaspoon salt
¼	teaspoon crushed red pepper
¼	teaspoon dry mustard

1. Combine all ingredients in a medium saucepan. Bring to a boil; reduce heat, and simmer, uncovered, 30 minutes or until thick. Serve warm or at room temperature. YIELD: 6 servings (serving size: ¼ cup).

POINTS value: 2; Exchanges: ½ Starch, 1½ Fruit;
Per serving: CAL 118 (3% from fat); PRO 0.5g;
FAT 0.4g (sat 0.0g); CARB 29.6g; FIB 2.6g;
CHOL 0mg; IRON 0.3mg; SOD 98mg; CALC 11mg

PORK CHOPS WITH ORANGE-OLIVE RELISH

prep: 28 minutes • cook: 20 minutes
other: 8 hours

1	cup fresh orange juice (about 2½ oranges)
½	cup dry white wine
¼	cup fresh lime juice (about 2 limes)
1	tablespoon ground cumin
1	tablespoon Dijon mustard
1½	teaspoons minced garlic
½	teaspoon salt
¼	teaspoon black pepper
⅛	teaspoon ground red pepper
6	(4-ounce) boneless center-cut loin pork chops (1½ inches thick), trimmed

Cooking spray
Orange-Olive Relish

1. Combine first 9 ingredients in a large zip-top plastic bag. Add pork to bag; seal. Marinate in refrigerator 8 hours, turning bag occasionally. Discard marinade.

2. Prepare grill.

3. Remove pork from bag.

4. Place pork on grill rack coated with cooking spray; cover and grill 10 minutes on each side or until pork is no longer pink. Serve with Orange-Olive Relish. YIELD: 6 servings (serving size: 1 chop and ⅓ cup relish).

(Total includes Orange-Olive Relish) *POINTS* value: 4;
Exchanges: ½ Fruit, 3 Lean Meat; Per serving:
CAL 207 (32% from fat); PRO 25.3g; FAT 7.4g
(sat 2.3g); CARB 9.0g; FIB 1.8g; CHOL 67mg;
IRON 1.6mg; SOD 299mg; CALC 56mg

ORANGE-OLIVE RELISH

1	teaspoon grated orange rind
1½	cups coarsely chopped oranges (about 2)
¼	cup chopped ripe olives
3	tablespoons chopped red onion
2	tablespoons chopped fresh cilantro
1½	tablespoons fresh lime juice (about 1 lime)
1	tablespoon fresh orange juice (about ½ orange)
¼	teaspoon sugar
¼	teaspoon salt
¼	teaspoon black pepper
⅛	teaspoon ground red pepper

1. Combine all ingredients in a bowl. Cover and chill 1 hour. YIELD: 6 servings (serving size: ⅓ cup).

POINTS value: 0; Exchange: ½ Fruit;
Per serving: CAL 33 (17% from fat); PRO 0.6g;
FAT 0.7g (sat 0.1g); CARB 7.1g; FIB 1.4g;
CHOL 0mg; IRON 0.3mg; SOD 148mg; CALC 26mg

APPLE-STUFFED PORK LOIN WITH MAPLE-MUSTARD SAUCE

prep: 25 minutes • cook 1 hour and 20 minutes • other: 30 minutes

½	cup raisins
¼	cup bourbon or apple juice
1½	teaspoons dried thyme
1	teaspoon ground coriander
½	teaspoon salt
¼	teaspoon pepper
2	teaspoons butter
½	cup chopped onion
½	cup chopped celery
1½	cups diced peeled Granny Smith apple
¼	teaspoon grated orange rind
1	(2-pound) boneless pork loin roast

Cooking spray
Maple-Mustard Sauce

1. Combine raisins and bourbon in a small microwave-safe bowl. Microwave at HIGH 45 seconds or until hot. Remove from microwave; cover and let stand 20 minutes.
2. Combine thyme and next 3 ingredients in a small bowl, stirring well.
3. Melt butter in a large nonstick skillet. Add onion and celery; sauté 5 minutes. Stir in apple and half of spice mixture. Sauté 3 minutes or until apple is crisp-tender. Stir in orange rind and raisins with liquid; cook 30 seconds. Set aside.
4. Trim fat from pork. Starting off-center, slice pork lengthwise, cutting to, but not through, other side. Open butterflied portions, laying pork flat. Turning knife blade parallel to surface of cutting board, slice larger portion of pork in half horizontally, cutting to, but not through, other side; open flat. Place plastic wrap over pork; pound to ½-inch thickness using a meat mallet or rolling pin.
5. Preheat oven to 325°.
6. Spread apple mixture over pork to within ½ inch of edges. Roll up pork, jelly roll fashion, starting with long side. Secure pork at 2-inch intervals with twine.
7. Rub pork with remaining spice mixture. Place on a broiler pan coated with cooking spray. Bake at 325° for 1 hour and 10 minutes or until a thermometer registers 160° (slightly pink). Let stand 10 minutes before slicing. Serve with Maple-Mustard Sauce. YIELD: 8 servings (serving size: about 3 ounces pork and about 1½ tablespoons sauce).

(Total includes Maple-Mustard Sauce) *POINTS* value: 5;
Exchanges: 1 Starch, ½ Fruit, 2½ Lean Meat;
Per serving: CAL 253 (23% from fat); PRO 25.5g;
FAT 6.6g (sat 2.2g); CARB 22.1g; FIB 1.9g;
CHOL 74mg; IRON 1.9mg; SOD 532mg; CALC 50mg

MAPLE-MUSTARD SAUCE

1½	cups fat-free, less-sodium chicken broth
5	tablespoons maple syrup
¼	cup Dijon mustard
1	tablespoon bourbon or apple juice

1. Combine first 3 ingredients in a saucepan. Bring to a boil; reduce heat, and simmer about 20 minutes or until mixture is reduced to ⅔ cup. Stir in bourbon. Serve warm. YIELD: 8 servings (serving size: about 1½ tablespoons).

POINTS value: 1; **Exchange:** ½ Starch;
Per serving: CAL 49 (12% from fat); PRO 1.1g;
FAT 0.7g (sat 0.0g); CARB 9.4g; FIB 0.1g;
CHOL 0mg; IRON 0.4mg; SOD 307mg; CALC 19mg

HOW TO DOUBLE BUTTERFLY AND STUFF A PORK LOIN

1. Starting off-center, slice pork lengthwise, cutting to, but not through, other side. Open butterflied portions, laying pork flat. Slice larger portion of pork in half horizontally, cutting to, but not through, other side; open flat.

2. Place plastic wrap over pork and pound to ½-inch thickness.

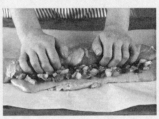

3. Spread apple mixture over pork and roll up, jelly roll fashion, starting with long side.

4. Secure pork with twine at 2-inch intervals.

Thin Feels Good

HEATHER MURRAY • **HEIGHT** 5'6" • **BEFORE** 175 LBS. • **AFTER** 139 LBS.

Motto: "Nothing tastes as good as thin feels."

Nothing tastes as good as thin feels. This phrase has guided Heather Murray, morning news radio editor, for the past four years. "To someone who's been overweight since the third grade, the feeling of being thin was foreign," she says. "But that was until January 2000 when something clicked and being thin was something I knew I could do."

In December 1999 Heather and her friends made New Year's Eve plans to ring in both the new year and the new millennium. "We talked about taking pictures at midnight and how one day they would be family heirlooms," Heather says. "But when I got the pictures back, I realized this was not how I wanted to look entering the next century. And that's when I joined *Weight Watchers*.

"I was determined." she says. "In my mind there was no room for defeat." Heather followed the program precisely. She counted the **POINTS** values, went to all the meetings, wrote down everything she ate, and began exercising. "It all worked," she says. "I was eating less and moving more. I even started running."

About one month after Heather committed to *Weight Watchers* and lost 15 pounds, Heather's leader said something that changed everything for Heather: Nothing tastes as good as thin feels. "It was just something that stuck with me," Heather says. "The moment of eating something is gone in an instant," she says. "But feeling good about yourself and being confident and proud of your accomplishment stays with you all the time.

"I learned I could control my weight by controlling what went into my mouth," Heather says. "A plate of fettuccine Alfredo tasted good, but it didn't feel good. I finally comprehended that there was joy in life in more than food. There was joy in health, in energy, and in fitness!"

As Heather's weight decreased, her confidence increased. "I didn't have to hide in sweatpants and sweatshirts," she says. "I could meet strangers and not think of myself as unworthy or uninteresting. I found my true self in my weight loss and discovered that it

> *"I learned I could control my weight by controlling what went into my mouth."*

was the same person I had always been. I just uncovered the confidence to let others find her, too."

Heather has now been at her goal weight for four years. "Reaching my goal was a big deal," she says. "But it's keeping the weight off that I'm most proud of. That and wearing a strapless size 6 wedding dress. That was definitely one of the big rewards!"

On December 7, 2002, Heather married her high school sweetheart. "I married someone who knew me when I was overweight, but fell in love with me anyway," she says. "And while we may not be happy with our New Year's 2000 photos, you can be sure that we will some day proudly show off our wedding photos to our grandchildren."

Pastitsio,
page 82

Filet Mignon with Sherry-
Mushroom Sauce,
page 86

Cumin Lamb Chops with
Pear Chutney,
page 86

Pork with Grapefruit-Mint Salsa,
opposite page

PORK WITH GRAPEFRUIT-MINT SALSA

(pictured on opposite page)

prep: 10 minutes • cook: 28 minutes
other: 35 minutes

For easy cleanup, line your jelly roll pan with foil and lightly coat with cooking spray before placing the pork in the pan. Simply remove the foil after cooking and throw it away. Serve the pork slices and salsa over 1 cup of wild rice for a hearty meal with a POINTS value of 7.

½   teaspoon ground allspice
½   teaspoon ground cinnamon
½   teaspoon ground cumin
¼   teaspoon crushed red pepper
¼   teaspoon salt
¼   teaspoon black pepper
1   pound pork tenderloin, trimmed
Cooking spray
½   cup finely chopped dried apricots
½   cup finely chopped yellow bell pepper
½   cup refrigerated red grapefruit sections, drained
¼   cup finely chopped red onion
¼   cup finely chopped fresh mint
1   tablespoon lemon juice
½   teaspoon sugar

1. Preheat oven to 425°.
2. Combine allspice and next 5 ingredients in a small bowl. Stir well, and rub evenly on pork. Place pork on a jelly roll pan coated with cooking spray.
3. Bake at 425° for 28 minutes or until a thermometer registers 160° (slightly pink).

4. While meat cooks, combine apricots and next 6 ingredients in a medium bowl. Let stand 30 minutes. Serve salsa over pork. YIELD: 4 servings (serving size: 3 ounces pork and about ⅓ cup salsa).

POINTS value: 4; **Exchanges:** 1 Fruit, 3 Lean Meat; **Per serving:** CAL 218 (17% from fat); PRO 25.2g; FAT 4.1g (sat 1.4g); CARB 19.2g; FIB 2.3g; CHOL 74mg; IRON 2.6mg; SOD 208mg; CALC 35mg

SPICY PORK WITH BLACK BEAN AND TOMATILLO SALSA

prep: 11 minutes • cook: 28 minutes
other: 20 minutes

For less heat in the salsa, substitute ⅓ cup chopped green bell pepper for the Anaheim chile.

1   teaspoon ground cumin
¾   teaspoon dried ground chipotle pepper
¼   teaspoon salt
1   pound pork tenderloin, trimmed
2   teaspoons olive oil
Black Bean and Tomatillo Salsa

1. Combine first 3 ingredients; rub over all sides of pork. Let stand 15 minutes. Heat a large nonstick skillet over medium-high heat; add oil. Add pork and cook 3 minutes; turn and cook 2 to 3 minutes on other side or until browned.
2. Preheat oven to 350°.
3. Wrap handle of pan with foil. Bake at 350° for 22 minutes or until a thermometer registers 160° (slightly pink). Remove from oven, tent with foil and let stand 5 minutes.

4. Slice pork; serve with Black Bean and Tomatillo Salsa. YIELD: 4 servings (serving size: 3 ounces pork and about ½ cup salsa).

(Total includes Black Bean and Tomatillo Salsa)
POINTS value: 4; **Exchanges:** ½ Very Lean Meat, 2½ Lean Meat, 1½ Fat; **Per serving:** CAL 223 (40% from fat); PRO 26.2g; FAT 9.8g (sat 2.3g); CARB 7.2g; FIB 4.0g; CHOL 74mg; IRON 2.3mg; SOD 429mg; CALC 20mg

BLACK BEAN AND TOMATILLO SALSA

⅔   cup avocado, chopped (about ½ medium)
⅓   cup black beans, rinsed and drained
⅓   cup tomatillos, chopped (about 2 medium)
¼   cup chopped fresh cilantro
1   Anaheim chile, seeded and chopped
1   tablespoon fresh lime juice
¼   teaspoon salt

1. Combine all ingredients in a large bowl. Toss gently to combine. YIELD: 4 servings (serving size: about ½ cup).

POINTS value: 1; **Exchanges:** 1 Vegetable, ½ Fat; **Per serving:** CAL 52 (50% from fat); PRO 1.6g; FAT 3.3g (sat 0.7g); CARB 6.0g; FIB 3.1g; CHOL 0mg; IRON 0.4mg; SOD 206mg; CALC 19mg

ROASTED ITALIAN PORK TENDERLOIN

prep: 3 minutes • cook: 23 minutes
other: 5 minutes

Our Test Kitchens staff thinks dry rubs really kick up the flavor of the meat and are great alternatives to marinades.

1 tablespoon Italian-seasoned breadcrumbs
1 teaspoon dried thyme
1 teaspoon dried basil
1 teaspoon instant dried onion flakes
¾ teaspoon salt
½ teaspoon freshly ground black pepper
1 pound pork tenderloin, trimmed
1 teaspoon olive oil
Cooking spray

1. Preheat oven to 375°.
2. Combine first 6 ingredients in a small bowl; rub over all sides of pork.
3. Heat oil in a large nonstick skillet coated with cooking spray over medium-high heat. Add pork and cook 3 minutes; turn and cook 2 minutes on other side or until browned.
4. Wrap handle of pan with foil. Bake at 375° for 18 minutes or until a thermometer registers 160° (slightly pink). Remove from oven, tent with foil, and let stand 5 minutes before slicing. YIELD: 4 servings (serving size: 3 ounces).

POINTS value: 3; **Exchanges:** 3 Lean Meat; **Per serving:** CAL 157 (29% from fat); PRO 24.2g; FAT 5.1g (sat 1.5g); CARB 2.1g; FIB 0.5g; CHOL 74mg; IRON 1.9mg; SOD 547mg; CALC 19mg

SKILLET SAUSAGE CASSEROLE

prep: 5 minutes • cook: 45 minutes
other: 3 minutes

½ cup uncooked brown rice
½ (12-ounce) package 50%-less-fat breakfast sausage
1½ cups chopped onion
1½ cups chopped red bell pepper
½ cup sliced carrot
1 poblano chile, cut into strips
1 (8-ounce) package presliced mushrooms
1 cup frozen whole-kernel corn, thawed and drained
1 teaspoon beef-flavored bouillon granules
¾ teaspoon dried thyme
⅛ teaspoon ground red pepper
¾ cup chopped fresh parsley
2 teaspoons olive oil
¼ teaspoon salt

1. Cook rice according to package directions, omitting salt and fat.
2. Cook sausage in a large nonstick skillet over medium-high heat 4 minutes, stirring to crumble. Set aside.
3. Add onion and next 3 ingredients to pan; cook 4 minutes or until onion is tender, stirring frequently. Add mushrooms and next 4 ingredients; cook 4 minutes or until carrot is crisp-tender.
4. Remove from heat; stir in sausage, parsley, oil, and salt. Cover and let stand 3 minutes. Toss with rice. YIELD: 4 servings (serving size: 1½ cups).

POINTS value: 6; **Exchanges:** 2 Starch, 1 Vegetable, 2 Medium-Fat Meat; **Per serving:** CAL 316 (32% from fat); PRO 13.8g; FAT 11.7g (sat 3.2g); CARB 42.6g; FIB 6.8g; CHOL 30mg; IRON 3.6mg; SOD 698mg; CALC 47mg

SKILLET HAM WITH PINEAPPLE-GINGER SALSA

prep: 9 minutes • cook: 2 minutes

Dried plums—also known as prunes—are a good source of vitamins A and B, and are high in fiber, iron, calcium, and phosphorus. Not only are they a tasty addition to recipes such as this one, they make a nutritious and delicious snack as well!

Cooking spray
4 (3-ounce) slices extralean, low-sodium ham
½ cup chopped fresh pineapple
½ cup chopped red bell pepper
4 orange essence dried plums, chopped
2 tablespoons pineapple juice
1 teaspoon grated peeled fresh ginger

1. Place a large nonstick skillet coated with cooking spray over medium-high heat. Add ham and cook 1 to 2 minutes on each side or until thoroughly heated.
2. Combine pineapple and next 4 ingredients in a small bowl; serve with ham. YIELD: 4 servings (serving size: 1 slice ham and ¼ cup salsa).
Note: Canned pineapple tidbits may be substituted for fresh pineapple. Drain tidbits, and reserve 2 tablespoons juice for recipe.

POINTS value: 3; **Exchanges:** 1 Fruit, 2 Very Lean Meat; **Per serving:** CAL 130 (20% from fat); PRO 14.6g; FAT 3.0g (sat 1.1g); CARB 12.4g; FIB 0.9g; CHOL 36mg; IRON 1.4mg; SOD 707mg; CALC 13mg

Poultry

PIZZA WITH CHICKEN, ARTICHOKES, AND BASIL

prep: 5 minutes • cook: 18 minutes

1   teaspoon olive oil
Cooking spray
1   (8-ounce) package presliced
       mushrooms
1   (14-ounce) Italian
       cheese-flavored pizza crust
       (such as Boboli)
1   cup tomato and basil pasta
       sauce (such as Classico)
1   cup chopped grilled chicken
       breast strips (such as Tyson
       Chicken Breast Strips)
1   cup drained canned artichoke
       hearts, coarsely chopped
1   cup (4 ounces) shredded
       part-skim mozzarella cheese
¼   cup thinly sliced fresh basil

1. Preheat oven to 450°.
2. Heat oil in a large nonstick skillet coated with cooking spray over medium-high heat. Add mushrooms; sauté 6 minutes.
3. Place pizza crust on an ungreased baking sheet; spoon pasta sauce onto crust, leaving a 1-inch border around edges. Top with mushrooms, chicken, and artichokes; sprinkle with cheese. Bake at 450° for 12 minutes or until crust is golden. Top with basil. Cut into 8 slices. YIELD: 8 servings (serving size: 1 slice).

POINTS value: *5;* **Exchanges:** 1½ Starch, 1 Vegetable, 1 Very Lean Meat, 1 Fat; **Per serving:** CAL 227 (25% from fat); PRO 15.3g; FAT 6.4g (sat 2.6g); CARB 27.2g; FIB 2.5g; CHOL 21mg; IRON 2.1mg; SOD 622mg; CALC 254mg

SOUTHWEST CHICKEN PIZZA

prep: 12 minutes • cook: 8 minutes

If you like a little more heat, use Monterey Jack cheese with jalapeño peppers and sprinkle with crushed red pepper. Serve with salsa.

1   (10-ounce) Italian
       cheese-flavored thin pizza
       crust (such as Boboli)
1   cup (4 ounces) shredded
       Monterey Jack cheese, divided
1   (6-ounce) package
       Southwest-flavor grilled
       chicken breast strips, coarsely
       chopped
½   cup thinly sliced red onion
⅓   cup frozen whole-kernel
       corn, thawed and drained
1   jalapeño pepper, seeded and
       chopped
2   tablespoons chopped fresh
       cilantro

1. Preheat oven to 450°.
2. Place pizza crust on an ungreased baking sheet. Sprinkle ½ cup cheese evenly over crust, leaving a ½-inch border around edges. Top with chicken and next 3 ingredients. Sprinkle with ½ cup cheese.
3. Bake at 450° for 8 to 10 minutes or until cheese melts. Sprinkle with cilantro. Cut into 8 slices. YIELD: 8 servings (serving size: 1 slice).

POINTS value: *4;* **Exchanges:** 1 Starch, 1 Vegetable, 1 Very Lean Meat, ½ High-Fat Meat; **Per serving:** CAL 183 (34% from fat); PRO 12.3g; FAT 7.0g (sat 3.6g); CARB 17.5g; FIB 0.6g; CHOL 26mg; IRON 1.2mg; SOD 458mg; CALC 201mg

CHICKEN AND SPINACH PIZZA

prep: 10 minutes • cook: 12 minutes

In a rush? Use rotisserie chicken from your supermarket's deli instead of cooking the chicken yourself. Keep in mind that one rotisserie chicken will yield approximately three cups of chopped chicken.

1   (10-ounce) Italian
       cheese-flavored thin pizza
       crust (such as Boboli)
1½   cups chopped cooked chicken
1   (10-ounce) package frozen
       chopped spinach, thawed,
       drained, and squeezed dry
1   cup spicy spaghetti sauce
       (such as Newman's Own)
1½   cups (6 ounces) shredded
       part-skim mozzarella cheese
2   tablespoons chopped fresh
       basil

1. Preheat oven to 450°.
2. Place crust on an ungreased baking sheet.
3. Combine chicken, spinach, and spaghetti sauce in a bowl; spoon evenly over crust. Top with cheese.
4. Bake at 450° for 12 minutes or until crust is browned and cheese melts. Top with basil; cut into 8 slices. YIELD: 8 servings (serving size: 1 slice).

POINTS value: *4;* **Exchanges:** 1½ Starch, ½ Vegetable, 1 Very Lean Meat, 1 Fat; **Per serving:** CAL 204 (27% from fat); PRO 17.1g; FAT 6.2g (sat 2.9g); CARB 20.0g; FIB 2.0g; CHOL 26mg; IRON 2.0mg; SOD 531mg; CALC 294mg

CHICKEN AND RICE ENCHILADAS

prep: 20 minutes • cook: 34 minutes
other: 5 minutes

Enjoy chicken, vegetables, and rice all rolled up in a soft flour tortilla.

1   (14-ounce) bag boil-in-bag brown rice (such as Success)
2   teaspoons olive oil
Cooking spray
1½   cups thinly sliced mushrooms
½   cup diced onion
1   (10-ounce) can enchilada sauce
½   cup tomato juice
1½   cups chopped cooked chicken
3   tablespoons finely chopped fresh flat-leaf parsley
2   tablespoons grated Parmesan cheese
½   teaspoon chili powder
½   teaspoon dried oregano
½   teaspoon ground cumin
¼   teaspoon salt
6   (8-inch) 97%-fat-free flour tortillas (such as Mission)
½   cup (2 ounces) shredded reduced-fat sharp Cheddar cheese
6   tablespoons low-fat sour cream

1. Preheat oven to 375°.
2. Cook rice according to package directions, omitting salt and fat.
3. Heat oil in a large nonstick skillet coated with cooking spray over medium-high heat. Add mushrooms and onion; sauté 5 minutes or until tender. Combine enchilada sauce, tomato juice, and mushroom mixture. Spoon ¼ cup mushroom mixture over bottom of an 11 x 7-inch baking dish coated with cooking spray.
4. Combine rice, chicken, and next 6 ingredients in a large bowl. Spoon about ½ cup chicken mixture in center of 1 tortilla; roll tightly and place, seam side down, in baking dish. Repeat procedure with remaining tortillas and chicken mixture.
5. Spoon remaining mushroom mixture over top of enchiladas. Cover and bake at 375° for 25 minutes. Uncover; sprinkle with Cheddar cheese. Bake an additional 4 minutes or until cheese melts. Let stand 5 minutes. Top each enchilada with 1 tablespoon sour cream. YIELD: 6 servings (serving size 1 enchilada and 1 tablespoon sour cream).

POINTS value: 6; **Exchanges:** 2 Starch, 1 Vegetable, 1½ Very Lean Meat, 1½ Fat; **Per serving:** CAL 293 (37% from fat); PRO 16.0g; FAT 12.4g (sat 5.9g); CARB 31.2g; FIB 2.8g; CHOL 46mg; IRON 1.9mg; SOD 512mg; CALC 156mg

---

SHORTCUTS TO COOKED CHICKEN

When salads and sandwich fillings call for cooked chicken, use skinless, boneless chicken breast halves.

On the cooktop: Bring 1 cup water to a boil in a large skillet over medium-high heat. Reduce heat to simmer, and add chicken; cover and cook 15 minutes or until done, turning chicken after 8 minutes. Drain.

In the microwave: Arrange chicken in an 11 x 7-inch baking dish with the thickest portions toward the outside of the dish. Cover with wax paper, and microwave at HIGH 6 to 8 minutes or until done, rotating dish a quarter-turn after 4 minutes.

SKILLET CHICKEN AND BISCUITS

prep: 4 minutes • cook: 13 minutes

1   (10-ounce) can condensed reduced-fat cream of chicken soup
⅓   cup low-fat sour cream
2½   cups diced cooked chicken breast
2½   cups frozen mixed vegetables, thawed
1   (4-ounce) jar diced pimiento, drained
½   teaspoon dried thyme
¼   teaspoon pepper
2   tablespoons chopped fresh parsley
1   (4-ounce) can reduced-fat refrigerated crescent dinner roll dough

1. Preheat oven to 450°.
2. Combine soup and sour cream in a large nonstick skillet; add chicken and next 4 ingredients. Bring to a boil; cover, reduce heat, and simmer 8 minutes or until vegetables are tender. Sprinkle with parsley.
3. Unroll dough, separating dough along perforations into triangles; cut each triangle in half. Bake at 450° for 6 to 7 minutes or until browned. Spoon chicken mixture over 2 pastry triangle halves. YIELD: 4 servings (serving size: 1 cup chicken mixture and 2 pastry triangle halves).

POINTS value: 6; **Exchanges:** 1 Starch, 2 Vegetable, 3 Very Lean Meat, 2 Fat; **Per serving:** CAL 319 (27% from fat); PRO 26.9g; FAT 9.5g (sat 2.9g); CARB 31.5g; FIB 3.5g; CHOL 58mg; IRON 2.2mg; SOD 791mg; CALC 58mg

CREAMED CHICKEN WITH NOODLES

prep: 13 minutes • cook: 17 minutes

Creamy white sauce, fresh vegetables, and precooked chicken breast combine to create a warm, hearty meal in just 30 minutes. The chicken can also be served over ½ cup hot cooked rice for the same POINTS value.

1	cup uncooked wide egg noodles
¼	cup all-purpose flour
½	teaspoon salt
¼	teaspoon dried rubbed sage
¼	teaspoon dried thyme
¼	teaspoon pepper
1¼	cups fat-free, less-sodium chicken broth
1¼	cups 1% low-fat milk
1	tablespoon butter
1	(8-ounce) package presliced mushrooms
½	cup chopped onion
½	cup thinly sliced celery
2	cups chopped cooked chicken breast
1	cup frozen green peas, thawed
¼	cup chopped fresh flat-leaf parsley

1. Prepare pasta according to package directions, omitting salt and fat.
2. While pasta cooks, combine flour and next 4 ingredients in a large bowl. Slowly whisk in broth and milk.
3. Melt butter in a large nonstick skillet over medium-high heat. Add mushrooms, onion, and celery; cook, stirring constantly, 6 minutes or until almost all liquid is absorbed and onion is tender. Stir in broth mixture; bring to a boil, reduce heat, and cook, stirring constantly, 4 minutes or until thick and bubbly. Add chicken and peas; cook 3 minutes or until thoroughly heated, stirring occasionally. Stir in parsley. Serve over hot cooked pasta. YIELD: 4 servings (serving size: about 1 cup chicken mixture and ½ cup noodles).

POINTS value: 6; Exchanges: 2½ Starch, 1 Vegetable, 3 Very Lean Meat; Per serving: CAL 324 (17% from fat); PRO 28.8g; FAT 6.1g (sat 2.3g); CARB 39.5g; FIB 3.8g; CHOL 74mg; IRON 2.9mg; SOD 819mg; CALC 132mg

PECAN-CRUSTED CHICKEN FINGERS WITH DIJON-MAPLE SAUCE

prep: 26 minutes • cook: 24 minutes

Baking these double-dipped chicken tenders in the oven allows the pecan crust to get crispy without the added fat and calories associated with deep-fat frying.

1½	pounds chicken breast tenders (about 12 pieces)
¾	teaspoon pepper, divided
½	teaspoon salt
1	cup all-purpose flour, divided
½	cup egg substitute
½	cup finely chopped pecans
2	teaspoons olive oil, divided
	Cooking spray
½	cup fat-free, less-sodium chicken broth
1	teaspoon cornstarch
¼	cup maple syrup
1½	tablespoons country-style Dijon mustard
2	teaspoons light butter
1	tablespoon fresh lemon juice

1. Preheat oven to 400°.
2. Sprinkle chicken with ½ teaspoon pepper and salt. Place ½ cup flour and egg substitute in separate shallow dishes. Combine ½ cup flour, pecans, and ¼ teaspoon pepper in a shallow dish.
3. Dredge each chicken tender in flour, shaking off excess flour. Dip each tender in egg substitute; dredge dipped tenders in pecan mixture.
4. Heat 1 teaspoon oil in a large nonstick skillet coated with cooking spray. Add half of chicken and cook 2 to 3 minutes on each side or until browned. Transfer chicken to a baking sheet lined with foil; lightly coat chicken with cooking spray. Repeat procedure with remaining oil and chicken tenders.
5. Bake at 400° for 12 minutes or until done.
6. Combine chicken broth and cornstarch; add chicken broth mixture to pan (do not wipe clean). Bring to a boil, reduce heat, and cook 1 to 2 minutes or until thick, scraping pan to loosen browned bits. Stir in maple syrup, mustard, butter, and lemon juice; cook 1 minute or until thoroughly heated. Serve immediately with chicken tenders. YIELD: 6 servings (serving size: 4 ounces chicken and 2½ tablespoons sauce).

POINTS value: 6; Exchanges: 1½ Starch, 4 Very Lean Meat, 1 Fat; Per serving: CAL 298 (26% from fat); PRO 31.5g; FAT 8.5g (sat 2.0g); CARB 28.2g; FIB 1.1g; CHOL 68mg; IRON 2.3mg; SOD 463mg; CALC 36mg

MARSALA-STYLE CHICKEN

(pictured on page 110)
prep: 17 minutes • cook: 16 minutes

*Tender chunks of chicken coated with
tangy mushroom sauce served over
wide egg noodles make a hearty meal.*

1½   pounds skinless, boneless
       chicken breast halves
⅓   cup all-purpose flour
½   teaspoon salt
¼   teaspoon pepper
1   teaspoon olive oil
¾   cup fat-free, less-sodium
       chicken broth
⅓   cup dry Marsala wine
2   teaspoons cornstarch
2   teaspoons chopped fresh
       thyme
2   teaspoons fresh lemon juice
¼   teaspoon salt
¼   teaspoon garlic powder
Cooking spray
1   (8-ounce) package presliced
       mushrooms
1   tablespoon light butter
1   tablespoon chopped fresh
       parsley

1. Place chicken between 2 sheets
of heavy-duty plastic wrap, and
flatten to ¼-inch thickness using a
meat mallet or rolling pin. Cut into
2-inch pieces.
2. Combine flour, salt, and pepper
in a large zip-top plastic bag. Add
chicken; seal and shake to coat.
3. Heat oil in a large nonstick
skillet over medium-high heat. Add
chicken; cook 4 to 5 minutes on
each side or until done. Remove
chicken from pan; keep warm.
4. Combine broth and next 6
ingredients in a small bowl.

5. Coat pan with cooking spray. Add
mushrooms; sauté 3 minutes or until
tender. Add broth mixture; bring to
a boil. Cook over medium-high heat
4 minutes or until thick, stirring
constantly. Stir in butter. Spoon over
chicken. Sprinkle with parsley. YIELD:
4 servings (serving size: 4 ounces
chicken and ⅓ cup sauce).

POINTS value: 5; **Exchanges:** ½ Starch,
4½ Very Lean Meat, ½ Fat; **Per serving:** CAL 262
(18% from fat); PRO 42.8g; FAT 5.0g (sat 1.8g);
CARB 10.1g; FIB 1.0g; CHOL 104mg; IRON 2.1mg;
SOD 674mg; CALC 30mg

SPICY CHICKEN TORTILLAS

prep: 19 minutes • cook: 14 minutes

*Try the spicy cooked chicken as a
topper for taco salad or as a
filling for enchiladas and burritos.*

½   cup chipotle pepper sauce
       (such as Tabasco)
1   teaspoon ground cumin
4   (6-ounce) skinless, boneless
       chicken breast halves
½   cup low-fat sour cream
3   tablespoons fresh lime juice,
       divided (about 2 limes)
¼   teaspoon salt, divided
2   cups quartered cherry
       tomatoes
½   cup chopped fresh cilantro
2   tablespoons cider vinegar
Cooking spray
½   cup chopped onion
4   (8-inch) 97%-fat-free flour
       tortillas (such as Mission)

1. Combine pepper sauce, cumin,
and chicken in a large zip-top plastic
bag; seal. Marinate in refrigerator 15
minutes, turning occasionally.

2. Meanwhile, combine sour cream, 1
tablespoon lime juice, and ⅛ teaspoon
salt in a small bowl; cover and chill.
3. Combine tomatoes, cilantro, vinegar, 2 tablespoons lime juice, and ⅛
teaspoon salt in a small bowl.
4. Heat a large nonstick skillet over
medium-high heat; coat with cooking
spray. Add onion; cook 5 minutes or
until lightly browned. Remove from
pan; keep warm.
5. Remove chicken from bag and
discard marinade. Recoat pan with
cooking spray. Add chicken; cook over
medium-high heat 4 minutes on each
side or until done. Remove chicken
from pan, and cut diagonally into thin
strips.
6. Warm tortillas according to package
directions. Spoon about ¾ cup chick-
en down center of each tortilla. Top
each with ½ cup tomato mixture and
2 tablespoons sour cream mixture.
Roll up tortilla. YIELD: 4 servings (serving size: 1 tortilla).

POINTS value: 6; **Exchanges:** 1½ Starch, 1 Vegetable,
4 Very Lean Meat; **Per serving:** CAL 325 (17% from fat);
PRO 33.0g; FAT 6.3g (sat 2.8g); CARB 33.2g;
FIB 3.7g; CHOL 81mg; IRON 3.2mg; SOD 683mg;
CALC 121mg

CIDER VINEGAR

Keep cider vinegar as well as
other vinegars in your pantry to
use in marinades for meat, in
salad dressings, or when
deglazing a skillet to make a
pan sauce. Cider vinegar adds
a delightfully sweet and tangy
flavor to a variety of foods and
stays good for a long time
when stored in a cool, dark
place.

CAJUN CHICKEN

prep: 12 minutes • cook: 17 minutes
other: 3 minutes

Cooking spray
4   (6-ounce) skinless, boneless chicken breast halves
⅛   teaspoon salt
⅛   teaspoon black pepper
4   ounces andouille sausage, finely chopped
1   cup chopped green bell pepper
1   cup finely chopped onion
1   cup finely chopped celery
½   teaspoon dried thyme
½   cup chopped fresh parsley
1   teaspoon olive oil
¼   teaspoon hot sauce
¼   teaspoon salt

1. Heat a large nonstick skillet coated with cooking spray over medium-high heat. Add chicken; cook 6 minutes. Turn and sprinkle with ⅛ teaspoon salt and pepper; cook 6 minutes or until chicken is done. Transfer chicken to a platter.
2. Wipe pan with paper towels. Coat pan with cooking spray; add sausage and next 4 ingredients. Coat mixture with cooking spray. Cook 5 minutes or until onion is tender, stirring frequently.
3. Remove from heat and stir in parsley, oil, hot sauce, and salt. Return chicken to pan and spoon vegetable mixture over chicken. Cover and let stand 3 minutes. YIELD: 4 servings (serving size: 1 chicken breast half and ½ cup vegetable mixture).

POINTS value: 6; **Exchanges:** 1 Vegetable, 5 Very Lean Meat, 1 Medium-Fat Meat; **Per serving:** CAL 295 (27% from fat); PRO 45.0g; FAT 8.5g (sat 2.8g); CARB 7.8g; FIB 1.6g; CHOL 119mg; IRON 2.7mg; SOD 592mg; CALC 56mg

ROSEMARY CHICKEN WITH WHITE BEANS

prep: 9 minutes • cook: 15 minutes

The chicken in this recipe is cooked over medium heat so the breadcrumbs will not brown too quickly.

3   tablespoons Italian-seasoned breadcrumbs
1½   tablespoons fresh minced rosemary, divided
½   teaspoon salt, divided
½   teaspoon freshly ground black pepper, divided
1   large egg white, lightly beaten
1   teaspoon water
4   (6-ounce) skinless, boneless chicken breast halves
2   teaspoons olive oil
3   garlic cloves, minced
1   (16-ounce) can navy beans, rinsed and drained
1½   cups chopped fresh tomato (about 2 medium)

1. Combine breadcrumbs, 1½ teaspoons rosemary, ¼ teaspoon salt, and ¼ teaspoon pepper in a shallow dish.
2. Combine egg white and water in a shallow dish.
3. Place each chicken breast in egg white mixture, allowing excess to drip back into dish. Dredge chicken in breadcrumb mixture.
4. Heat oil in a large nonstick skillet over medium heat. Add chicken; cook 6 to 7 minutes on each side or until chicken is done. Transfer chicken to a plate. Set aside and keep warm.
5. Add garlic to pan; cook, stirring constantly, 30 seconds. Stir in beans, tomato, 1 tablespoon rosemary, ¼ teaspoon salt, and ¼ teaspoon pepper.

Cook over medium heat 2 minutes or until thoroughly heated.
6. Spoon bean mixture onto serving plates and top with chicken. YIELD: 4 servings (serving size: 1 chicken breast half and ½ cup bean mixture).

POINTS value: 5; **Exchanges:** 1½ Starch, 3½ Very Lean Meat, ½ Fat; **Per serving:** CAL 270 (15% from fat); PRO 34.9g; FAT 4.4g (sat 0.9g); CARB 21.9g; FIB 4.9g; CHOL 69mg; IRON 2.8mg; SOD 698mg; CALC 70mg

HOW TO MAKE A POCKET IN A CHICKEN BREAST HALF

1. Insert tip of a clean, sharp knife into thickest side of chicken breast half. Make a 2-inch slit. Cut to, but not through, the opposite side.

2. Holding the knife blade parallel to the cutting board, guide the blade around the inside, creating a pocket. Be careful not to cut through sides.

TOMATO-BASIL-STUFFED CHICKEN BREASTS

prep: 15 minutes • cook: 20 minutes

¼   cup (2 ounces) ⅓-less-fat
      cream cheese, softened
1   tablespoon chopped
      sun-dried tomatoes
1   tablespoon chopped fresh basil
⅛   teaspoon salt
⅛   teaspoon black pepper
4   (6-ounce) skinless, boneless
      chicken breast halves
2   (1-ounce) slices whole wheat
      bread
2   tablespoons Dijon mustard
Cooking spray

1. Preheat oven to 375°.
2. Combine first 5 ingredients in a
small bowl. Cut a horizontal slit
through thickest portion of each
chicken breast half to form a pocket.
Divide cream cheese mixture evenly
among pockets. Place bread in a
food processor; pulse 10 times or
until coarse crumbs measure 1 cup.
Brush mustard evenly over tops of
chicken. Top with breadcrumbs,
pressing down slightly. Place chick-
en, crumb side up, on a baking sheet
coated with cooking spray.
3. Bake at 375° for 20 minutes or
until done. YIELD: 4 servings (serving
size: 1 stuffed chicken breast half).

POINTS value: 6; **Exchanges:** *½ Starch,*
5½ Very Lean Meat, 1 Fat; **Per serving:** *CAL 269*
(21% from fat); PRO 42.9g; FAT 6.1g (sat 2.4g);
CARB 9.0g; FIB 1.2g; CHOL 107mg; IRON 2.3mg;
SOD 511mg; CALC 59mg

STUFFED CHICKEN BREASTS WITH MARSALA CREAM SAUCE

prep: 20 minutes • cook: 31 minutes

The secret ingredient in this recipe
is the Marsala wine because of
the deep, smokey flavor it adds
to the sauce.

1   tablespoon olive oil, divided
1   (8-ounce) package presliced
      mushrooms, finely chopped
⅓   cup minced shallot (about 1
      small)
1   cup chopped fresh baby
      spinach
2   tablespoons chopped fresh
      parsley
⅓   cup dry breadcrumbs
1   large egg white
½   teaspoon salt, divided
½   teaspoon freshly ground black
      pepper, divided
4   (6-ounce) skinless, boneless
      chicken breast halves
¼   cup all-purpose flour
½   cup dry Marsala wine
½   (1.8-ounce) package white
      cream sauce mix (such as
      Knorr)
½   cup fat-free, less-sodium
      chicken broth
½   cup 1% low-fat milk
½   tablespoon fresh lemon juice

1. Preheat oven to 400°.
2. Heat 1 teaspoon oil in a large
nonstick skillet over medium-high
heat. Add mushrooms and shallot;
cook 6 minutes. Add spinach and
parsley; cook 1 minute. Transfer to a
bowl. Stir in breadcrumbs, egg
white, ¼ teaspoon salt, and ¼ teaspoon pepper.

3. Sprinkle chicken with ¼ teaspoon each salt and pepper. Arrange
chicken breasts between 2 sheets of
heavy-duty plastic wrap; flatten to
¼-inch thickness using a meat mallet.
4. Spoon mushroom mixture onto
center of chicken breasts. Roll up
and secure with wooden picks.
Dredge chicken breasts in flour,
shaking off excess.
5. Wipe pan clean with paper towels.
Heat 2 teaspoons oil in pan over
medium-high heat; add chicken.
Cook 5 minutes, turning frequently,
until browned. Transfer chicken to a
baking sheet lined with foil. Bake at
400° for 13 minutes or until done.
6. Add wine to pan; cook 2 minutes
over medium heat, scraping pan to
loosen browned bits.
7. Whisk together cream sauce mix,
broth, and milk; add to pan. Bring to
a boil; reduce heat, and simmer 1
minute. Stir in lemon juice.
8. Remove wooden picks from
chicken; cut into 1-inch-thick slices.
Spoon sauce onto serving plates;
arrange chicken over sauce. YIELD:
4 servings (serving size: 1 chicken
breast half and about ¼ cup sauce).

POINTS value: 7; **Exchanges:** *1 Starch, 1 Vegetable,*
5 Very Lean Meat, 1½ Fat; **Per serving:** *CAL 353*
(20% from fat); PRO 46.0g; FAT 7.6g (sat 1.4g);
CARB 23.3g; FIB 1.7g; CHOL 100mg; IRON 3.0mg;
SOD 815mg; CALC 93mg

CRANBERRY-ORANGE CHICKEN

prep: 10 minutes • cook: 1 hour and 8 minutes

Although we often use boneless chicken breasts in our recipes, purchasing "bone-in" chicken has its benefits as well. It's a good choice when baking—the bones make the meat more flavorful and moist.

4   (8-ounce) skinless, bone-in chicken breasts
¼   teaspoon salt
¼   teaspoon pepper
Cooking spray
1   (16-ounce) can whole-berry cranberry sauce
1   teaspoon grated orange rind
¼   cup fresh orange juice
3   tablespoons low-sodium soy sauce
1   tablespoon fresh lemon juice
1   teaspoon butter, melted
2   teaspoons cornstarch

1. Preheat oven to 350°.
2. Sprinkle chicken evenly with salt and pepper; coat with cooking spray.
3. Heat a nonstick skillet coated with cooking spray over medium-high heat. Add chicken, meat side down, to pan; cook 5 minutes or until browned. Transfer chicken to a 13 x 9-inch baking dish coated with cooking spray.
4. Combine cranberry sauce and next 5 ingredients in a small bowl, stirring until blended. Pour evenly over chicken. Cover and bake at 350° for 30 minutes. Uncover and bake an additional 30 minutes or until chicken is done. Transfer chicken to a serving platter, reserving drippings; keep warm.

5. Whisk together drippings and cornstarch in a small saucepan. Bring to a boil over medium-high heat; cook 1 minute or until slightly thick. Serve over chicken. YIELD: 4 servings (serving size: 1 chicken breast and ¼ cup sauce).

POINTS value: 7; **Exchanges:** 3 Fruit, 5 Very Lean Meat, ½ Fat; **Per serving:** CAL 378 (7% from fat); PRO 40.1g; FAT 3.1g (sat 1.0g); CARB 46.5g; FIB 1.9g; CHOL 101mg; IRON 1.6mg; SOD 689mg; CALC 24mg

MEXICAN-STYLE CHICKEN

prep: 12 minutes • cook: 48 minutes

The spicy-hot vegetable juice in this recipe really kicks up the flavor of this one-dish meal.

1   tablespoon chili powder
1   tablespoon sugar
1   teaspoon ground cumin
1   teaspoon dried oregano
¼   teaspoon salt
1   cup picante sauce
1   (5.5-ounce) can spicy-hot vegetable juice
¼   cup water
Cooking spray
4   chicken drumsticks, skinned
4   chicken thighs, skinned
¼   cup thinly sliced green bell pepper
1   cup thinly sliced onion

1. Combine first 5 ingredients in a small bowl; mix well. Combine picante sauce, vegetable juice, and water in a separate bowl.
2. Heat a large nonstick skillet coated with cooking spray over medium-high heat. Add chicken; sprinkle evenly with chili powder

mixture. Top with bell pepper and onion. Drizzle with picante sauce mixture. Bring to a boil; cover, reduce heat, and simmer 40 minutes or until chicken is no longer pink in the center, stirring occasionally. YIELD: 4 servings (serving size: 1 thigh, 1 drumstick, and ½ cup sauce).

POINTS value: 4; **Exchanges:** 2 Vegetable, 3 Lean Meat; **Per serving:** CAL 217 (22% from fat); PRO 26.9g; FAT 5.2g (sat 1.2g); CARB 15.7g; FIB 2.0g; CHOL 103mg; IRON 2.2mg; SOD 845mg; CALC 39mg

YELLOW PEPPER CHIPOTLE CHICKEN

prep: 8 minutes • cook: 39 minutes

Cooking spray
4   chicken thighs, skinned
4   chicken drumsticks, skinned
1¼   cups yellow bell pepper, chopped (about 1 large)
1   cup chopped onion
4   garlic cloves, minced
1   (14.5-ounce) can diced tomatoes with green peppers and onion, undrained
2   chipotle chiles, chopped
1½   teaspoons sugar
½   teaspoon salt
1   tablespoon fresh lime juice

1. Heat a nonstick skillet coated with cooking spray over medium-high heat. Add chicken, and cook 5 minutes; turn and cook 3 minutes. Remove chicken; keep warm.
2. Add bell pepper, onion, and garlic to pan; coat vegetables with cooking spray. Sauté vegetable mixture 2 minutes or until tender.

3. Add tomatoes, chipotle chiles, and next 2 ingredients; bring to a boil. Return chicken to pan; cover, reduce heat to medium-low, and cook 25 minutes or until chicken is done. Remove chicken from pan; keep warm.

4. Cook tomato mixture over medium-high heat 1 minute or until slightly thick, stirring constantly. Remove pan from heat; stir in lime juice. Serve tomato mixture over chicken. YIELD: 4 servings (serving size: 1 thigh, 1 drumstick, and about ⅓ cup tomato mixture).

POINTS value: 4; **Exchanges:** 2½ Vegetable, 3 Lean Meat; **Per serving:** CAL 229 (20% from fat); PRO 27.5g; FAT 4.8g (sat 1.2g); CARB 15.4g; FIB 2.9g; CHOL 103mg; IRON 1.9mg; SOD 800mg; CALC 49mg

BALSAMIC CHICKEN AND RICE SKILLET

prep: 12 minutes • cook: 33 minutes

1	teaspoon dried thyme
½	teaspoon salt
¼	teaspoon freshly ground black pepper
8	chicken thighs, skinned
2	teaspoons olive oil
1	cup uncooked jasmine rice
1	(14.5-ounce) can diced tomatoes, undrained
1	(14-ounce) can fat-free, less-sodium chicken broth
2	tablespoons chopped fresh parsley

1. Sprinkle thyme, salt, and pepper over 1 side of chicken.

2. Heat oil in a large nonstick skillet over medium-high heat. Add

chicken, seasoned side down; cook 4 minutes or until browned. Turn chicken; cook 3 minutes.

3. Transfer chicken to a plate; set aside and keep warm. Add rice to pan; cook, stirring constantly, 1 minute. Add tomatoes and broth; bring to a simmer. Return chicken to pan; cover, and simmer over medium-low heat 20 minutes or until chicken is done and rice is tender. Sprinkle chicken with parsley. YIELD: 4 servings (serving size: 2 thighs and about ¾ cup rice mixture).

POINTS value: 6; **Exchanges:** 1 Starch, 1½ Vegetable, 4½ Very Lean Meat, ½ Fat; **Per serving:** CAL 295 (23% from fat); PRO 30.0g; FAT 7.6g (sat 1.6g); CARB 26.4g; FIB 2.5g; CHOL 107mg; IRON 3.3mg; SOD 812mg; CALC 55mg

CHICKEN THIGHS PICCATA-STYLE

(pictured on page 111)
prep: 11 minutes • cook: 21 minutes

4	chicken thighs, skinned
1	tablespoon all-purpose flour
¼	teaspoon salt
¼	teaspoon pepper
1	large egg white, lightly beaten
1	teaspoon water
½	cup Italian-seasoned breadcrumbs
2	teaspoons olive oil
½	cup fat-free, less-sodium chicken broth
½	cup white wine
2	tablespoons fresh lemon juice
2	garlic cloves, minced
2	tablespoons chopped fresh parsley
1	tablespoon capers, drained
Grated lemon rind (optional)	

1. Place chicken in a heavy-duty zip-top plastic bag; add flour, salt, and pepper. Seal bag, and shake to coat chicken. Combine egg white and water in a shallow dish. Remove chicken from bag. Dip each piece in egg white mixture, and dredge in breadcrumbs.

2. Heat oil in a large nonstick skillet over medium-high heat. Add chicken to pan; cook 3 to 4 minutes on each side or until browned. Add broth, wine, lemon juice, and garlic to pan; bring to a boil. Cover, reduce heat, and simmer 8 minutes. Add parsley and capers, and simmer, uncovered, 5 minutes or until chicken is no longer pink in center. Sprinkle with grated lemon rind, if desired. YIELD: 4 servings (serving size: 1 thigh and about 2 tablespoons sauce).

POINTS value: 4; **Exchanges:** 1 Starch, 1½ Lean Meat, ½ Fat; **Per serving:** CAL 172 (28% from fat); PRO 16.6g; FAT 5.2g (sat 1.1g); CARB 14.1g; FIB 0.9g; CHOL 54mg; IRON 1.6mg; SOD 766mg; CALC 30mg

FOOD SAFETY

Food safety is important when handling any type of raw meat. When handling poultry, rinse thoroughly before cooking and pat dry with paper towels. Always use a clean knife and cutting board and make sure to sanitize those items before cutting any other raw food products like fruits and vegetables. Most importantly, wash your hands immediately after working with raw poultry to prevent cross-contamination with other foods.

HEARTY CHICKEN AND DUMPLINGS

prep: 6 minutes • cook: 1 hour and 30 minutes

Keep the dumplings frozen until ready to add to pan. Add one at a time to the broth to prevent them from sticking together.

4	chicken thighs, skinned
4	chicken drumsticks, skinned
4	cups fat-free, less-sodium chicken broth
3	cups water
½	cup chopped onion
⅓	cup sliced celery
⅓	cup sliced carrot
¾	teaspoon dried thyme
¼	teaspoon salt
1	(12-ounce) package frozen dumplings (such as Mary B's)
2	teaspoons light butter
¼	teaspoon freshly ground black pepper

1. Combine first 9 ingredients in a Dutch oven. Bring to a boil; partially cover. Reduce heat; simmer 45 minutes or until chicken is done. Transfer chicken and vegetables to a large bowl, using tongs; cool slightly.
2. Bring broth to a boil. Separate frozen dumpling strips; break each strip in half. Add dumplings to broth, 1 at a time, stirring often to prevent sticking. Cover, reduce heat, and simmer 25 minutes.
3. Meanwhile, remove chicken from bones; cut meat into bite-sized pieces.
4. Add chicken, butter, and pepper to dumpling mixture; stir well to combine. Simmer 10 minutes, covered, or until dumplings are tender. YIELD: 4 servings (serving size: 1½ cups).

POINTS value: 6; **Exchanges:** 1½ Starch, 3½ Lean Meat; **Per serving:** CAL 303 (26% from fat); PRO 32.4g; FAT 8.5g (sat 2.6g); CARB 23.4g; FIB 1.8g; CHOL 108mg; IRON 2.8mg; SOD 1,087mg; CALC 151mg

HERBED ROASTED CHICKEN

prep: 10 minutes • cook: 50 minutes other: 10 minutes

The flavors of fresh herbs penetrate the chicken as it cooks and remain even after the skin is removed.

⅓	cup Italian-flavored oil-packed sun-dried tomatoes
1	tablespoon chopped fresh basil
1	teaspoon chopped fresh chives
1	teaspoon chopped fresh parsley
1	teaspoon chopped fresh thyme
½	teaspoon salt
½	teaspoon black pepper
1	(3.75-pound) whole chicken
2	onions, cut into wedges

1. Preheat oven to 375°.
2. Drain tomatoes, reserving 1½ teaspoons oil; chop tomatoes. Combine tomato, reserved oil, basil, and next 5 ingredients in a small bowl. Set aside.
3. Remove and discard giblets and neck from chicken. Rinse chicken with cold water; pat dry. Trim excess fat. Remove backbone from chicken, using kitchen shears. Flatten chicken, skin side up, with palm of hand. Starting at neck cavity, loosen skin from breast and drumsticks by inserting fingers, gently pushing between skin and meat. Stuff tomato mixture under skin of chicken.
4. Place onion in center of a jelly roll pan lined with foil. Place chicken, skin side up, over onion.
5. Bake at 375° for 50 minutes or until a thermometer registers 170°. Let stand 10 minutes. Remove and discard skin. Cut chicken into serving pieces; sprinkle with tomato mixture. YIELD: 6 servings (serving size: 4 ounces).

POINTS value: 4; **Exchanges:** 3 Very Lean Meat, 1½ Lean Meat; **Per serving:** CAL 188 (24% from fat); PRO 30.2g; FAT 4.8g (sat 1.1g); CARB 4.8g; FIB 1.1g; CHOL 94mg; IRON 1.8mg; SOD 321mg; CALC 28mg

TURKEY AND BEAN ENCHILADAS

prep: 27 minutes • cook: 38 minutes

	Cooking spray
¾	pound ground turkey breast
½	cup chopped onion
3	garlic cloves, minced
2	teaspoons ground cumin
1	(15-ounce) can black beans, rinsed and drained
½	cup salsa
¼	teaspoon salt
1½	cups (6 ounces) preshredded reduced-fat Mexican blend cheese, divided
1	(10-ounce) can enchilada sauce, divided
12	(6-inch) corn tortillas
¼	cup chopped fresh cilantro
2	tablespoons chopped green onions
6	tablespoons fat-free sour cream
6	tablespoons salsa

1. Preheat oven to 375°.

2. Heat a large nonstick skillet coated with cooking spray over medium-high heat. Add turkey and next 3 ingredients; cook until browned, stirring to crumble. Stir in beans, salsa, and salt; cook 1 minute. Stir in ½ cup cheese and ¼ cup enchilada sauce.

3. Pour remaining enchilada sauce into a shallow dish. Dip tortillas, 1 at a time, into sauce. Spoon about ⅓ cup meat mixture onto 1 side of each tortilla; roll up tightly, and place in a baking dish coated with cooking spray. Bake, covered, at 375° for 25 minutes. Top with 1 cup cheese, and bake, uncovered, an additional 5 minutes or until cheese melts. Sprinkle with cilantro and green onions. Serve with sour cream and salsa. YIELD: 6 servings (serving size: 2 enchiladas, 1 tablespoon sour cream, and 1 tablespoon salsa).

POINTS value: 7; **Exchanges:** 2 Starch, 3 Very Lean Meat, ½ High-Fat Meat, ½ Fat; **Per serving:** CAL 339 (35% from fat); PRO 25.1g; FAT 14.0g (sat 7.2g); CARB 33.0g; FIB 5.7g; CHOL 58mg; IRON 1.8mg; SOD 828mg; CALC 291mg

---

TURKEY MEAT LOAF

When making meat loaf, place all the ingredients except the ground turkey in a large bowl and then crumble the turkey over the mixture. Use a spoon or your hands to knead the seasoning into the meat. After baking, use an instant-read thermometer to register the temperature of the center of a meat loaf to check for doneness. Allow the meat loaf to stand at room temperature for 10 minutes before cutting so the slices won't fall apart.

TURKEY MEAT LOAF WITH ROASTED RED BELL PEPPER SAUCE

prep: 15 minutes • cook: 1 hour and 2 minutes • other: 10 minutes

Use ground turkey in this dish (a combination of light and dark meat) for a juicy and flavorful meat loaf.

Cooking spray
1   cup minced onion
1   (8-ounce) package presliced mushrooms, finely chopped
1   cup preshredded carrot, finely chopped
1   tablespoon minced garlic
1   pound ground turkey (light and dark meat)
1   cup quick-cooking oats
¼   cup ketchup
⅓   cup chopped fresh parsley
1   tablespoon Worcestershire sauce
1   large egg, lightly beaten
1   teaspoon salt
½   teaspoon black pepper
2   tablespoons ketchup
Roasted Red Bell Pepper Sauce

1. Preheat oven to 375°.

2. Heat a large nonstick skillet coated with cooking spray over medium-high heat; add onion, mushrooms, and carrot. Cook, stirring occasionally, 6 to 8 minutes or until vegetables are tender and all liquid is evaporated. Add garlic; cook 1 minute. Remove from heat; cool slightly.

3. Combine onion mixture, ground turkey, oats, ¼ cup ketchup, and next 5 ingredients in a large bowl, mixing well. Press turkey mixture into an 8 x 4-inch loaf pan coated with cooking spray. Brush 2 tablespoons ketchup over top.

4. Bake at 375° for 55 minutes to 1 hour or until a thermometer registers 170°. Let stand 10 minutes. Remove from pan and slice. Serve with Roasted Red Bell Pepper Sauce. YIELD: 6 servings (serving size: 1 slice meat loaf and about 2 tablespoons sauce).

(Total includes Roasted Red Bell Pepper Sauce) *POINTS* value: 5; **Exchanges:** 1 Starch, 3 Vegetable, 3 Very Lean Meat; **Per serving:** CAL 253 (27% from fat); PRO 21.5g; FAT 8.0g (sat 0.5g); CARB 26.5g; FIB 3.1g; CHOL 83mg; IRON 2.5mg; SOD 819mg; CALC 68mg

ROASTED RED BELL PEPPER SAUCE

1   (7-ounce) jar roasted red bell peppers, drained
⅓   cup ketchup
1   teaspoon minced garlic
¼   teaspoon freshly ground black pepper

1. Combine all ingredients in a blender or food processor; process 1 to 2 minutes or until smooth. YIELD: 6 servings (serving size: about 2 tablespoons).

POINTS value: 0; **Exchange:** Free **Per serving:** CAL 20 (8% from fat); PRO 0.6g; FAT 0.3g (sat 0.0g); CARB 4.5g; FIB 0.3g; CHOL 0mg; IRON 0.2mg; SOD 216mg; CALC 7mg

SKILLET TURKEY PARMESAN

prep: 10 minutes • cook: 25 minutes

This dish uses a quick pasta sauce made with canned tomatoes, garlic, and fresh herbs. You can substitute a good quality bottled pasta sauce for the homemade one if you're short on time.

2½   teaspoons olive oil, divided
2   garlic cloves, minced
1   (14.5-ounce) can diced tomatoes, undrained
2   tablespoons chopped fresh basil, divided
2   tablespoons chopped fresh parsley, divided
1   tablespoon balsamic vinegar
1   tablespoon tomato paste
1   teaspoon sugar
¼   teaspoon salt, divided
½   cup Italian-seasoned breadcrumbs
2   tablespoons grated fresh Parmesan cheese, divided
¼   teaspoon freshly ground black pepper
1   pound (¼-inch-thick) turkey breast cutlets
¼   cup all-purpose flour
2   large egg whites, lightly beaten
¼   cup (1 ounce) finely shredded part-skim mozzarella cheese
Parsley sprigs (optional)

1. Heat ½ teaspoon oil in a small saucepan over medium heat. Add garlic; sauté 30 to 45 seconds or until tender. Add canned tomatoes, 1 tablespoon basil, 1 tablespoon parsley, vinegar, tomato paste, sugar, and ⅛ teaspoon salt. Bring to a boil; reduce heat, and simmer, uncovered, 15 minutes.

2. Combine breadcrumbs, 1 tablespoon Parmesan cheese, 1 tablespoon basil, 1 tablespoon parsley, ⅛ teaspoon salt, and ¼ teaspoon pepper in a shallow dish. Dredge 1 turkey cutlet in flour. Dip in egg white; dredge in breadcrumb mixture. Repeat procedure with remaining cutlets.

3. Heat 2 teaspoons oil in a nonstick skillet over medium-high heat. Add turkey; cook 4 to 5 minutes on each side or until cutlets are done. Leave turkey in pan and spoon ¼ cup tomato sauce on top of each turkey cutlet. Sprinkle mozzarella and 1 tablespoon Parmesan cheese evenly over tops of cutlets. Remove pan from heat. Cover and let stand until cheese melts. Garnish with parsley, if desired. YIELD: 4 servings (serving size: 1 turkey cutlet and ¼ cup sauce).

POINTS value: 6; **Exchanges:** 1½ Starch, 4 Very Lean Meat, 1 Lean Meat; **Per serving:** CAL 306 (18% from fat); PRO 36.5g; FAT 6.0g (sat 1.9g); CARB 25.1g; FIB 2.8g; CHOL 77mg; IRON 2.8mg; SOD 872mg; CALC 135mg

---

BALSAMIC VINEGAR

Balsamic vinegar is a great ingredient to keep on hand. It adds a delightfully sweet, tangy flavor to sauces, marinades, and vinaigrettes. It has a full-bodied, slightly sweet flavor with a hint of tartness. Balsamic vinegar ages to a dark brown color and is quite aromatic. Purchase it in large supermarkets and gourmet food stores.

TURKEY SCALOPPINE IN CRANBERRY-PORT SAUCE

prep: 10 minutes • cook: 15 minutes

1   pound (¼-inch-thick) turkey breast cutlets
½   teaspoon dried thyme
½   teaspoon salt
½   teaspoon freshly ground black pepper
2   teaspoons butter
¼   cup finely chopped shallot (about 1 small)
1   (14-ounce) can fat-free, less-sodium chicken broth, divided
2   teaspoons cornstarch
⅔   cup port or other sweet red wine
¼   cup dried cranberries

1. Sprinkle turkey evenly with thyme, salt, and pepper.

2. Melt butter in a large nonstick skillet over medium-high heat. Add turkey; cook 2 to 3 minutes on each side or until golden brown. Remove turkey and keep warm.

3. Reduce heat to medium; add shallot. Sauté 30 seconds or until tender. Combine 1 tablespoon chicken broth and cornstarch; set aside. Add remaining broth to pan; scrape pan to loosen browned bits. Add wine and cranberries; bring to a boil. Reduce heat, and simmer, uncovered, 7 minutes. Stir in cornstarch mixture; boil 1 minute. Spoon sauce over turkey. YIELD: 4 servings (serving size: 1 turkey cutlet and about ⅓ cup sauce).

POINTS value: 4; **Exchanges:** ½ Fruit, 3½ Very Lean Meat, ½ Fat; **Per serving:** CAL 182 (12% from fat); PRO 30.0g; FAT 2.4g (sat 1.0g); CARB 10.4g; FIB 0.6g; CHOL 50mg; IRON 1.9mg; SOD 675mg; CALC 11mg

CARIBBEAN GRILLED TURKEY KABOBS

prep: 15 minutes • cook: 10 minutes
other: 30 minutes

If you can't find turkey tenderloin in your store, you may use a frozen 3-pound boneless turkey breast, thawed (such as Butterball), discarding gravy packet and removing the skin. Save remaining turkey for another use.

1 pound turkey breast tenderloin, cut into 1½-inch chunks
2 teaspoons Caribbean jerk seasoning
1 small red onion, cut into 1-inch pieces
1 small green bell pepper, cut into 1-inch pieces
2 cups fresh pineapple chunks (2-inch pieces)
2 tablespoons mango chutney (such as Major Grey's)
1 tablespoon spicy brown mustard

1. Toss turkey with jerk seasoning in a bowl. Cover and chill 30 minutes.
2. Prepare grill.
3. Alternately thread turkey, onion, bell pepper, and pineapple onto 4 (12-inch) metal skewers.
4. Combine chutney and mustard, stirring well. Brush kabobs with chutney mixture.
5. Grill, covered, 5 minutes on each side or until turkey is done. YIELD: 4 servings (serving size: 1 kabob).

*POINTS value: 4; **Exchanges:** 1½ Fruit, ½ Vegetable, 3½ Very Lean Meat; **Per serving:** CAL 214 (7% from fat); PRO 29.0g; FAT 1.7g (sat 0.0g); CARB 23.1g; FIB 2.2g; CHOL 45mg; IRON 2.0mg; SOD 393mg; CALC 25mg*

TURKEY SAUSAGE AND PASTA BAKE

prep: 12 minutes • cook: 40 minutes

This cheesy, one-dish supper will be a family favorite in no time. Leftovers are easily reheated for lunches later.

3½ cups uncooked penne pasta
1¼ pounds hot turkey Italian sausage, casings removed
1½ cups chopped onion (about 1 large)
1 (8-ounce) package presliced mushrooms
¾ cup chopped celery (about 3 stalks)
2 (14.5-ounce) cans diced tomatoes with basil, garlic, and oregano (such as Hunt's)
1 (7-ounce) jar diced pimiento, drained
1 tablespoon minced garlic
Cooking spray
1 cup (4 ounces) shredded part-skim mozzarella cheese

1. Cook pasta according to package directions, omitting salt and fat.
2. Preheat oven to 400°.
3. Cook sausage in a large nonstick skillet over medium-high heat until browned, stirring to crumble. Add onion, mushrooms, and celery; cook 6 to 8 minutes or until tender. Add tomatoes, pimiento, and garlic. Bring to a boil; reduce heat, and simmer, uncovered, 8 to 10 minutes or until almost all liquid has evaporated.
4. Combine sausage mixture and hot cooked pasta in a large bowl, mixing well. Pour into a 13 x 9-inch baking dish coated with cooking spray. Sprinkle with cheese. Bake, uncovered, at 400° for 15 minutes or until

cheese melts. YIELD: 8 servings (serving size: about 1½ cups).

*POINTS value: 6; **Exchanges:** 1½ Starch, 1½ Vegetable, 3 Medium-Fat Meat; **Per serving:** CAL 303 (29% from fat); PRO 22.3g; FAT 9.6g (sat 3.6g); CARB 31.7g; FIB 2.4g; CHOL 68mg; IRON 3.1mg; SOD 769mg; CALC 142mg*

PERFECT PASTA EVERY TIME

Here are a few tips for preparing perfectly cooked pasta:

• **Use a large Dutch oven** or a stockpot to allow room for the pasta to move freely in the boiling water so it will cook evenly.

• **It's not necessary to add salt or oil** to the water; we omit them when preparing pasta.

• **Bring water to a rolling boil** and add the pasta gradually so the water will continue to boil. Once all the pasta has been added, stir and begin timing. Stir frequently—you can't stir too much!

• **Cooking times vary** depending on the shape and thickness of the pasta. Begin checking for doneness after the minimum cooking time. Remove a piece of pasta from the water and bite into it; perfectly cooked pasta will have a firm, tender consistency. This is called *al dente,* Italian for "to the tooth."

• **If the pasta is to be used** as part of a dish that requires further cooking, slightly undercook the pasta.

• **Refrigerate leftover pasta** in an airtight container for up to 1 week. Reheat by running hot water over the pasta, or place in a bowl, cover, and microwave at HIGH 30 seconds to 1 minute.

TURKEY CUTLETS WITH PUTTANESCA SAUCE

prep: 10 minutes • cook: 31 minutes

Puttanesca sauce is a spicy Italian sauce that includes tomatoes, onions, garlic, capers, olives, and oregano cooked together in olive oil. It is delicious served over noodles, chicken, or baked fish.

¼   cup all-purpose flour
¼   teaspoon black pepper
⅛   teaspoon salt
1   pound (¼-inch-thick) turkey breast cutlets
Cooking spray
1   tablespoon olive oil, divided
½   cup chopped onion
3   garlic cloves, chopped
1   (14.5-ounce) can no-salt-added diced tomatoes
¼   cup fat-free, less-sodium chicken broth
3   tablespoons capers, drained
2   tablespoons coarsely chopped ripe olives (about 4 large olives)
2   teaspoons chopped fresh oregano
½   teaspoon sugar
¼   teaspoon crushed red pepper
¼   teaspoon salt

1. Combine flour, pepper, and ⅛ teaspoon salt in a shallow dish. Dredge turkey in flour mixture, coating both sides; shake off excess flour.
2. Place a large nonstick skillet coated with cooking spray over medium-high heat. Add 1 teaspoon oil and half of cutlets; cook 3 minutes on each side or until lightly browned. Repeat procedure with 1 teaspoon oil and remaining cutlets; remove from pan and keep warm.
3. Pour 1 teaspoon oil into a medium saucepan; place over medium-high heat. Add onion and garlic; sauté 3 minutes or until tender. Add tomatoes and next 7 ingredients; bring to a boil. Reduce heat and simmer, uncovered, 10 minutes, stirring occasionally. Spoon sauce over turkey cutlets; serve immediately. **YIELD:** 4 servings (serving size: 1 cutlet and ⅓ cup sauce).

POINTS value: 4; **Exchanges:** ½ Starch, 1 Vegetable, 4 Very Lean Meat, 1 Fat; **Per serving:** CAL 225 (26% from fat); PRO 30.3g; FAT 4.75g (sat 0.8g); CARB 14.6g; FIB 2.7g; CHOL 70mg; IRON 2.4mg; SOD 584mg; CALC 44mg

ORIENTAL HENS

(pictured on page 112)
prep: 16 minutes • cook: 1 hour and 25 minutes • other: 4 hours and 5 minutes

Cornish hens are small, specially-bred chickens that typically weigh less than 1½ pounds and have tender meat. Cook the hens with the skin on to keep them perfectly moist throughout the cooking process, but remove and discard it before serving for a low-fat feast. Garnish with rosemary or thyme sprigs.

2   tablespoons low-sodium soy sauce
2   tablespoons dry sherry
1   tablespoon light brown sugar
2   teaspoons sesame oil
1   teaspoon ground allspice
1   teaspoon chopped fresh rosemary
2   garlic cloves, minced
2   (1½-pound) Cornish hens
Cooking spray

1. Preheat oven to 350°.
2. Combine first 7 ingredients in a small bowl.
3. Remove and discard giblets and necks from hens. Rinse hens under cold water; pat dry. Place hens in an 11 x 7-inch baking dish. Pour marinade evenly under skin and inside of hens. Cover and chill 4 hours. Drain; discard marinade.
4. Working with 1 hen at a time, tie ends of legs together with string. Place hens, meaty side up, on a broiler pan coated with cooking spray. Lift wing tips up and over back; tuck under hen. Insert a meat thermometer into meaty part of a thigh, making sure not to touch bone. Bake at 350° for 1 hour and 25 minutes or until thermometer registers 170°, basting occasionally. Let stand 5 minutes. Remove skin and discard. **YIELD:** 4 servings (serving size: 1 hen half).
Tip: Use a brush when basting your hens so that you can get under the skin and let the wonderful flavors soak into the meat.

POINTS value: 5; **Exchanges:** 3 Very Lean Meat, 2 Lean Meat; **Per serving:** CAL 216 (31% from fat); PRO 29.9g; FAT 7.2g (sat 1.6g); CARB 5.0g; FIB 0.4g; CHOL 133mg; IRON 1.4mg; SOD 369mg; CALC 29mg

All About Attitude

TAMI KRAMER • **HEIGHT** 5'4" • **BEFORE** 175 LBS. • **AFTER** 126 LBS.

Advice: "Don't focus all your attention on the numbers; look for non-scale victories."

"When I saw our European vacation photos, I was embarrassed at how I looked," Tami Kramer says. "I was 43, overweight, dressing frumpy, and feeling tired all the time. I knew I was too young to be looking and feeling so old!"

Tami remembered hearing someone once say that if you're overweight and out of shape, then you had to have a lifestyle to support it. "When I took a good look at my life, I knew it was true," she says. It was then that Tami realized she had to change her eating habits and start moving her body.

"From past experience I knew that *Weight Watchers* had a healthy food plan with lots of variety that would work for my entire family," Tami says. "I just needed to stick to it 100 percent. So I found a meeting with a motivating leader and supportive members, and committed that this was the last time I would ever have to lose weight."

Once on the *Weight Watchers* plan, Tami chose not to focus her attention on the numbers. Instead, Tami looked for non-scale victories, such as her belts and rings becoming too loose and her increased energy level. "I just had a lot of determination," she says.

One way Tami fought negative thoughts was to tell herself, "Act as if . . ." and then she would fill in the blank. For example, Tami didn't particularly care for exercise. So she would tell herself, "Act as if you like exercise." And she actually discovered that exercise is something she could enjoy.

"I never thought I would hear myself say I like to exercise," Tami says. "But it's a priority in my life now. I have found that it reduces my level of stress, gives me more energy, and helps me maintain my weight now that I've lost 49 pounds. I start each day feeling positive, and exercising first thing sets a good pace for my day.

"It feels good to feel good," Tami says. "I have gone from a size 14 to a 4, and clothes shopping has never been so much fun. I can finally wear cute clothes again!" In

> *"I start each day feeling positive, and exercising first thing sets a good pace for my day."*

line with her positive attitude, Tami gave away her "big" clothes once she lost the weight. "If the big clothes are still in your closet, then the message you are sending yourself is that you might go back," she says. "Having the clothes gone was a huge relief. Having them gone removed the possibility in my mind of going back.

"My daughter says that I am a happier person since I've lost weight," Tami says. "And I know that's true. I always liked who I was before, I just didn't like being overweight and the way it made me feel. I know I smile more now—because I have so many reasons to smile!"

Southwestern Turkey Burger, page 132

Marsala-Style Chicken, page 99

Chicken Thighs
Piccata-Style,
page 103

Oriental Hens,
page 108

Crunchy Pecan Greens
with Fresh Berries,
page 119

Chicken Taco Salad
with Chipotle Dressing,
page 124

Fresh Fruit Salad with Lime-Ginger Syrup, page 118

Meditterranean Couscous and Lentil Salad, page 122

Salad Primavera, page 119

Beating The Odds

DEBBIE RICHARDSON • **HEIGHT** 5'4" • **BEFORE** 248 LBS. • **AFTER** 145 LBS.

Philosophy: "Every week isn't going to be perfect, but if I keep going, I know I can keep the weight off. I know that despite my daily struggles, I am going to beat the odds!"

Debbie Richardson's weight-loss journey officially began April 1, 2000. Her goal: to lose 103 pounds and keep it off forever.

Debbie's weight woes were constant. She had been overweight her entire life, never learning to manage portion control successfully. Negative reinforcement from friends and family only contributed to her uncontrolled eating habits and her weight began to skyrocket.

"But I decided to change my life after dealing with the loss of my father," she says. "I went through a lot of anger for about a year after my dad passed away. I was hurt because he refused to do anything about his poor health habits.

"My father knew of our family's history of diabetes, heart disease, and high blood pressure, and chose not to change his life," Debbie says. "I didn't want my kids to go through the pain that I did with the loss of my dad. I knew I had to change my life so that I would be there for them."

And that's why Debbie chose *Weight Watchers.* "It was hard to swallow my pride," she says. "But I knew the only way I was going to change my life was to change the way I ate and how I lived my life. Walking into that 6 a.m. meeting room full of people for the first time was tough, but it was the best thing I've ever done."

For Debbie, going to the weekly meetings and having motivational leaders made all the difference. "All four of my leaders have added something to my life," Debbie says.

"They always had great ideas on how to get through holidays and other situations such as barbecues and birthday parties. They would give me great recipes to try and would come up with many different ways to help me with my weight loss."

After 2½ years, Debbie reached part of her goal—losing 103 pounds. And that's when step two of the journey began: keeping the weight off.

"It has been 13 months since I reached my goal weight," she says. "And it's been the hardest year. I give myself more freedom and sometimes too much.

"Walking into that 6 a.m. meeting room full of people for the first time was tough, but it was the best thing I've ever done."

Some months I'm up and some months I'm down. I just think I'm still learning about myself."

To help Debbie with maintenance, she still attends weekly meetings each Saturday. "Although the meeting time has changed, and the people come and go, I'm still there," she says.

"Mentally it is still a struggle to maintain my weight," Debbie says, "and I think it will be my entire life. I have to remind myself that every week isn't going to be perfect, but if I keep going, I know I can keep the weight off. Despite my daily struggles, I am going to beat the odds!"

Salads

ISLAND AMBROSIA

prep: 5 minutes • other: 15 minutes

If you prefer not to use rum, just leave it out—the delicious flavors will still come through.

1½ cups hulled strawberries, chopped (about 12 large)
1 (8-ounce) can pineapple tidbits in juice, drained
1 large naval orange, peeled and chopped (about ¾ cup)
⅓ cup flaked sweetened coconut, toasted
1 cubed peeled kiwifruit
2 tablespoons dark rum

1. Combine all ingredients in a medium bowl; toss gently. Let stand 15 minutes before serving. YIELD: 8 servings (serving size: ½ cup).

POINTS value: 1; **Exchange:** 1 Fruit;
Per serving: CAL 59 (17% from fat); PRO 0.7g;
FAT 1.2g (sat 0.9g); CARB 10.5g; FIB 1.6g;
CHOL 0mg; IRON 0.3mg; SOD 8.6mg; CALC 20mg

CANTALOUPE-PINEAPPLE-GINGER FRUIT SALAD

prep: 16 minutes • other: 5 minutes

1½ cups coarsely chopped cantaloupe
1 cup chopped fresh pineapple
½ cup dried cranberries
¼ cup chopped fresh mint or cilantro
2 tablespoons fresh lemon juice
1 teaspoon grated peeled fresh ginger
1 jalapeño pepper, seeded and finely chopped

1. Combine all ingredients in a medium bowl, tossing gently. Let stand 5 minutes before serving. YIELD: 6 servings (serving size: ½ cup).

POINTS value: 1; **Exchange:** 1 Fruit;
Per serving: CAL 60 (2% from fat); PRO 0.6g;
FAT 0.2g (sat 0.0g); CARB 15.7g; FIB 1.0g;
CHOL 0mg; IRON 0.2mg; SOD 8mg; CALC 9mg

FRESH FRUIT SALAD WITH LIME-GINGER SYRUP

(pictured on page 114)
prep: 15 minutes • cook: 7 minutes
other: 1 hour

Any combination of fresh fruit will work for this salad. The syrup can be made ahead and stored in the refrigerator until ready to use.

⅓ cup fresh lime juice
⅓ cup water
¼ cup fresh orange juice
2 tablespoons sugar
2 tablespoons honey
¼ teaspoon ground ginger
1 teaspoon grated lime rind
1 teaspoon grated orange rind
1½ cups (1-inch) cubed fresh pineapple
½ cup cubed peeled ripe mango (about 2 large)
½ cup fresh blueberries
2 kiwifruit, peeled and cubed

1. Combine first 6 ingredients in a small saucepan. Bring to a boil over medium heat; cook 5 minutes or until reduced to ½ cup, whisking constantly. Remove from heat; cool. Stir in lime and orange rinds.
2. Combine pineapple and next 3 ingredients in a large bowl. Pour syrup over fruit; toss gently to coat.

Cover and chill at least 1 hour. YIELD: 8 servings (serving size: about ½ cup).

POINTS value: 1; **Exchange:** 1 Fruit;
Per serving: CAL 73 (3% from fat); PRO 0.7g;
FAT 0.3g (sat 0.0g); CARB 19.0g; FIB 1.4g;
CHOL 0mg; IRON 0.3mg; SOD 1mg; CALC 15mg

APRICOT GREENS AND SWISS WITH GINGER VINAIGRETTE

prep: 9 minutes

2 tablespoons sugar
¼ cup dry white wine
2 tablespoons white balsamic vinegar
1 tablespoon vegetable oil
½ teaspoon grated peeled fresh ginger
¼ teaspoon crushed red pepper
¼ teaspoon salt
1 (5-ounce) package gourmet salad greens
4 ounces reduced-fat, reduced-sodium Swiss cheese, cut into ½-inch cubes
½ cup thinly sliced red bell pepper
½ cup thinly sliced green onions
½ cup thinly sliced dried apricots

1. Combine first 7 ingredients in a small bowl; stir well with a whisk.
2. Combine salad greens and next 4 ingredients in a bowl. Pour vinaigrette over salad; toss gently to coat. YIELD: 6 servings (serving size: 1⅓ cups).

POINTS value: 3; **Exchanges:** 1 Starch, 1 Vegetable, 1 Fat; **Per serving:** CAL 147 (38% from fat); PRO 6.5g; FAT 6.5g (sat 3.0g); CARB 15.8g; FIB 2.1g; CHOL 13mg; IRON 1.2mg; SOD 132mg; CALC 195mg

CRUNCHY PECAN GREENS WITH FRESH BERRIES

(pictured on page 113)
prep: 10 minutes • cook: 10 minutes

This summer salad received the highest rating from our Test Kitchens staff. We love the combination of garden-fresh flavors.

1	(3-ounce) package ramen noodles, broken into small pieces
½	cup chopped pecans
1	(5-ounce) package gourmet salad greens
2	cups quartered strawberries
1	cup blueberries
¾	cup thinly sliced red onion
⅓	cup white balsamic vinegar
3	tablespoons sugar
2	tablespoons sesame oil
¾	teaspoon curry powder
¼	teaspoon salt
⅛	teaspoon crushed red pepper

1. Heat a large nonstick skillet over medium heat. Add ramen noodles and pecans; cook 10 minutes or until lightly browned. Remove from heat, and cool to room temperature.
2. Combine ramen noodles, pecans, salad greens, and next 3 ingredients in a large bowl.
3. Combine balsamic vinegar and next 5 ingredients in a small bowl, stirring well with a whisk. Pour dressing over salad mixture; toss well. YIELD: 8 servings (serving size: 1 cup).

POINTS value: 4; **Exchanges:** 1½ Starch, 1 Fat; **Per serving:** CAL 173 (45% from fat); PRO 3.2g; FAT 9.2g (sat 1.0g); CARB 21.6g; FIB 2.8g; CHOL 0mg; IRON 1.2mg; SOD 197mg; CALC 34mg

SALAD PRIMAVERA

(pictured on page 115)
prep: 11 minutes • cook: 4 minutes

2	tablespoons sherry vinegar
2	tablespoons lemon juice
2	tablespoons extravirgin olive oil
1	teaspoon salt
1	teaspoon Dijon mustard
¼	teaspoon freshly ground black pepper
2	garlic cloves, minced
1½	cups (2-inch) sliced asparagus (about ½ pound)
4	cups baby spinach leaves
2	cups torn Boston lettuce
1	cup frozen petite green peas, thawed
½	cup julienne-cut red bell pepper
½	cup julienne-cut yellow bell pepper
¼	cup (¼-inch-thick) red onion wedges
¼	cup chopped fresh parsley
2	tablespoons chopped fresh basil

1. Combine vinegar and next 6 ingredients in a jar; cover tightly, and shake vigorously.
2. Cook asparagus in boiling water 4 minutes or just until crisp-tender. Drain and plunge asparagus into ice water; drain.
3. Place asparagus and next 8 ingredients in a large bowl; add dressing, and toss gently to coat. Serve immediately. YIELD: 6 servings (serving size: 2 cups).

POINTS value: 2; **Exchanges:** 3 Vegetable, 1 Fat; **Per serving:** CAL 107 (38% from fat); PRO 5.4g; FAT 5.1g (sat 0.7g); CARB 13.2g; FIB 5.0g; CHOL 0mg; IRON 2.4mg; SOD 462mg; CALC 69mg

PEAR, PROSCIUTTO, AND PINE NUT SALAD

prep: 12 minutes • cook: 5 minutes

Prosciutto can be found presliced in the deli at most grocery stores. If you have to ask for the prosciutto to be sliced, request that the slices be separated by deli paper to prevent them from sticking together. Ham may be substituted for the prosciutto.

2	tablespoons balsamic vinegar
1	tablespoon extravirgin olive oil
1½	teaspoons sugar
1½	teaspoons Dijon mustard
¼	teaspoon freshly ground black pepper
⅛	teaspoon salt
8	cups torn Boston lettuce
2	ounces thinly sliced prosciutto, cut into thin strips (about ⅔ cup)
1	ripe Bartlett pear, sliced
¼	cup pine nuts, toasted

1. Combine first 6 ingredients in a small bowl; stir with a whisk.
2. Divide lettuce evenly among 4 individual plates; top evenly with prosciutto, pear slices, and pine nuts. Drizzle 1½ tablespoons dressing over each salad. Serve immediately. YIELD: 4 servings (serving size: 1 salad).

POINTS value: 3; **Exchanges:** ½ Fruit, 1 Lean Meat, 1 Fat; **Per serving:** CAL 152 (52% from fat); PRO 6.8g; FAT 9.3g (sat 1.6g); CARB 13.0g; FIB 2.4g; CHOL 8mg; IRON 1.2mg; SOD 381mg; CALC 46mg

ASIAN SLAW WITH ROASTED PEANUTS

prep: 10 minutes

The vegetables in this salad soak up the rich flavors of its ginger dressing. Since preshredded red cabbage isn't readily available at most supermarkets, we used a chef's knife to thinly shred it. Preshredded white cabbage can be substituted for the red, if you prefer.

4	cups shredded red cabbage
1	cup matchstick-cut carrots
¼	cup coarsely chopped dry-roasted peanuts (1½ ounces)
1	yellow bell pepper, cut into thin strips
1	small jalapeño pepper, minced
3	tablespoons dark brown sugar
3	tablespoons balsamic vinegar
3	tablespoons low-sodium soy sauce
2	tablespoons dry sherry
1	tablespoon sesame oil
½	teaspoon grated peeled fresh ginger

1. Combine first 4 ingredients in a large bowl.
2. Combine jalapeño pepper and next 6 ingredients in a small bowl, stirring with a whisk. Pour dressing mixture over cabbage mixture, tossing to coat. YIELD: 6 servings (serving size: 1 cup).

POINTS value: 2; **Exchanges:** ½ Starch, 1½ Vegetable, 1 Fat; **Per serving:** CAL 118 (43% from fat); PRO 3.2g; FAT 6.0g (sat 0.8g); CARB 14.0g; FIB 2.5g; CHOL 0mg; IRON 0.9mg; SOD 340mg; CALC 44mg

EDAMAME SALAD

prep: 12 minutes

1	(10-ounce) package fully-cooked refrigerated shelled edamame
1	large navel orange, peeled and cut into sections
¼	cup minced red onion
1	tablespoon chopped fresh mint
1	teaspoon sugar
2	teaspoons fresh orange juice
1	teaspoon seasoned rice vinegar
1	teaspoon extravirgin olive oil
½	teaspoon salt
¼	teaspoon pepper

1. Combine first 4 ingredients in a large bowl.
2. Combine sugar, orange juice, and next 4 ingredients. Pour over edamame mixture; toss gently to coat. YIELD: 4 servings (serving size: about ½ cup).

POINTS value: 3; **Exchanges:** 1 Starch, ½ Fruit, ½ Fat; **Per serving:** CAL 132 (24% from fat); PRO 9.9g; FAT 3.6g (sat 0.2g); CARB 15.3g; FIB 1.9g; CHOL 0mg; IRON 1.5mg; SOD 363mg; CALC 94mg

EDAMAME

Edamame is the Japanese term for fresh soybeans. The bean has a sweet, nutty flavor and is delicious on salads, in casseroles or soups, or steamed and eaten straight out of the pod. Edamame is rich in vitamins, minerals, and phytoestrogens, which prevent certain cancers, fight heart disease, and act as an antioxidant to prohibit damage to healthy cells.

GREEN BEAN SALAD WITH CARAMELIZED ONIONS

prep: 15 minutes • cook: 27 minutes

Haricot verts is a French term used to describe young, tiny, slender green beans that are generally cooked whole. If you can't find haricot verts, use small green beans instead.

1	teaspoon vegetable oil
1	large onion, sliced into thin rings
2	tablespoons balsamic vinegar
2	tablespoons minced oil-packed sun-dried tomatoes
1	pound haricot verts or small green beans, trimmed
¼	teaspoon salt
¼	teaspoon freshly ground black pepper

1. Heat oil in a large nonstick skillet over medium-high heat. Add onion, and cook 5 minutes, stirring frequently. Reduce heat to medium; cook 15 to 20 minutes or until deep golden brown, stirring frequently. Add balsamic vinegar, and cook 2 minutes. Remove from heat. Add tomatoes.
2. Cook haricot verts in boiling water 2 minutes or until crisp-tender; drain. Set aside.
3. Combine haricot verts, onion mixture, salt, and pepper in a large bowl. Serve immediately. YIELD: 4 servings (serving size: 1 cup).

POINTS value: 1; **Exchanges:** 2 Vegetable, ½ Fat; **Per serving:** CAL 68 (22% from fat); PRO 1.8g; FAT 1.7g (sat 0.3g); CARB 11.7g; FIB 4.7g; CHOL 0mg; IRON 0.7mg; SOD 159mg; CALC 65mg

LEMON-DILL POTATO SALAD

prep: 20 minutes • cook: 35 minutes
other: 8 hours

Lemon and dill add a fresh flavor to this dish, which is perfect for a casual summer dinner. Sprinkle extra dill over the top of the potato salad for a beautiful presentation.

2   pounds red potatoes
¾   cup chopped red onion
½   cup fat-free sour cream
½   cup light mayonnaise
2   tablespoons chopped fresh dill
2   tablespoons lemon juice
1   teaspoon salt
2   teaspoons cider vinegar

1. Place potatoes in a Dutch oven, and cover with cold water; bring to a boil. Cook potatoes 30 minutes or until tender; drain and cool. Peel potatoes and cut into 1-inch cubes.
2. Combine potatoes and onion in a large bowl; toss gently. Combine sour cream and next 5 ingredients in a separate bowl. Spoon sour cream mixture over cooled potato mixture; toss gently to coat. Cover and chill 8 hours. YIELD: 12 servings (serving size: ½ cup).

POINTS value: 2; **Exchanges:** 1 Starch, ½ Fat;
Per serving: CAL 109 (38% from fat); PRO 2.1g;
FAT 4.6g (sat 1.3g); CARB 14.8g; FIB 1.5g;
CHOL 9mg; IRON 0.6mg; SOD 287mg; CALC 27mg

WARM POTATO AND SAUSAGE SALAD

prep: 7 minutes • cook: 23 minutes

3   pounds red potatoes, sliced
½   cup fat-free, less-sodium chicken broth
¼   cup white wine vinegar
2   tablespoons stone-ground mustard
1   tablespoon peanut oil
½   teaspoon salt
½   teaspoon black pepper
1   pound lite turkey, pork, or beef smoked sausage, thinly sliced (such as Hillshire Farms)
1   tablespoon maple syrup
¾   cup sliced green onions
¼   cup chopped fresh parsley

1. Cook potatoes in boiling water, covered, 10 to 12 minutes or just until tender; drain. Set aside; cool.
2. Combine chicken broth and next 5 ingredients; stir well with a whisk. Set aside.
3. Cook sausage in a large nonstick skillet over medium heat 5 minutes or until browned, stirring frequently. Add maple syrup; cook 1 minute.
4. Place potatoes in a large bowl. Add sausage, green onions, and parsley; toss gently.
5. Pour broth mixture into pan. Bring to a boil, scraping pan to loosen browned bits. Pour broth mixture over potato mixture; toss gently to coat. Serve immediately. YIELD: 18 servings (serving size: ½ cup).

POINTS value: 2; **Exchanges:** 1 Starch, ½ Lean Meat;
Per serving: CAL 100 (14% from fat); PRO 4.8g;
FAT 1.6g (sat 0.4g); CARB 16.2g; FIB 1.6g;
CHOL 9mg; IRON 1.1mg; SOD 328mg; CALC 24mg

BLACK BEAN AND COUSCOUS SALAD WITH JALAPEÑO-LEMON DRESSING

prep: 5 minutes • cook: 8 minutes
other: 5 minutes

Couscous, a staple of North African cuisine, is a form of semolina flour (the main ingredient in pasta). Brown rice can be substituted for couscous.

⅔   cup uncooked couscous
⅔   cup canned black beans, rinsed and drained
½   cup finely chopped green onions
1   teaspoon grated lemon rind
3   tablespoons fresh lemon juice
1   jalapeño pepper, minced
1   garlic clove, minced
1½   tablespoons olive oil
¾   teaspoon salt
¾   teaspoon chopped fresh cilantro

1. Prepare couscous according to package directions, omitting salt and fat.
2. Spread couscous on a baking sheet in a thin layer; let stand 5 to 10 minutes or until completely cooled.
3. Meanwhile, combine lemon rind and next 6 ingredients in a small bowl; set aside
4. Combine couscous, beans, and onion in a large bowl. Add reserved lemon mixture and toss gently. YIELD: 8 servings (serving size: ½ cup).

POINTS value: 2; **Exchanges:** 1 Starch, ½ Fat;
Per serving: CAL 91 (25% from fat); PRO 2.6g;
FAT 2.6g (sat 0.4g); CARB 14.8g; FIB 1.9g;
CHOL 0mg; IRON 0.5mg; SOD 277mg; CALC 11mg

MEDITERRANEAN COUSCOUS AND LENTIL SALAD

(pictured on page 115)
prep: 14 minutes • cook: 42 minutes
other: 5 minutes

1   cup dried lentils
1   (14-ounce) can fat-free, less-sodium chicken broth
1½ cups uncooked couscous
1   cup diced red bell pepper
1   cup chopped fresh mint
½   cup chopped fresh parsley
½   cup chopped green onions
½   cup fresh lemon juice
¼   cup olive oil
1   tablespoon Dijon mustard
1½ teaspoons minced garlic
½   teaspoon black pepper
1   cup (4 ounces) crumbled feta cheese

1. Place lentils in a large saucepan; cover with water 2 inches above lentils. Bring to a boil; cover, reduce heat, and simmer 25 to 30 minutes or until tender. Drain well; cool.
2. Bring broth to a boil in a medium saucepan; gradually stir in couscous. Remove from heat; cover and let stand 5 minutes. Fluff with a fork.
3. Combine lentils, couscous, bell pepper, and next 3 ingredients in a large bowl; stir gently.
4. Combine lemon juice and next 4 ingredients in a small bowl. Pour lemon juice mixture over couscous mixture; stir gently. Stir in cheese.
YIELD: 10 servings (serving size: 1 cup).

POINTS value: *5*; **Exchanges:** 1½ Starch, 2 Vegetable, 2 Fat; **Per serving:** CAL 276 (30% from fat); PRO 12.3g; FAT 9.2g (sat 3.1g); CARB 37.0g; FIB 7.8g; CHOL 13mg; IRON 2.8mg; SOD 318mg; CALC 116mg

OAT GRAIN-FETA SALAD

prep: 3 minutes • cook: 30 minutes
other: 3 hours

We substituted oat groats, which are hulled, whole kernels of the oat grain, for bulgur wheat in this traditional Mediterranean main-dish salad.

2   cups water
1   cup uncooked oat groats
1   cup chopped seeded cucumber
¾   cup chopped fresh parsley
½   cup chopped red onion
½   cup finely chopped celery
½   cup chopped fresh mint
1   teaspoon grated lemon rind
2   tablespoons fresh lemon juice
1   garlic clove, minced
½   teaspoon salt
1   (4-ounce) package crumbled feta cheese with basil and sun-dried tomatoes

1. Bring water to a boil in a medium saucepan; stir in groats. Bring mixture to a boil; cover, reduce heat, and simmer 24 to 26 minutes or just until tender.
2. Combine groats, cucumber, and next 8 ingredients in a bowl; set aside.
3. Drain groats and rinse under cold water. Drain well, and add to cucumber mixture. Cover and chill 3 hours.
4. Add feta cheese; toss gently before serving. YIELD: 4 servings (serving size: 1 cup).

POINTS value: *6*; **Exchanges:** 2 Starch, 1 Vegetable, 1 Medium-Fat Meat; **Per serving:** CAL 257 (33% from fat); PRO 11.4g; FAT 9.7g (sat 4.6g); CARB 33.9g; FIB 1.6g; CHOL 20mg; IRON 2.6mg; SOD 662mg; CALC 149mg

BARLEY AND VEGETABLE CHOPPED SALAD

prep: 15 minutes • cook: 17 minutes
other: 5 minutes

1½ cups water
⅔   cup uncooked quick-cooking barley
2   cups chopped mushrooms
1   cup chopped seeded tomato (1 large)
½   cup finely chopped green onions
1   (4.25-ounce) can chopped ripe olives, drained
¼   cup chopped fresh parsley
¼   cup capers
1½ tablespoons dried basil
2   tablespoons cider vinegar
1   tablespoon olive oil
1   garlic clove, minced
¼   teaspoon salt
½   cup (2 ounces) crumbled blue cheese

1. Bring water to a boil in a small saucepan; stir in barley. Cover, reduce heat, and simmer 12 minutes or until tender. Remove from heat and let stand, covered, 5 minutes. Place barley in a colander and run under cold water until completely cooled. Drain well.
2. Combine mushrooms and next 10 ingredients in a large bowl.
3. Add barley and blue cheese to mushroom mixture; toss gently. Let stand 5 minutes before serving. YIELD: 6 servings (serving size: 1 cup).

POINTS value: *3*; **Exchanges:** 1½ Starch, 1 Fat; **Per serving:** CAL 178 (37% from fat); PRO 6.1g; FAT 7.8g (sat 2.5g); CARB 23.3g; FIB 5.8g; CHOL 7mg; IRON 2.8mg; SOD 586mg; CALC 128mg

CRANBERRY RICE SALAD

prep: 10 minutes • cook: 40 minutes
other: 5 minutes

1½   cups water
⅔   cup uncooked long-grain
   brown rice
⅓   cup chopped pecans
1   (8-ounce) can sliced water
   chestnuts, drained and coarsely
   chopped
½   cup chopped green onions
½   cup dried cranberries (such as
   Craisins)
3   tablespoons sugar
3   tablespoons cider vinegar
3   tablespoons low-sodium soy
   sauce
1   teaspoon grated peeled fresh
   ginger
1   teaspoon grated orange rind
¼   teaspoon crushed red pepper

1. Place water in a small saucepan; bring to a boil. Add rice; cover, reduce heat, and cook over medium-low heat 30 minutes or until liquid is absorbed. Place rice on a baking sheet in a thin layer; let stand 5 to 10 minutes or until completely cooled.
2. Meanwhile, place a medium nonstick skillet over medium-high heat; add pecans, and cook 3 minutes, stirring frequently, until lightly browned. Remove from heat and set aside.
3. Combine rice, water chestnuts, and next 8 ingredients in a large bowl; stir in pecans, and toss gently. YIELD: 7 servings (serving size: ½ cup).

POINTS value: 3; **Exchanges:** 1½ Starch, 1 Fat; **Per serving:** CAL 169 (24% from fat); PRO 2.6g; FAT 4.7g (sat 0.5g); CARB 30.2g; FIB 3.3g; CHOL 0mg; IRON 7.3mg; SOD 234mg; CALC 16mg

ARTICHOKE-PEPPERONCINI PASTA SALAD

prep: 5 minutes • cook: 15 minutes
other: 10 minutes

Since this salad uses olive oil rather than mayonnaise, it is perfect for picnics or tailgating.

1   cup uncooked whole
   wheat rotini (about 4 ounces)
2   cups grape or cherry
   tomatoes, halved
1   (14.5-ounce) can artichoke
   hearts, drained and coarsely
   chopped
12   kalamata olives, pitted and
   chopped
¼   cup chopped fresh parsley
¼   cup chopped red onion
¼   cup pepperoncini peppers
1   tablespoon dried basil
2   tablespoons cider vinegar
2   tablespoons olive oil
1½   teaspoons dried oregano
1   garlic clove, minced
¼   teaspoon salt

1. Cook pasta according to package directions, omitting salt and fat.
2. Meanwhile, combine tomatoes and next 11 ingredients in a large bowl. Set aside.
3. Drain pasta and rinse with cold water; drain. Add pasta to salad mixture. Toss gently to coat. Let stand 10 minutes. YIELD: 7 servings (serving size: ¾ cup).

POINTS value: 3; **Exchanges:** 1 Starch, 1 Vegetable, 1 Fat; **Per serving:** CAL 144 (36% from fat); PRO 4.4g; FAT 6.0g (sat 0.8g); CARB 20.1g; FIB 3.6g; CHOL 0mg; IRON 1.5mg; SOD 575mg; CALC 34mg

SALMON SALAD

prep: 10 minutes • cook: 16 minutes
other: 2 hours

6   (6-ounce) salmon fillets
   Cooking spray
½   cup chopped red onion
⅓   cup fat-free mayonnaise
1   tablespoon Dijon mustard
1   teaspoon chopped fresh dill
1   teaspoon capers, drained
1   teaspoon fresh lemon juice
¼   teaspoon salt
⅛   teaspoon black pepper
6   Bibb lettuce leaves

1. Preheat oven to 350°.
2. Place fillets on a baking sheet lightly coated with cooking spray. Bake at 350° for 16 minutes or until fish flakes easily when tested with a fork. Cool 5 minutes.
3. Flake fillets with a fork into ½-inch pieces. Add onion and next 7 ingredients; stir to combine. Cover and chill 2 hours.
4. Place a lettuce leaf on each of 6 serving plates; top each leaf with ⅔ cup salad. YIELD: 6 servings (serving size: 1 lettuce leaf and ⅔ cup salmon mixture).

POINTS value: 4; **Exchanges:** 3½ Lean Meat; **Per serving:** CAL 194 (28% from fat); PRO 30.5g; FAT 5.9g (sat 0.9g); CARB 3.3g; FIB 0.6g; CHOL 80mg; IRON 1.4mg; SOD 384mg; CALC 29mg

PAN-SEARED SCALLOPS AND BACON SALAD

prep: 6 minutes • cook: 15 minutes

1½   pounds sea scallops (about 28)
½   teaspoon paprika
¼   teaspoon salt
⅛   teaspoon black pepper
⅓   cup light Italian dressing
1   tablespoon water
1   (8-ounce) package mixed salad
     greens
2   bacon slices

1. Rinse scallops; pat dry with paper towels. Combine paprika, salt, and pepper. Sprinkle ¾ teaspoon spice mixture evenly over scallops; set aside. Combine remaining spice mixture, dressing, and water; stir well with a whisk. Set aside.
2. Place salad greens in a large bowl; set aside.
3. Cook bacon in a large nonstick skillet over medium heat until crisp. Remove bacon from pan, pat dry with paper towels, and crumble.
4. Add scallops to drippings in pan. Cook 3 to 4 minutes on each side or until browned. Remove scallops from pan; set aside and keep warm. Add reserved dressing mixture to pan; bring quickly to a boil, scraping pan to loosen browned bits. Pour over salad greens; toss to coat. Divide salad greens evenly among 4 plates. Top evenly with scallops and bacon. YIELD: 4 servings (serving size: 1 cup greens, 7 scallops, and 1 tablespoon bacon).

POINTS value: 5; **Exchanges:** 1 Vegetable, 3 Very Lean Meat, 1 Medium-Fat Meat, 1 Fat; **Per serving:** CAL 247 (36% from fat); PRO 31.0g; FAT 9.5g (sat 2.1g); CARB 7.6g; FIB 1.6g; CHOL 64mg; IRON 1.4mg; SOD 683mg; CALC 79mg

CHICKEN AND BLACK BEAN TACO SALAD WITH CHIPOTLE DRESSING

(pictured on page 113)
prep: 30 minutes • cook: 5 minutes
other: 5 minutes

*Save time and reduce the **POINTS** value of this Southwestern salad to 6 by serving in large bowls instead of making your own tortilla shells.*

4   (8-inch) 97%-fat-free flour
     tortillas (such as Mission)
Cooking spray
6   cups shredded iceberg lettuce,
     divided
1½   cups chopped cooked chicken
     breast
⅓   cup taco sauce (such as
     Old El Paso)
½   teaspoon chopped canned
     chipotle chile in adobo
     sauce
¾   cup canned black beans, rinsed
     and drained
¾   cup frozen whole-kernel corn,
     thawed
1½   teaspoons chili powder
1   teaspoon minced garlic
1   cup chopped tomato
4   large tomatillos, coarsely
     chopped
2   tablespoons chopped fresh
     cilantro
¼   cup (1 ounce) shredded
     Monterey Jack cheese
2   tablespoons sliced green
     onions
¾   cup fat-free ranch
     dressing
1   tablespoon chopped canned
     chipotle chile in adobo sauce

1. Preheat oven to 400°.
2. Coat both sides of tortillas with cooking spray; place over 1-quart glass mixing bowls or 10-ounce pyrex bowls on baking sheets. Gently press tortillas around bowls. Bake at 400° for 5 minutes or just until lightly browned. Cool 5 minutes on bowls; remove from bowls and cool completely.
3. Place 1½ cups lettuce in each tortilla bowl.
4. Combine chicken, taco sauce, and ½ teaspoon chipotle chile in a small bowl. Spoon mixture evenly into each tortilla bowl.
5. Combine black beans, corn, chili powder, and garlic in a small bowl. Spoon evenly into each tortilla bowl.
6. Combine tomato, tomatillos, and cilantro in a small bowl. Spoon evenly into each tortilla bowl. Sprinkle salads evenly with cheese and green onions.
7. Combine ranch dressing and 1 tablespoon chipotle chile; drizzle over salads. YIELD: 4 servings (serving size: 1 salad).

POINTS value: 7; **Exchanges:** 3 Starch, 4 Very Lean Meat; **Per serving:** CAL 376 (16% from fat); PRO 28.1g; FAT 7.0g (sat 2.3g); CARB 52.1g; FIB 6.9g; CHOL 53mg; IRON 3.6mg; SOD 1,132mg; CALC 229mg

Sandwiches

PEAR AND CREAMY SWISS CHEESE ON WALNUT BREAD

(pictured on page 135)
prep: 10 minutes

The rustic walnut bread serves as a good source of fiber and is especially delicious when combined with a wedge of soft, creamy, spreadable Swiss cheese.

2   (¾-ounce) wedges light, creamy, Swiss-flavor spreadable cheese (such as The Laughing Cow)
4   (1.3-ounce) slices walnut bread
1   large Bartlett pear, cored and cut lengthwise into ¼-inch-thick slices
1   cup alfalfa sprouts
2   tablespoons light mayonnaise
1   teaspoon Dijon mustard

1. Spread 1 cheese wedge over each of 2 bread slices. Top each bread slice with half of pear slices and half of alfalfa sprouts.
2. Combine mayonnaise and mustard. Spread half of mustard mixture evenly over each of 2 remaining bread slices; place over sprouts, coated side down. Cut sandwiches in half diagonally. YIELD: 2 servings (serving size: 1 sandwich).

POINTS value: 7; **Exchanges:** 2 Starch, 1½ Fruit, 1 Vegetable, 1½ Fat; **Per serving:** CAL 350 (28% from fat); PRO 8.7g; FAT 11.4g (sat 1.3g); CARB 58.4g; FIB 10.4g; CHOL 10mg; IRON 2.6mg; SOD 755mg; CALC 141mg

OPEN-FACED EGGPLANT-OLIVE SANDWICHES

prep: 6 minutes • cook: 16 minutes

3   tablespoons light Caesar dressing, divided
4   (¾-inch-thick) slices eggplant (about ½ pound)
Cooking spray
¼   cup tomato and basil pasta sauce
4   (0.7-ounce) slices reduced-fat Havarti cheese, sliced
4   (1.1-ounce) slices Italian bread with sesame seeds, toasted
¼   cup chopped pimiento-stuffed olives
1   tablespoon capers, rinsed and drained

1. Preheat broiler.
2. Brush 2 tablespoons dressing evenly over both sides of eggplant slices.
3. Place eggplant on a foil-lined broiler pan coated with cooking spray; cook 8 minutes. Turn and spread pasta sauce evenly over eggplant; cook 7 minutes. Place 1 cheese slice on each eggplant slice; cook 1 minute or until cheese melts. Top each bread slice with eggplant.
4. Combine olives, capers, and 1 tablespoon dressing; sprinkle evenly over each sandwich. YIELD: 4 servings (serving size: 1 sandwich).

POINTS value: 4; **Exchanges:** 1½ Starch, 1 Vegetable, 1 Lean Meat; **Per serving:** CAL 200 (36% from fat); PRO 10.1g; FAT 8.2g (sat 0.7g); CARB 22.0g; FIB 1.2g; CHOL 11mg; IRON 1.2mg; SOD 637mg; CALC 194mg

GRILLED DOUBLE CHEESE AND TOMATO SANDWICHES

prep: 4 minutes • cook: 6 minutes

Our Test Kitchens staff loves this combination of hearty bread, juicy tomatoes, and two types of melted cheese. The fontina cheese and honey mustard put a new twist on a classic favorite.

4   teaspoons honey mustard
4   (1.1-ounce) slices seven-grain bread
2   (0.7-ounce) slices fat-free sharp Cheddar cheese
4   (¼-inch-thick) slices tomato (about 3 ounces)
2   (0.7-ounce) slices fontina cheese
½   teaspoon butter
Butter-flavored cooking spray

1. Spread 1 teaspoon mustard on each of 4 bread slices; top each of 2 bread slices with 1 Cheddar cheese slice, 2 tomato slices, and 1 fontina cheese slice. Top with remaining bread slices.
2. Melt butter in a large nonstick skillet over medium heat. Lightly coat both sides of sandwiches with cooking spray. Place sandwiches in pan; cook 3 to 4 minutes on each side or until golden brown. Serve immediately. YIELD: 2 servings (serving size: 1 sandwich).

POINTS value: 6; **Exchanges:** 2½ Starch, 1 Very Lean Meat, 1 Medium-Fat Meat; **Per serving:** CAL 311 (32% from fat); PRO 16.5g; FAT 11.4g (sat 5.0g); CARB 37.5g; FIB 4.6g; CHOL 26mg; IRON 2.4mg; SOD 785mg; CALC 266mg

PROVOLONE PANINI SANDWICHES

prep: 4 minutes • cook: 6 minutes

If you don't have a panini maker, warm the sandwiches in a grill pan over medium heat. Place a skillet or large saucepan as a weight over sandwiches as they cook. Cook 3 minutes on each side or until golden brown and cheese melts.

4   (1.1-ounce) slices firm white sandwich bread (such as Pepperidge Farm)
1   tablespoon light Caesar dressing
4   (0.5-ounce) slices light provolone cheese
½   cup bottled roasted red bell pepper strips, drained
8   large basil leaves

1. Lightly brush 1 side of each bread slice with dressing. Place 2 bread slices, dressing side down, on a sheet of wax paper; top each with 1 slice cheese. Arrange bell pepper strips and basil evenly over cheese slices. Top with remaining 2 slices of cheese and bread slices, placing bread with the dressing side up.
2. Cook sandwiches in a preheated panini maker or waffle iron for 3 minutes or until golden brown and cheese melts. YIELD: 2 servings (serving size: 1 sandwich).

*POINTS value: 6; **Exchanges:** 2 Starch, 1 Lean Meat, 1 Fat; **Per serving:** CAL 266 (29% from fat); PRO 16.7g; FAT 8.5g (sat 2.5g); CARB 32.9g; FIB 0.3g; CHOL 10mg; IRON 1.3mg; SOD 842mg; CALC 275mg*

FRESH VEGETABLE PO'BOYS

prep: 9 minutes • cook: 33 minutes
other: 10 minutes

1   whole garlic head
1   medium zucchini, cut into ½-inch-thick slices
1   medium-sized yellow squash, cut into ½-inch-thick slices
1   medium-sized red bell pepper, seeded and cut into bite-sized pieces
1   small red onion, cut into 8 wedges
2   plum tomatoes, quartered
    Cooking spray
1   tablespoon balsamic vinegar
1   teaspoon chopped fresh thyme
1   teaspoon extravirgin olive oil
½   teaspoon freshly ground black pepper
¼   teaspoon salt
1   (8-ounce) loaf French bread
⅓   cup (1.3 ounces) shredded part-skim mozzarella cheese

1. Preheat oven to 475°.
2. Remove white papery skin from garlic head (do not peel or separate the cloves). Place in center of a large baking sheet or shallow roasting pan. Arrange zucchini and next 4 ingredients around garlic; spray vegetables with cooking spray. Bake at 475° for 15 minutes, and turn vegetables with a spatula. Bake an additional 15 minutes or until vegetables are lightly browned and tender.
3. Spoon vegetables and pan juices into a bowl. Separate garlic cloves, and squeeze to extract garlic pulp. Discard skins. Stir garlic pulp into vegetables. Stir in vinegar and

next 4 ingredients; toss gently. Let vegetable mixture stand 10 minutes.
4. Split French bread in half lengthwise, cutting to, but not through, other side using a serrated knife. Spoon vegetables onto bread; sprinkle with cheese. Bake at 475° for 3 to 4 minutes or until cheese melts. Cut into 4 equal pieces. Serve immediately. YIELD: 4 servings (serving size: ¼ of loaf).

*POINTS value: 5; **Exchanges:** 2 Starch, 2 Vegetable, 1 Lean Meat; **Per serving:** CAL 273 (22% from fat); PRO 12.5g; FAT 6.9g (sat 3.7g); CARB 41.4g; FIB 3.5g; CHOL 14mg; IRON 3.0mg; SOD 585mg; CALC 259mg*

SERRATED KNIVES

A serrated knife, with its scalloped blade, comes in two forms: a "bread knife" and a "tomato knife." Both items make for neat and easy cutting because of their ability to cut foods with a tough exterior and delicate interior.

Bread knives make cutting a slice of bread or cake a cinch. For the perfect slice, exert only a small amount of pressure downward and slide the knife back and forth in a sawing motion. This motion will create a clean cut without mashing or tearing the soft insides of the loaf or cake.

The shorter tomato knife glides easily through tomatoes and other smooth-shelled, soft fruits and vegetables. It also works well on crusty baguette loaves.

FRESH LEMON GREENS ON RED PEPPER FOCACCIA

(pictured on page 136)
prep: 10 minutes • cook: 19 minutes

This knife-and-fork sandwich is a refreshing combination of salad greens, fresh vegetables, and warm bread.

1 (13.8-ounce) can refrigerated pizza crust dough
Cooking spray
1¼ cups red bell pepper strips (about 1 medium)
¼ cup (1 ounce) crumbled reduced-fat feta cheese with basil and sun-dried tomatoes
2 teaspoons olive oil
1 tablespoon lemon juice
1 teaspoon dried basil
1 teaspoon Dijon mustard
½ teaspoon bottled minced garlic
¼ teaspoon crushed red pepper
5 cups gourmet salad greens
¾ cup grape or cherry tomatoes, halved
⅓ cup thinly sliced red onion

1. Preheat oven to 400°.
2. Unroll pizza dough; place on a baking sheet coated with cooking spray. Press into a 13 x 9-inch rectangle. Arrange bell pepper strips in a single layer over crust. Bake 19 minutes or until crust is lightly browned. Remove from oven and immediately sprinkle with feta cheese.
3. While crust is baking, combine olive oil and next 5 ingredients in a small bowl; stir with a whisk. Combine salad greens, tomatoes, and onion in a large bowl. Pour dressing over salad; toss gently.

4. Cut focaccia into 4 rectangles; top each focaccia rectangle evenly with greens. Serve immediately. YIELD: 4 servings (serving size: 1 focaccia rectangle and 1¼ cups greens).

POINTS value: 6; **Exchanges:** 3 Starch, 1 Vegetable, 1½ Fat; **Per serving:** CAL 325 (20% from fat); PRO 11.9g; FAT 7.2g (sat 1.0g); CARB 53.2g; FIB 3.5g; CHOL 2mg; IRON 3.8mg; SOD 802mg; CALC 70mg

OPEN-FACED SALMON SALAD SANDWICHES

prep: 10 minutes

1 (6-ounce) can salmon, drained, skin and bones discarded
¼ cup minced celery
¼ cup light mayonnaise
2 teaspoons fresh lime juice
1 teaspoon prepared horseradish
⅛ teaspoon salt
⅛ teaspoon pepper
4 curly leaf lettuce leaves
4 (¼-inch-thick) slices tomato
2 English muffins, split and toasted

1. Place salmon in a small bowl; flake with a fork. Add celery; toss well.
2. Combine mayonnaise and next 4 ingredients; mix well. Add to salmon mixture; toss well to coat.
3. Place 1 lettuce leaf and 1 tomato slice on each muffin half. Top with ¼ cup salmon salad. YIELD: 4 servings (serving size: 1 sandwich).

POINTS value: 4; **Exchanges:** 1 Starch, 1 Lean Meat, ½ Fat; **Per serving:** CAL 167 (39% from fat); PRO 8.8g; FAT 7.1g (sat 1.3g); CARB 16.7g; FIB 1.4g; CHOL 16mg; IRON 1.1mg; SOD 478mg; CALC 131mg

SHRIMP PO'BOYS

(pictured on page 134)
prep: 8 minutes • cook: 12 minutes

2 tablespoons light mayonnaise
1½ teaspoons Creole seasoning, divided
4 (3¼-ounce) unsliced French rolls (such as Earth Grains French Rolls)
Butter-flavored cooking spray
1¼ pounds large shrimp, peeled and deveined
1 teaspoon olive oil
1 cup sliced yellow onion
1 cup shredded lettuce
4 (¼-inch-thick) slices tomato

1. Preheat oven to 375°.
2. Combine mayonnaise and ½ teaspoon Creole seasoning in a small bowl; cover and chill.
3. Split rolls lengthwise, cutting to, but not through, other side. Place on a baking sheet; coat insides of rolls with cooking spray. Bake at 375° for 4 minutes or until lightly toasted. Set aside.
4. Sprinkle 1 teaspoon Creole seasoning over shrimp; set aside.
5. Heat oil in a large nonstick skillet over medium-high heat. Add onion; sauté 4 minutes. Add shrimp; sauté 4 minutes or until shrimp are done.
6. Spread mayonnaise mixture evenly over cut sides of rolls; top each evenly with lettuce and tomato. Spoon shrimp mixture over tomato. Serve immediately. YIELD: 4 servings (serving size: 1 sandwich).

POINTS value: 8; **Exchanges:** 3 Starch, 3½ Very Lean Meat, 1 Fat; **Per serving:** CAL 414 (19% from fat); PRO 31.1g; FAT 8.4g (sat 2.8g); CARB 52.2g; FIB 2.8g; CHOL 175mg; IRON 6.2mg; SOD 976mg; CALC 184mg

FRESH TUNA BURGERS WITH MANGO-JALAPEÑO JAM

prep: 15 minutes • cook: 14 minutes

Cubing and chopping fresh tuna fillets may seem time-consuming, but the end product is delicious and worth the effort. Chopped and mixed with Asian seasonings, the tuna makes a nice alternative to beef burgers.

1¼   pounds tuna fillets, cut into 1-inch cubes
1   tablespoon minced green onion tops
2   teaspoons low-sodium soy sauce
¼   teaspoon salt
⅛   teaspoon freshly ground black pepper
1   teaspoon olive oil
Cooking spray
Mango-Jalapeño Jam

1. Prepare grill.
2. Place fillets and next 4 ingredients in a food processor; process until fish is finely chopped. Shape fish mixture into 4 (4-inch) patties. Brush patties evenly on each side with oil. Place on grill rack coated with cooking spray. Cover and grill 2 minutes on each side. Serve with Mango-Jalapeño Jam. YIELD: 4 servings (serving size: 1 burger and 3½ tablespoons jam).

(Total includes Mango-Jalapeño Jam)
POINTS value: 4; **Exchanges:** 1 Starch, 4 Very Lean Meat; **Per serving:** CAL 216 (11% from fat); PRO 33.6g; FAT 2.6g (sat 0.5g); CARB 13.7g; FIB 0.9g; CHOL 64mg; IRON 1.3mg; SOD 291mg; CALC 33mg

MANGO-JALAPEÑO JAM

1   cup diced peeled mango (about 1 large)
2   tablespoons brown sugar
2   tablespoons pineapple juice
2   tablespoons fresh lemon juice
1   tablespoon minced red onion
1   tablespoon chopped fresh cilantro
1   teaspoon diced seeded jalapeño pepper

1. Combine first 5 ingredients in a medium saucepan. Bring to a boil over medium-high heat; reduce heat, and simmer, uncovered, 8 minutes or until thickened, stirring occasionally. Remove from heat; stir in cilantro and jalapeño. Carefully pour mango mixture into a blender or food processor; process until smooth. Cover and chill. YIELD: 4 servings (serving size: 3½ tablespoons).

POINTS value: 1; **Exchanges:** ½ Starch, ½ Fruit; **Per serving:** CAL 51 (2% from fat); PRO 0.3g; FAT 0.1g (sat 0.0g); CARB 13.2g; FIB 0.8g; CHOL 0mg; IRON 0.2mg; SOD 3mg; CALC 9mg

SODIUM SOLUTIONS

Current recommendations for daily sodium intake for healthy adults range between 2,400 and 3,000 milligrams per day but some people may require less than that. Choosing a diet low in sodium helps reduce the risk of heart-related diseases. When eating higher-sodium foods like sandwich meat, bread, or condiments, be sure to choose lower-sodium accompaniments like fruit or vegetables to balance out the meal.

ROAST BEEF ON RYE SANDWICHES

prep: 6 minutes

This is the perfect make-ahead sandwich. Simply prepare it a day in advance, cover with plastic wrap, and keep it in your refrigerator. Toss it in your lunch bag with a piece of fruit for a simple lunch on the go!

3   tablespoons fat-free mayonnaise
1   tablespoon stone-ground mustard
2   teaspoons prepared horseradish
8   (1-ounce) slices reduced-calorie rye bread
2   cups loosely packed fresh baby spinach
10   ounces thinly sliced deli roast beef
4   slices red onion, separated into rings

1. Combine first 3 ingredients, stirring well. Spread mixture evenly over 1 side of each bread slice. Top half of bread with spinach, beef, and onion. Top with remaining bread slices. Cut sandwiches in half to serve. YIELD: 4 servings (serving size: 1 sandwich).

POINTS value: 3; **Exchanges:** 1 Starch, ½ Vegetable, 1 Very Lean Meat; **Per serving:** CAL 196 (18% from fat); PRO 19.0g; FAT 4.1g (sat 1.0g); CARB 22.8g; FIB 6.7g; CHOL 41mg; IRON 3.6mg; SOD 764mg; CALC 55mg

LOOSE MEAT SANDWICHES

prep: 10 minutes • cook: 40 minutes

This free-form burger was invented by an Iowa native in the 1920's and sold throughout the Midwest. It resembles a sloppy joe without the sauce.

1	pound ground round
1¼	cups finely chopped onion, divided
1	(14-ounce) can low-salt beef broth
¼	teaspoon pepper
¼	cup prepared mustard
5	(1.5-ounce) light wheat hamburger buns
15	small dill pickle slices

1. Cook beef in a large nonstick skillet over medium-high heat until browned; stir to crumble. Drain well; return meat to pan.

2. Add ¾ cup chopped onion and broth to pan; bring to a boil. Reduce heat, and simmer 25 minutes or until liquid is absorbed. Remove from heat; stir in pepper.

3. Spread mustard evenly over bottom and top half of each bun. Arrange pickle slices on bottom halves of buns; top evenly with ½ cup onion. Spoon ½ cup meat mixture onto bottom half of each bun; top with remaining halves. YIELD: 5 servings (serving size: 1 sandwich).

POINTS value: 4; **Exchanges:** 1½ Starch, ½ Vegetable, 2 Lean Meat; **Per serving:** CAL 204 (16% from fat); PRO 24.7g; FAT 4.4g (sat 1.2g); CARB 26.8g; FIB 5.0g; CHOL 48mg; IRON 3.2mg; SOD 797mg; CALC 55mg

ARTICHOKE, MUSHROOM, AND PROSCIUTTO CALZONES

**prep: 22 minutes • cook: 23 minutes
other: 5 minutes**

	Olive oil-flavored cooking spray
½	(9-ounce) package frozen artichoke hearts, thawed, drained, and coarsely chopped
1	(8-ounce) package presliced mushrooms
1	garlic clove, minced
¾	cup fat-free ricotta cheese
¼	cup (1 ounce) grated fresh Parmesan cheese
2	tablespoons chopped fresh basil
½	teaspoon pepper
1	(10-ounce) can refrigerated pizza crust dough
4	(¾-ounce) slices prosciutto
1	cup tomato and basil pasta sauce (such as Classico), warmed

1. Preheat oven to 425°.

2. Heat a large nonstick skillet coated with cooking spray over medium-high heat. Add artichoke hearts, mushrooms, and garlic; cook 6 minutes or until liquid is absorbed. Remove from heat.

3. Combine artichoke mixture, cheeses, basil, and pepper in a medium bowl. Set aside.

4. Divide pizza dough evenly into 4 pieces on a lightly floured surface; roll each piece into a round disk. Let stand 5 minutes. Pat or roll each disk into a 5-inch circle.

5. Arrange 1 prosciutto slice over each circle. Spoon ½ cup cheese filling on half of each circle, leaving a ½-inch border. Brush edges with water. Fold pizza dough over the cheese filling until edges almost meet. Bring bottom edge over top edge; crimp edges of dough with fingers to form a rim.

6. Place calzones on a baking sheet coated with cooking spray. Coat calzones with cooking spray. Cut 3 small slits into top of dough using a sharp knife.

7. Bake calzones at 425° for 17 minutes or until lightly browned. Serve with pasta sauce. YIELD: 4 servings (serving size: 1 calzone and ¼ cup pasta sauce).

POINTS value: 7; **Exchanges:** 2½ Starch, 1 Vegetable, 1½ Medium-Fat Meat; **Per serving:** CAL 339 (17% from fat); PRO 23.9g; FAT 6.6g (sat 1.7g); CARB 46.6g; FIB 4.7g; CHOL 20mg; IRON 3.3mg; SOD 1,187mg; CALC 238mg

BACON-EGG-ARUGULA SANDWICHES

prep: 15 minutes • cook: 20 minutes

Adding just two egg yolks to the salad mixture makes it taste richer while cutting out most of the fat and calories usually found in egg salad.

6	hard-cooked large eggs
3	tablespoons light mayonnaise
2	tablespoons chopped pitted green olives
1	tablespoon honey mustard
¼	teaspoon salt
⅛	teaspoon black pepper
8	(1-ounce) slices light white bread (such as Nature's Own)
4	40%-less-fat bacon slices, (such as Gwaltney), cooked and cut in half
1	cup trimmed arugula or spinach

1. Slice eggs in half lengthwise, and remove yolks. Discard 4 yolks. Chop egg whites and remaining 2 yolks. Add mayonnaise, green olives, mustard, salt, and pepper to eggs. Stir gently.

2. Spread egg mixture over 4 bread slices; place 2 bacon slice halves and ¼ cup arugula over egg mixture. Top each with 1 bread slice. YIELD: 4 servings (serving size: 1 sandwich).

POINTS value: 4; **Exchanges:** 1½ Starch, 1½ Very Lean Meat, 1 Fat; **Per serving:** CAL 221 (34% from fat); PRO 14.4g; FAT 9.5g (sat 1.6g); CARB 27.6g; FIB 6.6; CHOL 113mg; IRON 4.1mg; SOD 670mg; CALC 103mg

APPLE SLAW AND HAM SANDWICHES

prep: 15 minutes

We love the texture that the apple slaw adds to this otherwise traditional ham sandwich. It's also a great way to sneak a little fruit and fiber into your diet.

1	cup shredded green cabbage
2	tablespoons light mayonnaise
2	tablespoons fat-free sour cream
2	teaspoons lemon juice
1	teaspoon Dijon mustard
¼	teaspoon celery seeds
¼	teaspoon caraway seeds, crushed
¼	teaspoon sugar
½	pound thinly sliced, lean honey ham
8	(1-ounce) slices pumpernickel bread, toasted
1	red apple, sliced

1. To make slaw, combine first 8 ingredients in a small bowl, stirring well.

2. Divide ham evenly among 4 toasted bread slices. Place apple slices evenly over ham. Top with cabbage slaw and remaining 4 bread slices. YIELD: 4 servings (serving size: 1 sandwich).

POINTS value: 5; **Exchanges:** 2 Starch, ½ Fruit, 2 Very Lean Meat; **Per serving:** CAL 261 (23% from fat); PRO 15.8g; FAT 6.6g (sat 1.6g); CARB 37.8g; FIB 5.4g; CHOL 23mg; IRON 1.9mg; SOD 960mg; CALC 63mg

---

HOW TO MAKE HARD-COOKED EGGS

Here's a foolproof method for making perfect hard-cooked eggs every time:

Place eggs in a single layer in a saucepan and cover with cold water 1 inch above the eggs. Place over medium heat. When the water begins to simmer, remove the pan from the heat, cover, and let stand 15 minutes. Transfer the eggs to an ice water bath with a slotted spoon and let stand 5 minutes before peeling.

Because of a chemical reaction between iron in the yolk and sulfur in the white, overcooked eggs often have an unattractive greenish ring around the yolk. The eggs are still edible, but when hard-cooking next time, decrease the stand time by 1 minute.

Undercooked eggs often result in a soft yolk that is still edible but may not be the appropriate consistency for your dish. Add 1 minute to your stand time the next time you hard-cook eggs.

CHICKEN AND VEGETABLE GARDEN WRAPS

prep: 14 minutes

Wraps are a fun alternative to traditional sandwiches—kids will love them!

1½	(6-ounce) packages grilled chicken breast strips, diced
⅔	cup thinly sliced red bell pepper (about ½ medium)
½	cup thinly sliced celery (about 1 stalk)
½	cup vertically sliced red onion
½	cup frozen petite green peas
½	cup light ranch dressing
⅓	cup (1.3 ounces) crumbled blue cheese
4	cups chopped romaine lettuce
6	(8-inch) 98%-fat-free flour tortillas

1. Stir together first 7 ingredients in a medium bowl.

2. Spoon about ⅔ cup each of lettuce and chicken mixture onto center of each tortilla; fold edges of tortilla over filling. Roll up tortillas, and secure with wooden picks; wrap in wax paper. Chill. Cut diagonally in half; carefully remove wooden picks. YIELD: 6 servings (serving size: 1 wrap).

POINTS value: 6; **Exchanges:** 1½ Starch, 1 Vegetable, 2 Very Lean Meat, 1½ Fat; **Per serving:** CAL 291 (30% from fat); PRO 16.5g; FAT 9.6g (sat 2.9g); CARB 32.8g; FIB 3.4g; CHOL 36mg; IRON 2.5mg; SOD 976mg; CALC 99mg

GREEK CHICKEN SALAD PITA

prep: 9 minutes • cook: 5 minutes
other: 15 minutes

12   ounces skinless, boneless
      chicken breast tenders
1   teaspoon no-salt-added Greek
      seasoning (such as Cavender's)
4   teaspoons olive oil, divided
Cooking spray
1   (7-ounce) jar sliced roasted
      red bell peppers, drained
1   teaspoon grated lemon rind
2   tablespoons fresh lemon juice
1   tablespoon chopped fresh
      mint
½   teaspoon salt
¼   teaspoon freshly ground black
      pepper
2   whole wheat pita bread
      rounds, cut in half crosswise
4   romaine lettuce leaves
⅔   cup thinly sliced cucumber
3   tablespoons crumbled feta
      cheese

1. Sprinkle chicken with Greek
seasoning.
2. Heat 1 teaspoon oil in a large
nonstick skillet coated with cooking
spray over medium-high heat. Add
chicken; cook 2 to 3 minutes on
each side or until lightly browned.
3. Combine chicken and roasted
bell peppers in a medium bowl.
4. Combine 1 tablespoon oil, lemon
rind, and next 4 ingredients in a
small bowl. Pour marinade over
chicken mixture; toss gently. Let
stand 15 minutes.
5. Line each pita half with 1 lettuce
leaf and cucumber slices. Carefully fill
each pita pocket with ½ cup chicken
mixture. Sprinkle evenly with feta

cheese. YIELD: 4 servings (serving size:
1 pita half).

POINTS value: 4; **Exchanges:** 1 Starch,
2½ Very Lean Meat, 1 Fat; **Per serving:** CAL 207
(33% from fat); PRO 22.8g; FAT 7.7g (sat 2.1g);
CARB 11.5g; FIB 1.7g; CHOL 56mg; IRON 1.5mg;
SOD 652mg; CALC 59mg

GRILLED MOZZARELLA CHICKEN SANDWICHES

prep: 10 minutes • cook: 8 minutes

2   tablespoons light mayonnaise
4   teaspoons sweet pickle relish
8   (1.2-ounce) slices whole-grain
      bread
1   (4.9-ounce) package roasted
      skinless, boneless chicken
      breast, thinly sliced
4   (0.7-ounce) slices part-skim
      mozzarella cheese
2   cups trimmed arugula or
      spinach
Butter-flavored cooking spray

1. Combine mayonnaise and relish;
spread evenly over 4 bread slices. Top
evenly with chicken, cheese, and
arugula. Top with remaining bread
slices. Coat both sides of sandwiches
with cooking spray.
2. Place a nonstick skillet coated with
cooking spray over medium-high
heat. Add 2 sandwiches to pan; cook
2 to 3 minutes on each side or until
lightly browned. Repeat with remaining sandwiches. YIELD: 4 servings
(serving size: 1 sandwich).

POINTS value: 6; **Exchanges:** 2 Starch,
2 Very Lean Meat, ½ Medium-Fat Meat, ½ Fat;
Per serving: CAL 286 (26% from fat); PRO 19.0g;
FAT 8.6g (sat 2.9g); CARB 35.2g; FIB 4.6g;
CHOL 32mg; IRON 2.6mg; SOD 690mg;
CALC 182mg

SOUTHWESTERN TURKEY BURGERS

(pictured on page 110)
prep: 11 minutes • cook: 7 minutes

1   pound ground turkey breast
⅓   cup crushed baked tortilla
      chips
⅓   cup bottled salsa
¼   cup chopped fresh cilantro
2   tablespoons finely chopped
      green onions
1   teaspoon ground cumin
¼   teaspoon salt
¼   teaspoon black pepper
Cooking spray
4   (1.5-ounce) light wheat
      hamburger buns
4   curly leaf lettuce leaves
4   slices ripe tomato
¼   cup bottled salsa

1. Combine first 8 ingredients.
Divide mixture into 4 equal portions,
shaping each into a ½-inch-thick
patty.
2. Heat a large nonstick skillet over
medium heat. Coat patties with
cooking spray. Add patties to pan;
cook 3 minutes. Carefully turn patties over; cook 4 minutes or until
done.
3. Top bottom halves of buns with
lettuce and tomato slices. Place patties
over tomato slices, and top each with
salsa and top halves of buns. YIELD: 4
servings (serving size: 1 burger).

POINTS value: 5; **Exchanges:** 1½ Starch, 1 Vegetable,
3 Very Lean Meat; **Per serving:** CAL 245
(17% from fat); PRO 28g; FAT 5.3g (sat 1.2g);
CARB 30.2g; FIB 6.1g; CHOL 56mg; IRON 3mg;
SOD 948mg; CALC 75mg

A Picture Is Worth A Thousand Words

TENA CLARK • **HEIGHT** 5'8" • **BEFORE** 178 LBS. • **AFTER** 136 LBS.
EVERETTE CLARK • **HEIGHT** 6'2" • **BEFORE** 252 LBS. • **AFTER** 186 LBS.

Philosophy: "We don't feel like we are missing out on anything...because we aren't!"

In December 2002, Tena and Everette Clark went to a party decked in their holiday best. They were disappointed when they later saw pictures from the event. "I couldn't believe the pudgy faces staring back at me," Tena says. "And we thought that we looked nice!" Fortunately, it was that photo that made them realize their need to lose weight, and the one that motivated them to succeed.

For Tena, her weight issues began with the 10 pounds she never lost after the birth of her son. "I kept meaning to lose the weight, but never did," she says. "So after 13 years of putting on a few

"Joining Weight Watchers is definitely one of the best decisions we ever made."

pounds each year, I had grown from a size 7 to a size 12. And I simply refused to buy bigger clothes."

Everette's weight problem was a strain on his health and his work. As an electrical inspector, he sometimes has to crawl into small spaces. The extra weight he was carrying around made executing his job something of a challenge. "The strain on my back from the extra weight caused leg and back pain and also resulted in sleep apnea,"

he says. "It was even affecting my golf game.

"So when Tena finally suggested that we go to a *Weight Watchers* meeting, I agreed," Everette says. "I was a bit skeptical at first, but when I lost 7.4 pounds the first week, I became a believer."

"We put that ugly 'before' picture on the refrigerator as a motivator," Tena says. "It was definitely an encouragement. Looking at that every day makes you want to lose the weight."

Everette and Tena have been going to *Weight Watchers* meetings every week since June 2, 2003. "*Weight Watchers* quickly became a way of life for us," Tena says. "With encouragement and inspiration from our group leader, we have been amazed at how easy it is to lose the weight and keep it off."

Along with following the food program step by step, the Clarks also put their feet to the street. "Tena and I walk 3 to 4 times a week for exercise. It made a big difference in losing the weight and keeping it off," Everette says.

On December 29, 2003, both Tena and Everette became lifetime members. "We don't feel like we are missing out on anything," Tena says, "because we aren't!"

"Together we have lost over 108 pounds," Everette says. "Joining *Weight Watchers* is definitely one of the best decisions we ever made."

133

Shrimp Po'Boy,
page 128

Chive-Parmesan
Potato Chips,
page 15

Pear and Creamy Swiss
Cheese on Walnut Bread,
page 126

Fresh Lemon Greens
on Red Pepper
Focaccia,
page, 128

Maple-Pecan Sweet Potatoes,
page 147

Barley and Brussels Sprouts,
page 149

Moroccan Carrots,
page 145

Zesty White Beans
and Tomatoes,
page 143

Green Bean Casserole,
page 142

Shopping Once Again

SANDRA MARINO FISCH • **HEIGHT** 5'6" • **BEFORE** 245 LBS. • **AFTER** 135 LBS.

Advice: "Don't look at it as a diet. You can eat anything as long as it is in moderation."

After battling a weight problem off and on since she was a teenager, Sandra Marino Fisch finally decided to take action. The stresses and constraints of being a single parent along with the loss of her job had taken their toll. "Trying to find a new career and trying to take care of my son caused me to start gaining weight again," Sandra says. "So in January 2002, I decided to take a look at what *Weight Watchers* could offer me in terms of helping me with my weight problem."

Sandra walked into the *Weight Watchers* center, asked a few questions, and, feeling extremely overwhelmed, walked out without even joining. But as winter turned to spring, Sandra became increasingly unhappy with her weight and realized that shopping for new clothes—one of the joys of her life—had become a miserable experience.

"I would look at myself in the dressing room mirror and the image that I saw was not what I wanted to see anymore," she says. "I was disgusted with myself. This wasn't the person I was on the inside."

"I still love food and enjoy eating, but I'm just not overeating anymore."

By April, Sandra decided to take charge. She joined *Weight Watchers* in April 2002 and began learning everything she could about the program.

"My first week I lost 9.2 pounds," Sandra says, "and that gave me the incentive to continue with the program. As weeks went by, I started learning more and more and I was actually eating more than I was before. The difference was that I was learning how to eat a balanced diet and control portion sizes."

By the 20th week, Sandra had lost 50 pounds and was gaining confidence. "I had finally learned how to make the lifestyle changes that I needed for healthy weight loss," she says. "And the program was so easy to follow. It became so natural to look at foods and mentally calculate the **POINTS** values."

For Sandra, the beauty of *Weight Watchers* was that it didn't dictate what foods she could or could not eat. "They don't tell you that you can't eat something," she says. "After all, I am Italian. You can't tell me that I can't have bread and pasta! The **POINTS** system just makes it so easy. I still love food and enjoy eating, but I'm just not overeating anymore."

Today, Sandra is not only eating healthier, but she's weighing less, too. After a year and two months, Sandra reached her weight-loss goal. She has lost a total of 110 pounds and has never felt better.

"Since losing the weight I can now look forward to going shopping without dreading the image in the mirror," she says. "I am now a size 4 and have *Weight Watchers* to thank.

"The only problem now is that it is more difficult to find clothes than it was before," she says with a chuckle. "Isn't that horrible! But I enjoy it. I'd rather search for a size 4 than go back to a 22 or 24 any day. Thank you, *Weight Watchers,* for developing a great program that is really easy to follow and one that has enabled me to look and feel fantastic."

Sides

ASPARAGUS SPEARS WITH LEMON-TARRAGON BUTTER

prep: 13 minutes • cook: 3 minutes

*Substitute fresh thyme for fresh tarragon
if you prefer. The herb butter can also
be served over baked fish fillets.*

1	pound asparagus spears
2	tablespoons light butter
2	teaspoons grated lemon rind
2	tablespoons fresh lemon juice
2	teaspoons chopped fresh tarragon
½	teaspoon salt

1. Snap off tough ends of asparagus.
2. Cook asparagus in boiling water
in a large skillet 1 minute or until
crisp-tender. Drain well, and return
asparagus to pan.
3. Add butter and remaining ingredients. Cook over medium heat
2 minutes; toss gently to coat. YIELD:
4 servings (serving size: ¼ of
asparagus).

POINTS value: 0; **Exchanges:** 1½ Vegetable;
Per serving: CAL 42 (21% from fat); PRO 2.7g;
FAT 1.0g (sat 0.7g); CARB 5.8g; FIB 2.6g;
CHOL 3mg; IRON 0.5mg; SOD 307mg; CALC 28mg

TARRAGON SPRING VEGETABLES

prep: 3 minutes • cook: 4 minutes

*Many of the vegetables called
for in this recipe are frozen, but if
fresh are available, they would
make a delicious substitute.*

1	pound fresh asparagus, trimmed and cut into 2-inch pieces
2	cups frozen sugar snap peas
½	cup frozen green peas
1	tablespoon butter
1	tablespoon finely chopped shallots
1	tablespoon chopped fresh tarragon
2	teaspoons chopped fresh parsley
½	teaspoon salt
¼	teaspoon freshly ground black pepper
¼	teaspoon grated lemon rind

1. Arrange asparagus, sugar snap peas,
and green peas in a vegetable steamer.
Steam, covered, 3 to 4 minutes or
until tender. Remove from heat;
drain vegetables and return to pan.
2. Stir in butter and remaining
ingredients. Heat over medium heat
1 minute or until butter melts, tossing gently. YIELD: 4 servings (serving
size: 1 cup).

POINTS value: 1; **Exchanges:** 2 Vegetable, ½ Fat;
Per serving: CAL 71 (34% from fat); PRO 3.3g;
FAT 2.7g (sat 1.3g); CARB 8.5g; FIB 3.6g;
CHOL 5mg; IRON 0.9mg; SOD 229mg; CALC 50mg

GREEN BEAN CASSEROLE

(pictured on page 139)
prep: 7 minutes • cook: 27 minutes

*We reduced the fat but not
the flavor in this family favorite
recipe by substituting crushed Melba
rounds and onion flakes for the
canned fried onion rings.*

1	(16-ounce) package frozen French-cut green beans
¼	cup chopped onion
¼	cup water
⅓	cup shredded Parmesan cheese
¼	teaspoon salt
¼	teaspoon freshly ground black pepper
1	(10¾-ounce) can condensed reduced-fat, reduced-sodium cream of mushroom soup
Cooking spray	
15	onion melba rounds, crushed
1	tablespoon instant onion flakes
2	teaspoons butter, melted

1. Preheat oven to 350°.
2. Combine green beans, onion, and
water. Cover and microwave at
HIGH 7 minutes.
3. Combine cheese and next 3
ingredients in a bowl. Stir in bean
mixture. Spoon into an 8-inch
square baking dish coated with
cooking spray.
4. Combine melba rounds, onion
flakes, and butter. Sprinkle crumb
mixture over bean mixture. Bake at
350° for 20 to 25 minutes or until
bubbly. YIELD: 6 servings (serving size:
about ¾ cup).

POINTS value: 2; **Exchanges:** 2 Vegetable, 1 Fat;
Per serving: CAL 100 (39% from fat); PRO 4.2g;
FAT 4.8g (sat 2.0g); CARB 12.2g; FIB 2.8g;
CHOL 8mg; IRON 1.0mg; SOD 486mg; CALC 105mg

ZESTY WHITE BEANS AND TOMATOES

(pictured on page 138)
prep: 9 minutes

With its cool, refreshing blend of lemon juice, fresh basil and parsley, and grape tomatoes, this side is a colorful complement to any grilled dinner.

1   (16-ounce) can navy beans, rinsed and drained
½   cup quartered grape or cherry tomatoes
2   tablespoons chopped fresh parsley
1   tablespoon chopped fresh basil
1   tablespoon lemon juice
1   tablespoon extravirgin olive oil
1   garlic clove, minced
¼   teaspoon salt

1. Combine all ingredients in a small bowl. Serve at room temperature or chilled. YIELD: 4 servings (serving size: ½ cup).

POINTS value: 2; **Exchanges:** 1 Starch, ½ Vegetable, ½ Fat; **Per serving:** CAL 113 (29% from fat); PRO 5.4g; FAT 3.8g (sat 0.5g); CARB 15.4g; FIB 3.8g; CHOL 0mg; IRON 1.5mg; SOD 332mg; CALC 38mg

LEMON BROCCOLI

prep: 5 minutes • cook: 11 minutes

Finish this dish with a splash of balsamic vinegar for an extra flavor punch.

2   teaspoons olive oil
Cooking spray
1   pound broccoli, trimmed and cut into florets
2   garlic cloves, chopped
½   cup fat-free, less-sodium chicken broth
⅛   teaspoon grated lemon rind
2   teaspoons fresh lemon juice
½   teaspoon salt
⅛   teaspoon crushed red pepper

1. Heat oil in a large nonstick skillet coated with cooking spray. Add broccoli and garlic. Sauté 6 to 8 minutes or until crisp-tender. Remove broccoli mixture; keep warm.
2. Add broth and next 4 ingredients to pan. Bring to a boil. Cook 3 minutes or until liquid is reduced to ¼ cup. Add broccoli mixture, and cook 1 minute or until thoroughly heated. YIELD: 4 servings (serving size: 1 cup).

POINTS value: 1; **Exchanges:** ½ Starch, ½ Fat; **Per serving:** CAL 57 (36% from fat); PRO 3.9g; FAT 2.7g (sat 0.4g); CARB 6.9g; FIB 3.4g; CHOL 0mg; IRON 1.1mg; SOD 395mg; CALC 60mg

BRUSSELS SPROUTS WITH TOMATO, OLIVES, AND BACON

prep: 5 minutes • cook: 15 minutes

Brussels sprouts are an excellent source of vitamins A and C and a good source of the mineral, iron.

1   (16-ounce) package frozen Brussels sprouts
3   slices 40%-less-fat bacon (such as Gwaltney)
1   cup finely chopped onion
1   teaspoon bottled minced garlic
1   (14.5-ounce) can diced tomatoes with roasted garlic, drained
⅓   cup sliced green olives
¼   teaspoon salt
¼   teaspoon pepper

1. Partially thaw Brussels sprouts in microwave at HIGH 3½ minutes; cut sprouts in half. Set aside.
2. Cook bacon in a large nonstick skillet over medium heat until crisp. Remove bacon from pan, reserving 1 tablespoon drippings in pan. Drain bacon on paper towels; crumble and set aside. Add onion to drippings in pan; sauté 2 minutes. Add garlic; sauté 1 minute. Stir in Brussels sprouts; cook, stirring occasionally, 4 minutes or until mixture is browned. Stir in tomatoes and next 3 ingredients; cook until thoroughly heated. Sprinkle reserved bacon over top. YIELD: 4 servings (serving size: 1 cup).

POINTS value: 2; **Exchanges:** 4 Vegetable, ½ Fat; **Per serving:** CAL 133 (20% from fat); PRO 7.6g; FAT 2.9g (sat 0.6g); CARB 21.8g; FIB 6.1g; CHOL 4mg; IRON 2.3mg; SOD 602mg; CALC 100mg

CITRUS ROASTED BRUSSELS SPROUTS

prep: 7 minutes • cook: 18 minutes

Roasting Brussels sprouts mellows their pungent flavor. Select Brussels sprouts that are about the same size so they roast evenly.

1   pound Brussels sprouts, trimmed and halved (about 4 cups)
Cooking spray
2   teaspoons olive oil
¼   teaspoon salt
½   teaspoon grated orange rind
1   tablespoon fresh orange juice
1   tablespoon fresh lemon juice
⅛   teaspoon freshly ground black pepper

1. Preheat oven to 450°.
2. Place Brussels sprouts on a foil-lined jelly roll pan coated with cooking spray. Drizzle with 2 teaspoons oil and ¼ teaspoon salt. Bake at 450° for 18 minutes or until lightly browned, stirring once.
3. Meanwhile, combine orange rind, orange juice, lemon juice, and pepper in a large bowl.
4. Add Brussels sprouts to orange juice mixture and toss gently to coat. Serve immediately. YIELD: 3 servings (serving size: 1 cup).

POINTS value: 1; **Exchanges:** 2 Vegetable, ½ Fat; **Per serving:** CAL 81 (33% from fat); PRO 4.0g; FAT 3.4g (sat 0.5g); CARB 11.6g; FIB 4.6g; CHOL 0mg; IRON 1.7mg; SOD 226mg; CALC 51mg

CABBAGE, ONION, AND PEPPER TOSS

prep: 11 minutes • cook: 19 minutes
other: 3 minutes

Just because you want to have a healthy diet doesn't mean you have to cut out fat altogether. We used only two slices of bacon in this recipe, which gave it just the right amount of flavor without adding excess fat.

2   slices bacon, uncooked
5   cups coarsely chopped cabbage (about ½ large head)
1   cup chopped onion (about 1 medium)
1   cup chopped green bell pepper (about 1 large)
2   garlic cloves, minced
½   teaspoon salt
⅛   teaspoon black pepper

1. Cook bacon in a Dutch oven over medium-high heat 9 minutes or until crisp. Remove bacon from pan, reserving drippings in pan. Drain bacon on paper towels, and crumble; set aside
2. Cook cabbage and next 3 ingredients in bacon drippings over medium-high heat 10 minutes; stir often. Remove from heat. Stir in bacon, salt, and black pepper. Cover, and let stand 3 minutes. YIELD: 4 servings (serving size: ¾ cup).

POINTS value: 2; **Exchanges:** 2 Vegetable, 1 Fat; **Per serving:** CAL 105 (42% from fat); PRO 3.7g; FAT 5.3g (sat 1.8g); CARB 12.6g; FIB 1.2g; CHOL 8mg; IRON 1.0mg; SOD 412mg; CALC 68mg

CARROT-EDAMAME SAUTÉ

prep: 10 minutes • cook: 10 minutes

Shallots, a member of the onion family, have a flavor similar to sweet onions and garlic. You may substitute ¼ cup finely chopped white onion for the shallot.

2   teaspoons olive oil
½   cup finely chopped shallot (about 1 large)
1   (8-ounce) package preshredded carrot
⅓   cup fully-cooked refrigerated shelled edamame
¼   cup diced red bell pepper
¼   cup diced green bell pepper
1   tablespoon minced fresh parsley
1   teaspoon butter
2   teaspoons fresh lemon juice
¼   teaspoon dried thyme
¼   teaspoon salt
¼   teaspoon freshly ground black pepper

1. Heat oil in a large nonstick skillet over medium heat. Add shallot, and sauté 3 to 4 minutes or until soft. Add carrot and edamame; sauté 5 minutes or until vegetables are almost tender. Add bell peppers; sauté 2 minutes. Add parsley and butter, stirring until butter melts. Stir in lemon juice, thyme, salt, and black pepper. Serve immediately. YIELD: 5 servings (serving size: about ½ cup).

POINTS value: 1; **Exchanges:** 2 Vegetable, ½ Fat; **Per serving:** CAL 72 (39% from fat); PRO 2.1g; FAT 3.1g (sat 0.7g); CARB 9.8g; FIB 2.4g; CHOL 2mg; IRON 0.8mg; SOD 148mg; CALC 29mg

MOROCCAN CARROTS

(pictured on page 138)
prep: 9 minutes • **cook:** 16 minutes

Cumin and garlic complement the naturally sweet flavor of carrots. Serve with Mustard-Glazed Halibut with Warm Scallions, page 55, for a meal with a POINTS value of 6.

4   cups diagonally cut carrot
    (about 1¾ pounds)
2   teaspoons olive oil
3   garlic cloves, thinly sliced
¼   teaspoon cumin seeds
1½ tablespoons chopped fresh
    cilantro
1   teaspoon honey
½   teaspoon salt
½   teaspoon freshly ground black
    pepper
¼   teaspoon ground cumin

1. Steam carrots, covered, 14 minutes or until tender. Drain.
2. Meanwhile, heat oil in a large nonstick skillet over medium heat. Add garlic and cumin seeds; sauté 1½ minutes or until lightly browned. Stir in carrots, cilantro, and remaining ingredients. YIELD: 6 servings (serving size: ½ cup).

POINTS value: 1; **Exchanges:** 2 Vegetable;
Per serving: CAL 55 (28% from fat); PRO 1.0g;
FAT 1.7g (sat 0.2g); CARB 9.9g; FIB 2.6g;
CHOL 0mg; IRON 0.6mg; SOD 225mg; CALC 27mg

GARLICKY CAULIFLOWER

prep: 5 minutes • **cook:** 9 minutes

Pan-roasted garlic breadcrumbs add crunch to this mild-tasting vegetable. Serve with roast beef or pork.

1   cauliflower, trimmed and cut
    into florets (about 6 cups)
2   (1-ounce) slices whole
    wheat bread (such as
    Pepperidge Farm Light Style
    Wheat Bread)
1   tablespoon olive oil
4   garlic cloves, minced
1   tablespoon minced fresh
    parsley
½   teaspoon salt
Olive oil-flavored cooking spray

1. Arrange cauliflower in a vegetable steamer. Steam, covered, 8 to 10 minutes or until tender. Drain well.
2. Meanwhile, place bread in a food processor or blender; process until fine breadcrumbs form.
3. Heat oil in a large nonstick skillet over medium heat. Add garlic; sauté 1 to 1½ minutes or until lightly browned. Stir in breadcrumbs; cook, stirring frequently, until browned. Remove from heat; stir in parsley and salt.
4. Coat cauliflower with cooking spray; toss with breadcrumb mixture. YIELD: 6 servings (serving size: about 1 cup).

POINTS value: 1; **Exchanges:** ½ Starch, 1 Vegetable,
½ Fat; **Per serving:** CAL 96 (27% from fat); PRO 4.7g;
FAT 2.8g (sat 0.5g); CARB 16.2g; FIB 4.4g;
CHOL 0mg; IRON 1.2mg; SOD 333mg; CALC 41mg

CORN AND PECAN PILAF

prep: 5 minutes • **cook:** 15 minutes

This side is delicious enough to impress your friends at a dinner party and easy enough to make for supper tonight. Best of all, no one will guess it took you only 20 minutes to make!

½   cup uncooked instant brown
    rice (such as Uncle Ben's)
Cooking spray
1   cup chopped onion
    (about 1 medium)
¾   cup frozen whole-kernel
    corn, thawed
½   teaspoon dried basil
⅓   cup finely chopped fresh
    parsley
¼   cup chopped pecans, toasted
2   teaspoons yogurt-based spread
    (such as Brummel & Brown)
½   teaspoon salt

1. Cook rice according to package directions, omitting salt and fat.
2. Meanwhile, coat a large nonstick skillet with cooking spray; add onion, and cook 5 to 6 minutes or until brown. Add corn and basil; cook 2 minutes, stirring constantly. Remove from heat; add rice, parsley, pecans, yogurt-based spread, and salt. Toss gently. YIELD: 4 servings (serving size: ½ cup).

POINTS value: 3; **Exchanges:** 1½ Starch, 1 Fat;
Per serving: CAL 162 (36% from fat); PRO 3.3g;
FAT 6.9g (sat 0.7g); CARB 24.0g; FIB 3.0g;
CHOL 0mg; IRON 1.0mg; SOD 315mg; CALC 32mg

SUMMER CORN AND TOMATOES

prep: 15 minutes • cook: 10 minutes

Nothing says summer like sweet corn and fresh tomatoes. Serve this at your next cookout along with Lime-Marinated Flank Steak, page 83, or Caribbean Grilled Turkey Kabobs, page 107.

5   ears corn
1   tablespoon yogurt-based spread (such as Brummel & Brown)
1   cup diced onion (about 1 small)
1   pint grape or cherry tomatoes, cut in half
1   tablespoon chopped fresh parsley
¼   teaspoon salt
⅛   teaspoon freshly ground black pepper

1. Remove and discard husks and silks from corn. Cut off corn kernels into a bowl; scrape milk and remaining pulp from cob with a paring knife to measure 3 cups. Set corn aside.
2. Heat yogurt-based spread in a large nonstick skillet over low heat; add onion. Cook over medium heat 3 minutes, stirring occasionally. Add corn and cook 4 minutes, stirring frequently. Add tomatoes; cook 3 minutes. Stir in parsley, salt, and pepper. YIELD: 4 servings (serving size: 1 cup).

POINTS value: 2; **Exchanges:** 1½ Starch, 1 Vegetable;
Per serving: CAL 142 (19% from fat); PRO 4.9g;
FAT 2.9g (sat 0.5g); CARB 29.0g; FIB 4.7g;
CHOL 0mg; IRON 1.1mg; SOD 195mg; CALC 16mg

ROASTED POBLANO AND POTATO GRATIN

prep: 6 minutes • cook: 51 minutes
other: 15 minutes

1   large poblano pepper
1   garlic clove, halved
Olive oil–flavored cooking spray
4   large baking potatoes, peeled
2   tablespoons butter, melted and divided
½   teaspoon salt, divided
¼   teaspoon freshly ground black pepper, divided
1   cup (4 ounces) shredded reduced-fat sharp Cheddar cheese, divided
1¾   cups 1% low-fat milk

1. Preheat broiler.
2. Place pepper on a foil-lined baking sheet; broil 6 to 8 minutes or until blackened, turning occasionally. Place pepper in a zip-top plastic bag. Seal and let stand 15 minutes. Peel pepper and cut in half lengthwise. Discard seeds and membranes, and chop pepper.
3. Reduce oven temperature to 425°.
4. Rub sides and bottom of a 2½-quart gratin dish with garlic; discard garlic. Coat sides of dish with cooking spray.
5. Slice potatoes crosswise into ⅛-inch-thick rounds. Arrange half of potato slices in bottom of prepared dish; top with half of chopped poblano. Drizzle 1 tablespoon butter over potato mixture and sprinkle with ¼ teaspoon salt and ⅛ teaspoon pepper. Sprinkle with ½ cup cheese. Layer remaining potato slices on top of cheese, and top with 1 tablespoon butter, ¼ teaspoon salt, and ⅛ teaspoon pepper. Sprinkle with ½ cup cheese.

6. Place milk in a 4-cup glass measure. Microwave at HIGH 2 minutes or until gently boiling. Pour milk over potato mixture.
7. Bake at 425° for 45 minutes or until mixture is bubbly and potatoes are tender. YIELD: 7 servings (serving size: ¾ cup).

POINTS value: 3; **Exchanges:** 1 Starch, 1½ Fat;
Per serving: CAL 153 (39% from fat); PRO 6.7g;
FAT 6.7g (sat 4.2g); CARB 16.3g; FIB 1.6g;
CHOL 20mg; IRON 0.5mg; SOD 328mg;
CALC 175mg

OVEN-ROASTED POTATO WEDGES

prep: 5 minutes • cook: 30 minutes

2   large baking potatoes (about 14 ounces)
½   teaspoon salt
½   teaspoon garlic powder
1   teaspoon black pepper
¼   teaspoon paprika
Cooking spray

1. Preheat oven to 425°.
2. Cut each potato lengthwise into 12 wedges.
3. Combine salt and next 3 ingredients in a bowl; toss well. Arrange potatoes, flesh side down, in a single layer on a baking sheet coated with cooking spray. Coat potatoes with cooking spray.
4. Bake at 425° for 15 minutes. Turn potatoes, and bake an additional 15 minutes or until golden brown and tender. YIELD: 4 servings (serving size: 6 wedges).

POINTS value: 1; **Exchange:** 1 Starch;
Per serving: CAL 81 (1% from fat); PRO 2.3g;
FAT 0.1g (sat 0.0g); CARB 18.6g; FIB 1.5g;
CHOL 0mg; IRON 1.1mg; SOD 299mg; CALC 16mg

GORGONZOLA AND CHIVE MASHED POTATOES

prep: 15 minutes • cook: 34 minutes

Gorgonzola cheese and chives give classic mashed potatoes an updated taste. If you can't find Gorgonzola, any type of blue cheese makes a fine substitute.

2	large Yukon gold potatoes, peeled and cut into 1-inch cubes (about 1½ pounds)
1	teaspoon olive oil
2	tablespoons minced red onion
⅔	cup 1% low-fat milk
½	cup (2 ounces) crumbled Gorgonzola cheese
¼	cup chopped fresh chives
½	teaspoon salt
¼	teaspoon freshly ground black pepper

1. Place potatoes in a medium saucepan; add water to cover. Bring to a boil; cover, reduce heat, and simmer 20 minutes or until potatoes are tender. Drain; return potatoes to pan. Mash with a potato masher.
2. Heat oil in a small nonstick skillet over medium heat. Add onion, and cook 3 minutes or until soft; stir in milk and cheese. Reduce heat to low; cook 4 to 5 minutes or until heated and cheese begins to melt. Add milk mixture to mashed potatoes. Stir in chives, salt, and pepper. YIELD: 6 servings (serving size: about ½ cup).

POINTS value: 3; **Exchanges:** 1½ Starch, ½ Medium-Fat Meat; **Per serving:** CAL 156 (23% from fat); PRO 7.3g; FAT 4.5g (sat 2.7g); CARB 26.4g; FIB 3.3g; CHOL 11mg; IRON 1.1mg; SOD 405mg; CALC 122mg

MAPLE-PECAN SWEET POTATOES

(pictured on page 137)
prep: 11 minutes • cook: 35 minutes

We've combined brown sugar and maple syrup to make a delicious glaze for this simple side dish. Our Test Kitchens staff loved the sweet potatoes paired with crunchy pecans.

2	large sweet potatoes (about 2 pounds), peeled
½	teaspoon salt
1	tablespoon olive oil
	Cooking spray
2	tablespoons finely chopped pecans
1	tablespoon brown sugar
2	tablespoons maple syrup
1	tablespoon butter, cut into small pieces

1. Preheat oven to 450°.
2. Cut sweet potatoes in half lengthwise. Cut each half crosswise into ½-inch pieces. Place sweet potato in a large heavy-duty zip-top plastic bag. Sprinkle with salt and drizzle with oil. Seal bag; toss to coat. Place potato on a foil-lined baking sheet coated with cooking spray. Bake at 450° for 35 minutes or until browned.
3. Place pecans and next 3 ingredients in a serving bowl. Add potato; toss gently until coated. Serve immediately. YIELD: 6 servings (serving size: ⅔ cup).

POINTS value: 3; **Exchanges:** 1½ Starch, 1 Fat; **Per serving:** CAL 175 (30% from fat); PRO 1.8g; FAT 6.0g (sat 1.7g); CARB 29.4g; FIB 3.0g; CHOL 5mg; IRON 0.6mg; SOD 225mg; CALC 35mg

GRILLED PORTOBELLO MUSHROOMS

prep: 2 minutes • cook: 8 minutes

4	(4-inch) portobello mushroom caps
1	tablespoon olive oil
2	garlic cloves, minced
1	teaspoon low-sodium Worcestershire sauce
½	teaspoon freshly ground black pepper
¼	teaspoon salt
	Cooking spray

1. Prepare grill.
2. Place portobello caps, stem side up, on a plate. Combine olive oil and next 4 ingredients. Drizzle oil mixture over mushrooms.
3. Place mushrooms on grill rack coated with cooking spray; cover and grill 4 minutes on each side or until tender. YIELD: 4 servings (serving size: 1 mushroom cap).

POINTS value: 1; **Exchanges:** 1 Vegetable, ½ Fat; **Per serving:** CAL 54 (60% from fat); PRO 2.1g; FAT 3.6g (sat 0.5g); CARB 4.8g; FIB 1.3g; CHOL 0mg; IRON 0.6mg; SOD 153mg; CALC 11mg

PORTOBELLO MUSHROOMS

When selecting portobellos, look for those with a tight underside and lighter-colored gills. If the gill area appears very black and spread out, that's a sign the mushroom is old and should not be chosen.

Never submerge a portobello in water. The gills act like a sponge, absorbing water quickly. This dilutes their flavor and makes it more difficult to brown the mushrooms if they're to be cooked.

MEDITERRANEAN SAUTÉED SPINACH

prep: 2 minutes • cook: 4 minutes

A splash of fresh lemon juice makes a quick substitute for the tomato and cheese.

1	teaspoon olive oil
	Cooking spray
2	garlic cloves, minced
1	(7-ounce) package baby spinach
¼	teaspoon salt
¼	teaspoon freshly ground black pepper
½	cup chopped tomato
3	tablespoons crumbled feta cheese

1. Heat oil in a large nonstick skillet coated with cooking spray over medium heat. Add garlic; sauté 1 minute. Add spinach, and cook 3 to 4 minutes or just until spinach wilts. Sprinkle spinach mixture with salt and remaining ingredients, and serve immediately. YIELD: 4 servings (serving size: ¾ cup).

POINTS value: 1; **Exchanges:** 1 Vegetable, ½ Fat;
Per serving: CAL 47 (55% from fat); PRO 2.7g;
FAT 2.9g (sat 1.2g); CARB 3.7g; FIB 1.7g;
CHOL 6mg; IRON 1.5mg; SOD 267mg; CALC 88mg

SAUTÉED GRAPE TOMATOES

prep: 3 minutes • cook: 4 minutes

*With a **POINTS** value of 1 and less than 5 minutes of cooking time, tomatoes never tasted so good! Serve with Filet Mignon with Rosemary-Port Sauce, page 85, Herb-Roasted Chicken, page 104, or Pan-Seared Salmon with Honey-Balsamic Sauce, page 56.*

1½	teaspoons olive oil
1	pint grape tomatoes
¼	teaspoon ground cumin
¼	teaspoon chili powder
¼	teaspoon salt
⅛	teaspoon crushed red pepper

1. Heat oil in a nonstick skillet over medium-high heat. Add tomatoes; sauté 2 minutes. Sprinkle tomatoes with cumin, chili powder, salt, and crushed red pepper; toss gently. YIELD: 4 servings (serving size: ½ cup).

POINTS value: 1; **Exchange:** 1 Vegetable;
Per serving: CAL 32 (56% from fat); PRO 0.7g;
FAT 2.0g (sat 0.3g); CARB 3.6g; FIB 0.9g;
CHOL 0mg; IRON 0.4mg; SOD 155mg; CALC 5mg

YELLOW SQUASH RICE

prep: 6 minutes • cook: 12 minutes

*Toss in some cooked chicken or turkey and you have a one-dish meal with a **POINTS** value of about 4.*

½	cup uncooked instant brown rice (such as Uncle Ben's)
	Cooking spray
1	cup chopped onion (about 1 medium)
1	garlic clove, minced
1¼	cups chopped yellow squash (about 1 medium)
½	teaspoon dried oregano
2	tablespoons finely chopped parsley
1	tablespoon light butter
¼	teaspoon salt

1. Cook rice according to package directions, omitting salt and fat.
2. Meanwhile, place a medium nonstick skillet coated with cooking spray over medium heat. Add onion and garlic; sauté 3 minutes. Add squash and oregano; sauté 3 minutes. Stir in rice, parsley, butter, and salt; toss well. YIELD: 5 servings (serving size: ½ cup).

POINTS value: 1; **Exchanges:** ½ Starch, 1 Vegetable;
Per serving: CAL 66 (21% from fat); PRO 1.7g;
FAT 1.6g (sat 0.8g); CARB 11.7g; FIB 1.6g;
CHOL 4mg; IRON 0.5mg; SOD 137mg; CALC 19mg

PARMESAN-HERB ZUCCHINI

prep: 4 minutes • cook: 4 minutes

Parmesan cheese and fresh basil make these zucchini rounds a perfect match for Italian-inspired recipes like Roasted Italian Pork Tenderloin, page 94, Rosemary Chicken with White Beans, page 100, or Skillet Turkey Parmesan, page 106.

1 teaspoon olive oil
2 medium zucchini, sliced into ¼-inch rounds
1 garlic clove, chopped
1 teaspoon lemon juice
¼ cup chopped fresh basil
¼ teaspoon salt
¼ teaspoon freshly ground black pepper
2 tablespoons shredded Parmesan cheese

1. Heat oil in a nonstick skillet over medium-high heat. Add zucchini and garlic; cook 4 minutes or until lightly browned. Remove from heat; stir in lemon juice and next 3 ingredients. Sprinkle with cheese. Serve immediately. YIELD: 2 servings (serving size: 1 cup).

POINTS value: 1; **Exchanges:** 2 Vegetable;
Per serving: CAL 70 (46% from fat); PRO 4.2g;
FAT 4.0g (sat 1.2g); CARB 6.2g; FIB 2.4g;
CHOL 4mg; IRON 1.0mg; SOD 384mg; CALC 100mg

BLACK BEANS AND BARLEY

prep: 4 minutes • cook: 20 minutes
other: 5 minutes

Look for quick-cooking barley next to the hot cereal in the supermarket.

2 teaspoons olive oil
½ cup chopped onion
2 garlic cloves, minced
¾ teaspoon ground cumin
½ teaspoon paprika
¼ teaspoon salt
⅛ teaspoon ground red pepper
⅛ teaspoon ground cinnamon
1 (15-ounce) can black beans, rinsed and drained
1 cup fat-free, less-sodium chicken broth
½ cup uncooked quick-cooking barley
½ cup bottled roasted red bell peppers

1. Heat oil in a small saucepan over medium-high heat. Add onion and garlic; sauté 3 minutes. Stir in cumin and next 4 ingredients; cook, stirring constantly, 2 minutes. Add beans, broth, and barley; bring to a boil. Cover; reduce heat, and simmer 10 minutes or until liquid is absorbed. Add red bell pepper; cover, and let stand 5 minutes. Fluff with a fork before serving. YIELD: 6 servings (serving size: ½ cup).

POINTS value: 2; **Exchanges:** 1½ Starch;
Per serving: CAL 115 (16% from fat); PRO 5.2g;
FAT 2.1g (sat 0.3g); CARB 19.9g; FIB 5.2g;
CHOL 0mg; IRON 1.4mg; SOD 362mg; CALC 28mg

BARLEY AND BRUSSELS SPROUTS

(pictured on page 137)
prep: 12 minutes • cook: 24 minutes

Our Test Kitchens staff loved this hearty side dish. Increase the serving size to 1 cup for a 4 POINTS value meatless meal.

1 cup uncooked quick-cooking barley
2 cups fat-free, less-sodium chicken broth
2 teaspoons olive oil
Cooking spray
½ cup chopped onion
2 garlic cloves, minced
2 cups Brussels sprouts, shredded
¼ teaspoon salt
⅛ teaspoon black pepper
½ cup (2 ounces) shredded Parmesan cheese
4 teaspoons toasted chopped walnuts

1. Cook barley according to package directions, substituting broth for water. Set aside; keep warm.
2. Heat oil in a large nonstick skillet coated with cooking spray over medium-high heat. Add onion and garlic; cook 3 minutes or until tender, stirring frequently. Add Brussels sprouts, salt, and pepper.
3. Stir in reserved barley, Parmesan cheese, and walnuts. Serve immediately. YIELD: 10 servings (serving size: ½ cup).

POINTS value: 2; **Exchanges:** 1 Starch, 2 Vegetable,
½ Fat; **Per serving:** CAL 145 (22% from fat);
PRO 6.2g; FAT 3.7g (sat 1.2g); CARB 23.3g;
FIB 5.0g; CHOL 3mg; IRON 1.0mg; SOD 322mg;
CALC 84mg

ORANGE-KISSED BERRY PILAF

prep: 6 minutes • cook: 1 hour and 10 minutes

Hazelnut oil is a strong-flavored, nutty-tasting oil that is sold in specialty stores and supermarkets. Hazelnut oil goes rancid quickly, so store it in the refrigerator for up to 3 months. Olive oil can be substituted for the hazelnut oil.

1	cup uncooked wheat berries
4½	cups water
¾	teaspoon salt, divided
2	teaspoons grated orange rind
5	tablespoons fresh orange juice
1½	tablespoons hazelnut oil
½	cup sweetened dried cranberries
⅓	cup chopped hazelnuts, toasted

1. Combine wheat berries, cups water, and ¼ teaspoon salt in a large saucepan. Bring to a boil; cover, reduce heat, and simmer 1 hour or until tender. Drain.
2. Combine cooked wheat berries, ½ teaspoon salt, and remaining ingredients in a large bowl. YIELD: 8 servings (serving size: ½ cup).

POINTS value: 3; **Exchanges:** 1½ Starch, 1 Fat;
Per serving: CAL 160 (31% from fat); PRO 3.8g;
FAT 5.8g (sat 0.5g); CARB 25.5g; FIB 3.8g;
CHOL 0mg; IRON 0.3mg; SOD 222mg; CALC 6mg

PARMESAN POLENTA

prep: 3 minutes • cook: 3 minutes

Polenta, a staple of northern Italy, is traditionally made from cornmeal. We added a little Southern flair to this dish by replacing the cornmeal with grits.

2¾	cups boiling water
2	cups uncooked instant grits
¼	cup (1 ounce) shredded Parmesan cheese
1	teaspoon chopped fresh rosemary
½	teaspoon black pepper
¼	teaspoon salt

1. Combine boiling water and grits in a medium bowl. Stir in cheese and remaining ingredients. Serve immediately. YIELD: 6 servings (serving size: ½ cup).

POINTS value: 2; **Exchange:** 1 Starch;
Per serving: CAL 86 (12% from fat); PRO 3.0g;
FAT 1.2g (sat 0.6g); CARB 15.8g; FIB 0.4g;
CHOL 2mg; IRON 0.8mg; SOD 157mg; CALC 47mg

WHEAT BERRIES

With a nutty flavor and chewy texture, wheat berries provide protein, carbohydrates, and B vitamins when added to salads, breads, and side dishes, or eaten on their own. Wheat berries are sold loose or prepackaged at health food stores, and have a shelf life of up to 1 year. Soaking wheat berries overnight allows the wheat to cook quicker. Like rice or pasta, wheat berries can be cooked ahead of time and then refrigerated or frozen for later use.

LEMON ARTICHOKE RISOTTO

prep: 8 minutes • cook: 23 minutes

The microplane grater is a favorite tool in the Test Kitchens. Use it to quickly grate lemon, lime, or orange rind without picking up the bitter white pith underneath.

2	(14-ounce) cans vegetable broth
1¾	cups water
1	teaspoon olive oil
2	garlic cloves, minced
1½	cups Arborio rice or other short-grain rice
½	cup dry white wine
1	(14-ounce) can artichoke hearts, rinsed, drained, and coarsely chopped
¼	cup (1 ounce) grated fresh Parmesan cheese
1	teaspoon grated lemon rind
¼	teaspoon crushed red pepper

1. Bring broth and water to a simmer in a medium saucepan (do not boil). Keep warm over low heat.
2. Heat oil in a large saucepan over medium-high heat. Add garlic; sauté 1 minute. Add rice; sauté 1 minute. Stir in wine; cook 1 minute or until liquid is nearly absorbed, stirring constantly. Add warm broth, ½ cup at a time, stirring constantly until each portion of broth is absorbed before adding the next (about 17 minutes total). Remove from heat; stir in artichokes and remaining ingredients. YIELD: 5 servings (serving size: 1 cup).

POINTS value: 3; **Exchanges:** 2 Starch;
Per serving: CAL 156 (15% from fat); PRO 6.0g;
FAT 2.7g (sat 0.8g); CARB 27.7g; FIB 0.4g;
CHOL 4mg; IRON 1.0mg; SOD 800mg; CALC 49mg

Soups & Stews

GINGERED PEACH FRUIT SOUP

prep: 11 minutes

2	cups sliced peeled peaches
1½	cups orange juice, chilled
3	(6-ounce) containers vanilla low-fat yogurt (about 2 cups)
2	tablespoons sugar
1	tablespoon fresh lemon juice
1	tablespoon grated peeled fresh ginger

1. Place peaches and orange juice in a blender or food processor; process until smooth. Pour half of peach mixture into a bowl. Add yogurt and next 3 ingredients to peach mixture in blender; process until smooth. Pour yogurt mixture into reserved peach mixture; stir well. Serve cold. YIELD: 6 servings (serving size: 1 cup).

POINTS value: 3; **Exchanges:** 1 Fruit, 1 Skim Milk; **Per serving:** CAL 140 (8% from fat); PRO 5.2g; FAT 1.3g (sat 0.7g); CARB 28.2g; FIB 0.2g; CHOL 4mg; IRON 0.3mg; SOD 57mg; CALC 156mg

---

DAILY DAIRY

One serving of dairy is 8 ounces (1 cup) of milk, 1-1½ ounces of cheese, or 8 ounces (1 cup) of yogurt. Consuming at least 3 servings of dairy daily may play a vital role in weight loss and management. Studies find that the nutrient mix in dairy, especially calcium and protein, may improve the body's ability to burn fat and speed up metabolism. Plus, dairy foods help build and strengthen bones and reduce the risk of osteoporosis, high blood pressure, and certain cancers.

CHILLED MEXICAN-STYLE SALSA SOUP

(pictured on page 158)
prep: 17 minutes • other: 1 hour

This cold, chunky tomato soup may remind you of gazpacho, but the red pepper gives it a spicier flavor.

2	cups grape or cherry tomatoes
1½	cups green bell pepper, cut into 1-inch pieces
1	cup vegetable juice (such as V8)
¾	cup diced seeded peeled cucumber
⅓	cup chopped red onion
6	tablespoons fresh lime juice (about 3 medium limes)
¼	cup firmly packed cilantro leaves
2	teaspoons paprika
¾	teaspoon salt
¼	teaspoon ground red pepper (optional)
¼	cup low-fat sour cream (optional)

1. Place first 9 ingredients and ground red pepper, if desired, in a blender; process until finely minced. Cover and chill thoroughly. Top each serving with 1 tablespoon sour cream, if desired. YIELD: 4 servings (serving size: 1 cup).

POINTS value: 1; **Exchanges:** 2 Vegetable; **Per serving:** CAL 58 (5% from fat); PRO 2.1g; FAT 0.4g (sat 0.1g); CARB 13.5g; FIB 3.2g; CHOL 0mg; IRON 1.1mg; SOD 569mg; CALC 31mg

---

SPICED CARROT SOUP

prep: 15 minutes • cook: 27 minutes

Sweet and savory spices and a splash of coconut milk give this thick carrot soup a rich, full flavor.

2	teaspoons olive oil
½	cup coarsely chopped onion
¾	teaspoon curry powder
½	teaspoon salt, divided
½	teaspoon ground cumin
⅛	teaspoon ground cinnamon
4	cups fat-free, less-sodium chicken broth
1½	pounds carrots (about 15), peeled and coarsely chopped into ½-inch pieces
1	cup water, divided
⅓	cup light coconut milk

1. Heat oil in a Dutch oven. Add onion, and sauté 3 to 4 minutes or until tender. Add curry powder, ¼ teaspoon salt, cumin, and cinnamon; cook 2 minutes. Slowly stir in chicken broth; bring to a boil. Add carrots; bring to a boil. Reduce heat, and simmer, covered, 8 to 10 minutes or until carrots are tender. Add ½ cup water and ¼ teaspoon salt.
2. Place soup in batches in a blender or food processor; process until smooth.
3. Return mixture to Dutch oven. Stir in ½ cup water and coconut milk. Cook over medium heat 2 to 3 minutes. YIELD: 7 servings (serving size: 1 cup).

POINTS value: 1; **Exchanges:** ½ Starch, 1½ Vegetable; **Per serving:** CAL 78 (21% from fat); PRO 4.5g; FAT 1.8g (sat 0.6g); CARB 11.1g; FIB 3.2g; CHOL 0mg; IRON 1.5mg; SOD 337mg; CALC 49mg

LEMON GRASS VEGETABLE STEW

prep: 22 minutes • cook: 37 minutes

If you can't find lemon grass, stir in 1 tablespoon fresh grated lemon rind, to taste, just before serving.

2	small stalks chopped peeled fresh lemon grass
1	tablespoon olive oil
½	cup chopped onion
1¼	teaspoons salt, divided
1	teaspoon ground turmeric
¼	teaspoon ground ginger
¼	teaspoon crushed red pepper
2	large sweet potatoes, peeled and coarsely chopped (about 1 pound)
2	large baking potatoes, peeled and coarsely chopped (about 1 pound)
3	large carrots, peeled and coarsely chopped
2	cups thinly sliced shiitake mushroom caps
3	cups vegetable broth
1	cup water
1	cup frozen green peas, thawed
1	(13.5-ounce) can light coconut milk
¼	cup chopped fresh cilantro

1. Remove and discard tough outer leaves of lemon grass, saving about a 3-inch section of tender white root. Slice root in half lengthwise. Lightly crush lemon grass, using the side of a knife.
2. Heat oil in a Dutch oven over medium-high heat. Add lemon grass and onion; sauté 3 minutes. Stir in ¼ teaspoon salt, turmeric, ginger, and red pepper. Sauté 2 minutes or until vegetables are tender. Add sweet potato, baking potato, carrot, and mushrooms. Sauté 2 to 3 minutes or until vegetables are lightly browned. Stir in broth and water; bring to a boil. Cover, reduce heat, and simmer 23 to 25 minutes or until potato and carrot are tender.
3. Remove lemon grass. Stir in peas, coconut milk, and 1 teaspoon salt. Cook, uncovered, 2 to 3 minutes or until peas are thoroughly heated. Stir in cilantro. YIELD: 6 servings (serving size: 1⅔ cups).

POINTS value: 3; **Exchanges:** 1½ Starch, 1 Vegetable; **Per serving:** CAL 154 (21% from fat); PRO 3.0g; FAT 3.6g (sat 1.4g); CARB 28.3g; FIB 3.8g; CHOL 0mg; IRON 1.8mg; SOD 355mg; CALC 32mg

BABY LIMA BEAN SOUP WITH CRISPY SAGE

prep: 17 minutes • cook: 2 hours
other: 1 hour and 10 minutes

A quick way to thicken a bean soup is to mash a cup of the cooked beans and stir them back into the soup.

1	(16-pounce) package dried baby lima beans
7½	cups water
1	teaspoon salt, divided
2	bay leaves
3	cups coarsely chopped carrot
1	tablespoon olive oil
12	fresh sage leaves
2	center-cut bacon slices, cut into small pieces
2	cups coarsely chopped onion
6	garlic cloves, minced
1	(14-ounce) can vegetable broth
¼	teaspoon freshly ground black pepper

1. Sort and wash beans; place beans in a large Dutch oven. Cover with water to 2 inches above beans; bring to a boil, and cook 2 minutes. Remove from heat; cover and let stand 1 hour. Drain beans and return to pan.
2. Add 7½ cups water, ½ teaspoon salt, and bay leaves to pan. Bring to a boil; cover, reduce heat, and simmer 1 hour and 10 minutes. Add carrot; cook 20 minutes or until beans and carrot are tender.
3. Meanwhile, heat 1 tablespoon oil in a medium nonstick skillet over medium heat. Add sage leaves; sauté 1 to 2 minutes or until crisp. Remove leaves from pan; drain on paper towels. Crumble and set aside.
4. Cook bacon in same pan 4 minutes or until crisp. Stir in onion; sauté 3 to 4 minutes or until crisp-tender. Add garlic, and cook 3 to 4 minutes or until onion is tender. Remove from heat.
5. Drain beans, reserving ½ cup cooking liquid in a small bowl. Discard bay leaves and return beans to pan. Add 1 cup beans to reserved cooking liquid; mash with a fork until mixture forms a paste. Stir broth, bean paste, onion mixture, ½ teaspoon salt, pepper, and half of crumbled sage into cooked beans. Bring to a boil; reduce heat, and simmer 4 to 5 minutes or until mixture is thoroughly heated (mixture will be thick).
6. Ladle soup into individual bowls, and sprinkle with remaining crumbled sage. Serve immediately. YIELD: 7 servings (serving size: 1 cup).

POINTS value: 5; **Exchanges:** 3½ Starch, ½ Fat; **Per serving:** CAL 292 (11% from fat); PRO 15.7g; FAT 3.6g (sat 0.7g); CARB 51.9g; FIB 15.9g; CHOL 2mg; IRON 4.5mg; SOD 642mg; CALC 82mg

CLASSIC FRENCH ONION SOUP

(pictured on page 3)

prep: 20 minutes • cook: 1 hour and 4 minutes

Apple juice is the secret ingredient in this soup. Its mellow flavor balances out the strong flavors of the white wine and onions and gives the soup a subtle sweetness.

1	tablespoon butter
8	cups thinly sliced sweet onion (about 3 large)
1	cup dry white wine
1	cup apple juice
4	cups low-salt beef broth
1	(10½-ounce) can beef consommé
12	(½-inch-thick) slices diagonally cut French bread
1	cup (4 ounces) shredded light Jarlsberg cheese
2	tablespoons chopped fresh parsley

1. Melt butter in a large Dutch oven over medium-low heat; add onion. Cover and cook 30 minutes or until dark brown, stirring occasionally. Add wine and apple juice; bring to a boil. Boil, uncovered, 10 minutes or until liquid is reduced to about ½ cup. Stir in broth and consommé; bring to a boil. Reduce heat, and simmer, uncovered, 15 minutes.
2. Preheat broiler.
3. Arrange bread slices on a large baking sheet. Broil 1 minute on each side or until golden.
4. Place 6 (2-cup) ovenproof bowls or soup crocks on a large baking sheet. Spoon soup into bowls. Top each bowl of soup with 2 slices toasted French bread, 1½ tablespoons cheese, and 1 teaspoon parsley. Broil 2 to 3 minutes or just until cheese melts. YIELD: 6 servings (serving size: 1¼ cups soup, 2 slices toast, 1½ tablespoons cheese, and 1 teaspoon parsley).

POINTS value: 5; **Exchanges:** 1½ Starch, 3 Vegetable, 1 Lean Meat, ½ Fat; **Per serving:** CAL 275 (18% from fat); PRO 14.4g; FAT 5.6g (sat 2.9g); CARB 42.6g; FIB 3.9g; CHOL 15mg; IRON 1.5mg; SOD 779mg; CALC 278mg

CHIPOTLE RED PEPPER SOUP

(pictured on page 160)

prep: 10 minutes • cook: 41 minutes other: 20 minutes

6	small red bell peppers
1	(14-ounce) can fat-free, less-sodium chicken broth
1	cup chopped onion
½	cup thinly sliced carrot
½	cup thinly sliced celery
2	garlic cloves
2	drained canned chipotle chiles in adobo sauce
¾	cup half-and-half
¾	teaspoon salt
¼	cup low-fat sour cream
¼	cup chopped fresh cilantro

1. Cut bell peppers in half lengthwise; discard seeds and membranes. Place pepper halves, skin sides up, on a foil-lined baking sheet; flatten with hand. Broil 18 minutes or until bell peppers are blackened. Place in a zip-top plastic bag; seal. Let stand 20 minutes. Peel.
2. Place bell peppers, broth, and next 4 ingredients in a large saucepan. Bring to a boil over high heat; cover, reduce heat, and simmer 13 minutes or until carrot is tender.
3. Place 1 chipotle chile and half of pepper mixture in a blender; process until smooth. Repeat procedure with remaining chile and pepper mixture. Return pureed mixture to pan; stir in half-and-half and salt. Cook soup over medium heat 5 minutes or until thoroughly heated.
4. Ladle soup into 4 bowls. Top each serving evenly with sour cream and cilantro. YIELD: 4 servings (serving size: 1¼ cups).

POINTS value: 2; **Exchanges:** ½ Starch, 2½ Vegetable, ½ Fat; **Per serving:** CAL 128 (18% from fat); PRO 3.8g; FAT 2.5g (sat 1.2g); CARB 22.4g; FIB 2.0g; CHOL 6mg; IRON 1.0mg; SOD 852mg; CALC 84mg

ROASTED PEPPER AND CORN CHOWDER

(pictured on page 159)

prep: 1 hour • cook: 1 hour and 7 minutes

2	poblano chiles
1	red bell pepper
8	ears shucked corn
3	cups fat-free, less-sodium chicken broth
2	tablespoons butter
1½	cups chopped onion
½	cup chopped celery
2	teaspoons minced garlic
1	cup 2% reduced-fat milk
¼	teaspoon ground cumin
¼	teaspoon salt
¼	teaspoon freshly ground black pepper
¼	cup chopped fresh cilantro
	Finely chopped red bell pepper (optional)

1. Preheat broiler.

2. Cut poblano chiles and bell pepper in half lengthwise. Discard seeds and membranes. Place pepper halves, skin sides up, on a foil-lined baking sheet. Flatten peppers with hand and broil 15 to 20 minutes or until roasted. Place peppers in a zip-top plastic bag and seal. Let stand 5 minutes. Peel and coarsely chop. Set aside.

3. Cut kernels from ears of corn to measure 8 cups, reserving cobs; set kernels aside.

4. Combine reserved cobs and chicken broth in a large Dutch oven, and bring to a boil. Cover; reduce heat to medium-low, and simmer 15 minutes. Remove and discard cobs.

5. Add 1½ cups corn kernels to broth and bring to a boil. Cover; reduce heat, and simmer 10 minutes. Drain, reserving broth and kernels.

6. Meanwhile, melt butter in a large Dutch oven over low heat. Add onion, celery, and garlic; sauté over medium-high heat 5 minutes. Add reserved broth and remaining 6½ cups uncooked corn kernels to pan; bring to a boil. Cover; reduce heat, and simmer 10 minutes. Stir in roasted peppers; cool slightly.

7. Place corn mixture in batches in a blender or food processor. Process until smooth, scraping sides of bowl.

8. Strain mixture, in batches, through a fine sieve, into a pan. Discard solids. Stir in reserved cooked 1½ cups kernels, milk, cumin, salt, and pepper. Cook over medium heat 5 minutes or until thoroughly heated, stirring occasionally. Stir in cilantro. Sprinkle

with red bell pepper, if desired. YIELD: 6 servings (serving size: 1 cup).

POINTS value: 5; Exchanges: 2½ Starch, 1 Vegetable, 1 Fat; Per serving: CAL 279 (22% from fat); PRO 10.9g; FAT 7.6g (sat 2.5g); CARB 50.3g; FIB 3.5g; CHOL 13mg; IRON 2.0mg; SOD 500mg; CALC 75mg

TWO POTATO CHOWDER

prep: 23 minutes • cook: 1 hour and 3 minutes

Fresh corn and edamame are colorful additions to this hearty vegetarian chowder. For more information on edamame, see page 120. Serve on a cold winter day with crusty French bread.

1   large sweet potato, peeled and cut into ½-inch pieces (about ½ pound)
1   large Yukon gold potato, peeled and cut into ½-inch pieces (about ½ pound)
1½   tablespoons olive oil
1   cup chopped onion
½   cup diced red bell pepper
¼   cup diced celery
1   cup frozen whole-kernel corn, thawed
2   cups vegetable broth
1   cup 1% low-fat milk
¾   cup shelled edamame
2   tablespoons chopped fresh parsley
2   teaspoons chopped fresh chives
½   teaspoon salt
¼   teaspoon freshly ground black pepper
Fresh chives (optional)

1. Place sweet potato and Yukon gold potato in a medium saucepan;

add water to cover. Bring to a boil; reduce heat, and simmer, uncovered, 20 to 25 minutes or until potatoes are tender. Drain. Remove half of potatoes and set aside. Mash the remaining half of potatoes with a potato masher; set aside.

2. Heat olive oil in a Dutch oven over medium heat. Stir in onion, bell pepper, and celery. Cook 8 to 10 minutes or until vegetables are tender. Stir in mashed potato, corn kernels, and next 7 ingredients. Simmer, uncovered, 15 minutes. Add reserved potatoes and cook 10 minutes or until soup becomes thick. Ladle into 5 individual bowls. Garnish with fresh chives, if desired. YIELD: 5 servings (serving size: 1 cup).

POINTS value: 4; Exchanges: 2 Starch, 1 Vegetable, 1 Fat; Per serving: CAL 223 (25% from fat); PRO 8.1g; FAT 6.3g (sat 0.9g); CARB 36.9g; FIB 5.1g; CHOL 2mg; IRON 1.5mg; SOD 695mg; CALC 103mg

---

YUKON GOLD POTATOES

Yukon gold potatoes are truly versatile—they are good for baking, broiling, frying, and mashing. Their moist, creamy texture and sweet, buttery flavor make them the favorite of the gold potatoes.

Yukon golds are slightly flat and oval in shape with light gold, thin skin and light yellow flesh. When purchasing, make sure they have the same color all around, and are free of sprouts. Unlike traditional baking potatoes, Yukon golds should be stored in the refrigerator to prevent them from turning green and bitter.

CURRIED PUMPKIN STEW WITH ROASTED PEPITAS

prep: 10 minutes • cook: 35 minutes

Look for pepitas (pumpkin seeds) with Mexican ingredients or on the bulk food aisle of your supermarket. They are available in several forms, roasted or raw, with or without the hulls. For this recipe we used hulled raw pepitas.

1	tablespoon olive oil, divided
2	cups thinly sliced leeks
1	tablespoon minced peeled fresh ginger
3	garlic cloves, minced
1	tablespoon curry powder
½	teaspoon minced seeded Serrano chile
3	cups water
3	cups cubed peeled fresh pumpkin (about 1 pound)
1	cup light coconut milk
2	teaspoons brown sugar
1	(16-ounce) can white kidney beans, rinsed and drained
¼	cup chopped fresh cilantro
1	tablespoon lime juice
½	teaspoon salt
¼	cup hulled raw pepitas (pumpkin seeds)

1. Heat 1 teaspoon oil in a large Dutch oven over medium heat. Add leeks; sauté until tender, about 4 minutes. Stir in ginger and next 3 ingredients; cook 1 minute. Add water and next 3 ingredients. Bring to a boil; reduce heat, and simmer until pumpkin is tender, about 15 to 20 minutes. Stir in beans and next 3 ingredients; cook until beans are heated through, about 2 to 3 minutes.
2. Heat 2 teaspoons oil in a small saucepan over medium heat. Add pepitas, and sauté, stirring frequently, until lightly browned, about 2 to 3 minutes. Ladle stew into shallow bowls and top each serving with 1 tablespoon roasted pepitas. YIELD: 4 servings (serving size: 1½ cups stew and 1 tablespoon pepitas).

POINTS value: 6; **Exchanges:** 2 Starch, 2 Vegetable, 1½ Fat; **Per serving:** CAL 280 (35% from fat); PRO 9.1g; FAT 11.0g (sat 2.3g); CARB 38.7g; FIB 2.2g; CHOL 0mg; IRON 5.8mg; SOD 327mg; CALC 234mg

GINGERED BUTTERNUT SQUASH SOUP

prep: 27 minutes • cook: 1 hour and 35 minutes

This smooth and delicious soup would be an elegant first course at an autumn dinner party. Acorn squash is a good substitute for the butternut squash. You'll need about 4 pounds of acorn squash.

2	butternut squash (about 4½ pounds)
	Cooking spray
2	tablespoons butter
1½	cups chopped onion (about 1 large)
1	cup peeled, cored, and chopped pear (about 1 large)
1	tablespoon minced peeled fresh ginger
2	(14-ounce) cans fat-free, less-sodium chicken broth, divided
1	cup fat-free half-and-half
1½	tablespoons honey
1	teaspoon ground coriander
½	teaspoon curry powder
¼	teaspoon salt
⅛	teaspoon ground red pepper

1. Preheat oven to 375°.
2. Cut squash in half lengthwise. Remove seeds. Reserve seeds for toasting. Place squash, cut sides down, on a jelly roll pan coated with cooking spray.
3. Bake at 375° for 50 minutes or until skin pierces easily with a fork. Scoop out pulp; set aside. Reduce oven temperature to 325°.
4. To toast seeds, rinse seeds and pat dry. Place on a foil-lined baking sheet coated with cooking spray. Bake at 325° for 15 minutes or until crisp and lightly browned, stirring every 5 minutes.
5. Melt butter in a Dutch oven over medium-high heat. Add onion, pear, and ginger. Sauté 10 minutes or until tender. Add squash pulp and 1 can broth. Bring to a boil. Reduce heat; simmer, uncovered, 10 minutes.
6. Place mixture in a blender or food processor. Process in batches until smooth. Pour mixture through a strainer into a bowl, pressing with the back of a spoon.
7. Return soup to Dutch oven. Add 1 can broth, half-and-half, and next 5 ingredients. Cook over medium heat until thoroughly heated, stirring often. Spoon into serving bowls, and top with toasted seeds. YIELD: 5 servings (serving size: 1 cup).

POINTS value: 3; **Exchanges:** 1 Starch, ½ Fruit, 3 Vegetable; **Per serving:** CAL 192 (23% from fat); PRO 3.9g; FAT 4.9g (sat 2.3g); CARB 33.6g; FIB 3.8g; CHOL 12mg; IRON 0.9mg; SOD 741mg; CALC 101mg

Comfortable At Last

CARRIE MEYER • **HEIGHT** 5'8" • **BEFORE** 236 LBS. • **AFTER** 145 LBS.

Philosophy: "With *Weight Watchers*, you don't have to deprive yourself. You can still go out to eat; you can still have a normal, real, functioning lifestyle like everyone else."

Carrie Meyer says that she had never been quite "comfortable in her skin." "I was never really 'fat' per se, but I had been 'chunky' most of my childhood and adult life," she says. And then she met her future husband, Jeff.

"While we were dating, Jeff cooked for us all the time," Carrie says. "I was so spoiled! We ate real butter, real cream, real everything! And while everything was real good, I never realized until it was too late that I had put on over 80 pounds."

On Carrie and Jeff's wedding day, instead of feeling like a "pretty princess," Carrie says she felt like a "bloated white whale." "What should have been one of the happiest days of my life ended up being bittersweet. I hated the way I looked in my wedding dress," she says.

Soon after her wedding, Carrie began to suffer acid reflux and had trouble breathing when walking up and down stairs. With a

"For me, Weight Watchers is the only way to lose weight."

history of family health problems that included stroke, diabetes, heart and kidney failure, and cancer, Carrie knew that if she didn't take action, she was headed down a grim road.

So in early 2000 Carrie joined a *Weight Watchers* at Work program. "My motivation was really more about being healthy than anything else," Carrie says. "I wanted to know I had a long, healthy life ahead of me."

Carrie loved going to *Weight Watchers* meetings during her lunch hour and was amazed at how easy the program was. "After I lost 9 pounds, my acid reflux went away. And over the course of the next year I dropped over 90 pounds!"

During Carrie's weight-loss journey, her mother passed away from ovarian cancer. "I will never forget one of the last conversations I had with her," Carrie says. "She told me how proud she was of me for taking the step that she never had been able to take—shedding the extra pounds that she fought with most of her adult life. I know Mom would be even more proud of me now. I am more confident, happy, and healthy than I ever have been. And I believe I have the *Weight Watchers* program to thank for it."

Carrie is now entering her fourth year of maintenance and couldn't be happier. "I wear a size 4 or 6 now and I love it," she says. "I am smaller now than I ever was in high school and I'm well within my healthy weight range. For me, *Weight Watchers* is the only way to lose weight. I've learned how to manage and how to eat real food. You don't have to deprive yourself. You can still go out to eat; you can still have a normal, real, functioning lifestyle like everyone else.

"*Weight Watchers* has been such a blessing. It is definitely the best thing that has ever happened to me. Thank you, *Weight Watchers,* for helping me to be comfortable in my own skin at last!"

Weight-loss results not typical.

157

Chilled Mexican-Style
Salsa Soup,
page 152

Spicy Andouille Posole,
page 163

Roasted Pepper and
Corn Chowder,
page 154

Chipotle Red Pepper Soup,
page 154

CREAMY TOMATO SOUP WITH ROASTED GARLIC AND BASIL

prep: 10 minutes • cook: 1 hour and 15 minutes • other: 10 minutes

Tomato paste adds a deep, rich, tomato flavor to the soup. Look for tomato paste in the traditional small can or now in the more convenient, easy-to-use tube.

1   whole garlic head
1   tablespoon olive oil
1   cup chopped onion (about 1 medium)
1   (28-ounce) can diced tomatoes, undrained
2   tablespoons tomato paste
3   cups fat-free, less-sodium chicken broth, divided
2   tablespoons all-purpose flour
½   cup chopped fresh basil
½   cup fat-free half-and-half
¼   teaspoon pepper

1. Preheat oven to 350°.
2. Remove white papery skin from garlic head (do not peel or separate the cloves). Wrap head in foil. Bake at 350° for 40 minutes; cool 10 minutes. Separate cloves; squeeze to extract garlic pulp. Discard skins.
3. Heat oil in a Dutch oven. Add garlic and onion; sauté until onion is tender. Add tomatoes and tomato paste; simmer 5 minutes. Add 2½ cups chicken broth. Combine ½ cup broth and flour in a small bowl; stir with a whisk. Add flour mixture to tomato mixture. Bring to a boil; reduce heat, and simmer, uncovered, 30 minutes or until mixture thickens, stirring occasionally.
4. Place soup in batches in a blender or food processor; process until smooth. Return mixture to Dutch oven; stir in basil, half-and-half, and pepper. YIELD: 7 servings (serving size: 1 cup).

POINTS value: 1; **Exchanges:** 2 Vegetable, ½ Fat; **Per serving:** CAL 87 (21% from fat); PRO 4.2g; FAT 2.0g (sat 0.3g); CARB 12.5g; FIB 2.6g; CHOL 0mg; IRON 1.4mg; SOD 239mg; CALC 49mg

ROASTED VEGETABLE AND WHITE BEAN SOUP

prep: 16 minutes • cook: 43 minutes other: 5 minutes

Lining the baking sheet with foil makes for easier cleanup.

2   cups chopped green bell pepper (about 2 large)
1   cup chopped onion (about 1 medium)
1   cup chopped yellow squash (about 1 large)
½   cup chopped carrot (about 2)
Cooking spray
1   (16-ounce) can navy beans, rinsed and drained
1   (14-ounce) can fat-free, less-sodium chicken broth
1   (14.5-ounce) can diced tomatoes, undrained
1   tablespoon olive oil
1   teaspoon dried oregano
2   teaspoons minced chipotle chile in adobo sauce (about 1 chile)
¼   teaspoon salt
¼   teaspoon sugar

1. Preheat oven to 450°.
2. Place first 4 ingredients on a foil-lined baking sheet coated with cooking spray. Coat vegetables with cooking spray.
3. Bake at 450° for 30 minutes.
4. Stir together roasted vegetables, beans, and remaining ingredients in a large saucepan. Bring to a boil; cover, reduce heat, and simmer 10 minutes. Remove from heat; let stand 5 minutes. YIELD: 4 servings (serving size: about 1½ cups).

POINTS value: 3; **Exchanges:** 1 Starch, 1 Vegetable, ½ Fat; **Per serving:** CAL 162 (22% from fat); PRO 8.7g; FAT 4.4g (sat 0.6g); CARB 26.9g; FIB 7.5g; CHOL 0mg; IRON 2.5mg; SOD 597mg; CALC 61mg

CHIPOTLE CHILES IN ADOBO SAUCE

Chipotle chiles are red jalapeño peppers that have been ripened, dried, and smoked. These chiles give off a warm heat and smoky flavor. The chiles are packed adobo sauce, a red sauce made from lightly seasoned tomato broth. Chipotle chiles are about 2 to 4 inches long and are excellent in sauces, soups, and as seasonings for meats. After opening a can of chiles, store remaining chiles and adobo sauce in the refrigerator in an airtight container. Look for these recipes throughout this book featuring chipotle chiles in adobo sauce:
• Spicy Andouille Posole, page 163
• Creamy Chipotle Shrimp Bisque, page 162
• Bean and Roasted Vegetable Burritos, page 64
• Chicken and Black Bean Taco Salad with Chipotle Dressing, page 124

CREAMY CHIPOTLE SHRIMP BISQUE

prep: 8 minutes • cook: 16 minutes

The sour cream added to this bisque helps cool your tongue from the spicy flavor.

Cooking spray
1   cup sliced green onions (about 8 small)
¼   cup light butter
3   tablespoons all-purpose flour
1   (14.5-ounce) can diced tomatoes, undrained
1   (10½-ounce) can condensed chicken broth, undiluted
½   cup fat-free half-and-half
½   cup dry white wine
1   chipotle chile in adobo sauce, finely chopped
1   tablespoon chopped fresh oregano
1   teaspoon Old Bay seasoning
8   ounces peeled and deveined medium shrimp, coarsely chopped
½   cup low-fat sour cream
¼   cup chopped fresh cilantro

1. Heat a large saucepan over medium heat; coat with cooking spray. Add onions; cook 1 minute or until tender. Add butter, stirring until butter melts. Add flour; cook 1 minute, stirring constantly. Gradually stir in tomatoes and next 6 ingredients. Cook 9 minutes or until slightly thickened, stirring occasionally.
2. Pour tomato mixture into a blender; process until smooth. Return tomato mixture to pan.
3. Stir in shrimp. Cook 3 minutes or until shrimp are done. Divide soup evenly into bowls and top each serving with sour cream. Sprinkle with cilantro. YIELD: 5 servings (serving size: 1⅓ cups).

*POINTS value: 2; **Exchanges:** ½ Starch, 1 Very Lean Meat, ½ Fat; **Per serving:** CAL 99 (41% from fat); PRO 7.2g; FAT 4.5g (sat 2.5g); CARB 7.3g; FIB 0.9g; CHOL 42mg; IRON 1.1mg; SOD 395mg; CALC 53mg*

BEEF MINESTRONE

prep: 12 minutes • cook: 1 hour and 5 minutes

1   pound ground round
2½   cups chopped onion (about 2 medium)
2½   cups sliced carrot (about 5)
1   cup chopped celery
4   garlic cloves, minced
1   (32-ounce) carton fat-free, less-sodium chicken broth
1   (14.5-ounce) can petite diced tomatoes, undrained
1   cup water
1   teaspoon dried oregano
¾   teaspoon salt
¼   teaspoon black pepper
3   cups cubed zucchini (about 2 medium)
⅔   cup uncooked gnocchi or shell pasta

1. Heat a large Dutch oven over medium heat. Add beef; cook until browned, stirring to crumble. Remove beef with a slotted spoon, leaving drippings in pan.
2. Cook onion and next 3 ingredients in pan over medium heat 10 minutes; stir frequently. Add chicken broth and next 5 ingredients. Bring to a boil; cover, reduce heat, and simmer 15 minutes.
3. Stir in zucchini and pasta; bring to a simmer over medium heat. Cook, uncovered, 15 to 20 minutes or until pasta is tender. Return beef to pan; cook 5 minutes or until thoroughly heated. YIELD: 10 servings (serving size: 1¼ cups).

*POINTS value: 4; **Exchanges:** 1 Starch, 2 Vegetable, 2 Very Lean Meat; **Per serving:** CAL 208 (10% from fat); PRO 18.3g; FAT 2.4g (sat 0.7g); CARB 29.3g; FIB 3.4g; CHOL 24mg; IRON 2.5mg; SOD 524mg; CALC 46mg*

PORK AND GARBANZO BEAN CHILI

prep: 15 minutes • cook: 1 hour and 39 minutes

1   (14.5-ounce) can whole tomatoes, undrained
1   tablespoon vegetable oil
2½   pounds lean boneless pork loin, trimmed and cut into bite-sized pieces
1   cup chopped onion
2   to 3 jalapeño peppers, seeded and minced
1   teaspoon minced garlic
2   tablespoons chili powder
1   tablespoon ground cumin
¼   to ½ teaspoon black pepper
2   (14.5-ounce) cans no-salt-added diced tomatoes, undrained
1   (19-ounce) can chickpeas (garbanzo beans), rinsed and drained
1   (15.5-ounce) can white hominy, rinsed and drained
2   (4½-ounce) cans chopped green chiles, drained
¾   teaspoon salt
10   tablespoons low-fat sour cream
½   cup diced peeled avocado

1. Place whole tomatoes in a blender or food processor; process until pureed. Set aside.

2. Heat oil in a Dutch oven over medium-high heat. Add pork, and cook 5 minutes or until browned, stirring occasionally. Stir in onion, jalapeño pepper, and garlic; cook 3 to 5 minutes or until vegetables are tender. Add chili powder, cumin, and black pepper; cook 1 minute. Add reserved pureed tomatoes and diced tomatoes. Bring to a boil; reduce heat, and simmer, partially covered, 1 to 1½ hours or until pork is tender, stirring occasionally.

3. Add chickpeas, hominy, chiles, and salt. Bring to a boil; cover, reduce heat, and simmer 30 minutes. Spoon into individual serving bowls. Top each serving with 1 tablespoon sour cream. Sprinkle 2½ teaspoons avocado evenly over each serving. YIELD: 10 servings (serving size: 1 cup).

POINTS value: 6; **Exchanges:** 1 Starch, 2 Vegetable, 4 Very Lean Meat, 1 Fat; **Per serving:** CAL 289 (28% from fat); PRO 28.7g; FAT 8.8g (sat 2.8g); CARB 23.2g; FIB 6.3g; CHOL 79mg; IRON 3.1mg; SOD 648mg; CALC 119mg

---

HOMINY

Hominy is made from dried corn kernels from which the hull and germ have been removed. Hominy is sold canned, ready-to-eat, or dried.

Find hominy for Pork and Garbanzo Bean Chili, page 162, and Spicy Andouille Posole, page 163, in the canned vegetable section of the supermarket near the corn.

SPICY ANDOUILLE POSOLE

(pictured on page 159)
prep: **14 minutes** • cook: **12 minutes**

1   teaspoon olive oil
2   links (6.5 ounces) andouille sausage, thinly sliced
1   red bell pepper, cut into 1-inch pieces
1   large zucchini, diced (about 8 ounces)
2½   cups fat-free, less-sodium chicken broth
1   (15.5-ounce) can white hominy, rinsed and drained
2   teaspoons pureed chipotle chiles in adobo sauce (about 1 chile)
¼   cup chopped fresh cilantro

1. Heat oil in a large saucepan over medium-high heat; add andouille, and cook 1 minute. Add bell pepper and zucchini; cook 1 minute, stirring occasionally.

2. Add broth, hominy, and chiles. Bring to a boil; reduce heat, and simmer, uncovered, 8 minutes or until vegetables are tender. Sprinkle with cilantro before serving. YIELD: 4 servings (serving size: about 1⅓ cups).

POINTS value: 4; **Exchanges:** ½ Starch, 1 Vegetable, 1 High-Fat Meat; **Per serving:** CAL 199 (45% from fat); PRO 11.6g; FAT 10.3g (sat 3.5g); CARB 16.2g; FIB 2.8g; CHOL 33mg; IRON 1.8mg; SOD 850mg; CALC 26mg

---

CHICKEN WONTON SOUP

prep: **15 minutes** • cook: **1 hour and 25 minutes**

1   (3.25-pound) whole chicken, cut into pieces and skinned
2   celery stalks, cut into thirds
2   carrots, cut into thirds
1   small onion, quartered
8   cups water
1   tablespoon chicken-flavored bouillon granules
½   teaspoon salt
½   teaspoon freshly ground black pepper
20   wonton wrappers, cut in half
¼   cup chopped fresh parsley

1. Place first 4 ingredients in a Dutch oven; cover with 8 cups water. Bring to a boil; cover, reduce heat, and simmer 1 hour or until chicken is done. Transfer chicken to cutting board; remove chicken from bones, discarding bones. Coarsely chop chicken.

2. Strain broth through a sieve over a bowl, discarding vegetables and solids. Return broth to pan. Add chopped chicken, bouillon granules, salt, and pepper.

3. Bring to a simmer; add wonton wrapper halves, 1 at a time, to broth. Simmer 8 minutes; stir in parsley. YIELD: 7 servings (serving size: 1 cup).

POINTS value: 3; **Exchanges:** 1 Starch, 1 Very Lean Meat, 1 Lean Meat; **Per serving:** CAL 174 (17% from fat); PRO 17.6g; FAT 3.2g (sat 0.8g); CARB 17.8g; FIB 1.7g; CHOL 46mg; IRON 1.7mg; SOD 493mg; CALC 41mg

Easy Weeknight Supper

Serves 4 • Total **POINTS** value: 11

Spaghetti Pie • **Creamy Veggie Dip**
green salad with fat-free salad dressing • **Parmesan–Herb Bread**
Root Beer Floats

GAME PLAN

1. Prepare **Creamy Veggie Dip** up to 2 days in advance.

2. Pepare and bake **Spaghetti Pie.**

3. While pie bakes, slice vegetables to serve with dip.

4. Prepare green salad.

5. Remove pie from oven; increase oven temperature to broil. Broil **Parmesan–Herb Bread.**

6. Prepare **Root Beer Floats**, and serve immediately.

SPAGHETTI PIE

prep: 9 minutes • cook: 30 minutes

This is an incredibly easy entrée to plan into a busy workweek. Double the recipe to feed a large crowd. If you're cooking for 1 to 2, make the recipe as directed and divide between two small casserole dishes instead of one deep-dish pie plate. Bake one casserole tonight and freeze the other for later. Remember to thaw overnight in the refrigerator and bake as directed in the recipe.

6	ounces uncooked spaghetti
8	ounces extralean ground round
¾	cup chopped onion
1	teaspoon minced garlic
1½	cups tomato and basil pasta sauce
2	tablespoons tomato paste
½	teaspoon salt
Cooking spray	
¾	cup (3 ounces) shredded part-skim mozzarella cheese

1. Preheat oven to 375°.
2. Cook pasta according to package directions, omitting salt and fat.
3. Meanwhile, cook beef, onion, and garlic in a large nonstick skillet over medium–high heat until browned, stirring to crumble. Stir in pasta sauce, tomato paste, and salt. Bring to a boil; reduce heat, and simmer 5 minutes or until slightly thickened.
4. Spoon half of pasta into a 10-inch deep-dish pie plate coated with cooking spray. Spoon half of tomato sauce evenly over pasta; repeat layers, ending with tomato sauce. Sprinkle with cheese.
5. Cover and bake at 375° for 15 minutes or until cheese melts. YIELD: 4 servings (serving size: 1¼ cups).
Tip: To prevent cheese from sticking to foil, spray the foil with cooking spray or use nonstick foil.

POINTS value: 6; **Exchanges:** 2½ Starch, 2 Very Lean Meat, 1 Medium-Fat Meat; **Per serving:** CAL 332 (18% from fat); PRO 24.0g; FAT 6.5g (sat 2.7g); CARB 44.1g; FIB 3.4g; CHOL 41mg; IRON 3.3mg; SOD 717mg; CALC 195mg

CREAMY VEGGIE DIP

prep: 20 minutes • other: 2 hours

This healthy afternoon snack can be made ahead of time and ready for your family when they arrive home from school or work. Serve with sliced vegetables that have a POINTS value of zero such as celery, cucumbers, zucchini, or broccoli florets.

½ (8-ounce) tub light garden vegetable cream cheese, softened (such as Philly Light)
½ (8-ounce) container low-fat sour cream
3 tablespoons finely chopped seeded peeled cucumber
2 tablespoons minced green onions
1 tablespoon chopped fresh parsley
½ teaspoon minced garlic
⅛ teaspoon salt
⅛ teaspoon pepper

1. Stir together all ingredients. Cover and chill 2 hours or up to 2 days. Serve with vegetable sticks. YIELD: 4 servings (serving size: ¼ cup).

Tip: Drain chopped cucumber on paper towels before adding to cream cheese mixture.

POINTS value: 2; Exchanges: 1 Vegetable, 1½ Fat; Per serving: CAL 100 (66% from fat); PRO 4.0g; FAT 7.7g (sat 4.6g); CARB 4.9g; FIB 0.3g; CHOL 24mg; IRON 0.2mg; SOD 287mg; CALC 82mg

PARMESAN-HERB BREAD

prep: 8 minutes • cook: 2 minutes

Chop a little extra fresh basil and oregano as you prepare the meal. Sprinkle over Spaghetti Pie just before serving.

1 tablespoon yogurt-based spread (such as Brummel & Brown)
1 teaspoon minced garlic
2 teaspoons chopped fresh basil
2 teaspoons chopped fresh oregano
4 (½-inch-thick) slices diagonally cut French bread (about 2 ounces)
1 tablespoons shredded fresh Parmesan cheese

1. Preheat broiler.
2. Combine yogurt-based spread and next 3 ingredients in a small bowl. Spread garlic mixture evenly over top of each bread slice.
3. Place bread slices on a baking sheet; broil 2 minutes or until edges begin to brown. Sprinkle with cheese. Serve immediately. YIELD: 4 servings (serving size: 1 slice).

POINTS value: 1; Exchanges: ½ Starch, ½ Fat; Per serving: CAL 57 (32% from fat); PRO 1.8g; FAT 2.0g (sat 0.6g); CARB 7.7g; FIB 0.5g; CHOL 1mg; IRON 0.4mg; SOD 130mg; CALC 30mg

ROOT BEER FLOATS

prep: 6 minutes

Dessert doesn't have to be served with a spoon or a fork. Instead, stir up an old-fashioned root beer float using diet root beer and low-fat ice cream. Serve with a straw. The best part is that there are no leftovers to tempt you.

2 cups vanilla low-fat ice cream
3 (12-ounce) bottles diet root beer, chilled

1. Scoop ½ cup ice cream into each of 4 glasses. Slowly fill each glass with 1 cup root beer. Serve immediately. YIELD: 4 servings (serving size: 1 float).

POINTS value: 2; Exchanges: 1 Low-Fat Milk, ½ Fat; Per serving: CAL 110 (17% from fat); PRO 3.0g; FAT 2.0g (sat 1.0g); CARB 19.0g; FIB 1.0g; CHOL 5mg; IRON 0.0mg; SOD 88mg; CALC 100mg

Quick Tip: Three of the recipes in this menu call for minced garlic. To save time, mince all of the garlic at one time, and use the amounts called for in each recipe. You'll need 3 cloves of garlic to yield about 3 teaspoons of minced garlic. Or, if you prefer, use bottled preminced garlic from the produce section of the grocery store.

Simple Sunday Brunch

Serves 8 • Total **POINTS** value: 12

Mushroom Quiche • Turkey Sausage Patties
Spinach Salad with Grapefruit and Fennel • Roasted Sweet Potatoes

GAME PLAN

1. Make **Turkey Sausage Patties,** and freeze up to 2 weeks ahead.

2. Complete the first four steps of **Roasted Sweet Potatoes** a day ahead.

3. Prepare **Mushroom Quiche.**

4. While quiche bakes, prepare **Spinach Salad with Grapefruit and Fennel.**

5. While quiche stands, cook sausage patties and complete roasting of sweet potatoes.

MUSHROOM QUICHE

prep: 15 minutes • cook: 37 minutes • other: 15 minutes

Use cheese shreds to patch any cracks that may develop in the baked pastry. The cheese will melt into the cracks.

½ (15-ounce) package refrigerated pie dough
Cooking spray
1 cup (4 ounces) reduced-fat Swiss cheese
1 tablespoon olive oil
¼ cup chopped shallot (about 1 medium)
5 cups coarsely chopped fresh mushrooms
¼ teaspoon salt
⅛ teaspoon pepper
¾ cup egg substitute
¾ cup 2% reduced-fat milk
⅛ teaspoon ground nutmeg
¼ cup (1 ounce) grated fresh Parmesan cheese

1. Preheat oven to 375°.
2. Roll dough to an 11-inch circle. Fit dough into a 9-inch pie plate coated with cooking spray. Fold edges of dough under, and press to make sure edge is secured onto the rim of pie plate. Flute edge, if desired. Pierce bottom of dough with a fork.
3. Bake at 375° for 15 minutes. Remove from oven; sprinkle with Swiss cheese and set aside.
4. Meanwhile, heat oil in a large nonstick skillet over medium-high heat. Add shallot and sauté 2 minutes. Add mushrooms, salt, and pepper; sauté until mushrooms release their liquid. Continue to cook until liquid evaporates and mushrooms are brown.
5. Spoon mushroom mixture over cheese in crust.
6. Combine egg substitute and next 3 ingredients in a bowl; beat well with a whisk. Pour milk mixture over mushroom mixture.
7. Bake at 375° for 22 minutes or until set. Let stand 15 minutes before cutting into wedges. Serve warm.
YIELD: 8 servings (serving size: 1 wedge).

POINTS value: 6; **Exchanges:** 1 Starch, 1 Very Lean Meat, 1 Medium-Fat Meat, 2 Fat; **Per serving:** CAL 263 (49% from fat); PRO 14.5g; FAT 13.7g (sat 6.3g); CARB 17.9g; FIB 0.8g; CHOL 8mg; IRON 0.9mg; SOD 385mg; CALC 306mg

TURKEY SAUSAGE PATTIES

prep: 30 minutes • cook: 16 minutes
other: 8 hours

1   pear, peeled and cored
1   apple, peeled and cored
1¼   pounds lean ground turkey
½   cup chopped fresh parsley
¼   cup finely chopped fresh sage
1½   teaspoons salt
½   teaspoon pepper
¼   teaspoon ground allspice
¼   teaspoon red pepper flakes
¼   cup egg substitute
2   teaspoons olive oil

1. Coarsely shred pear and apple with a hand grater; press well to drain excess liquid.
2. Combine pear, apple, turkey, and next 7 ingredients in a bowl; stir until blended. Shape mixture into 16 patties (about 2 tablespoons each); place patties on a wax paper–lined baking sheet. Cover, and chill 8 hours or overnight.
3. Heat oil in a large nonstick skillet over medium heat; cook patties, in batches, about 4 minutes per side or until browned and no longer pink inside. YIELD: 8 servings (serving size: about 2 patties).
Note: Instead of chilling, patties may be wrapped in wax paper and foil, and frozen up to 2 weeks. Thaw frozen patties and cook according to directions 5 to 6 minutes on each side.

POINTS value: 3; **Exchanges:** ½ Fruit, 2 Lean Meat; **Per serving:** CAL 148 (39% from fat); PRO 15.9g; FAT 6.7g (sat 0.2g); CARB 7.9g; FIB 2.2g; CHOL 44mg; IRON 1.7mg; SOD 511mg; CALC 61mg

SPINACH SALAD WITH GRAPEFRUIT AND FENNEL

prep: 8 minutes

To cut prep time, we used a jar of refrigerated grapefruit sections. For a fresh grapefruit option, peel and section about 4 grapefruits.

1   (24-ounce) jar refrigerated unsweetened grapefruit sections, undrained (such as Del Monte SunFresh)
3   tablespoons red wine vinegar
1   tablespoon extravirgin olive oil
½   teaspoon salt
¼   teaspoon freshly ground black pepper
2   (6-ounce) packages fresh baby spinach
2   cups thinly sliced fennel bulb (about 1 medium)
⅓   cup thinly sliced red onion
3   tablespoons chopped pecans, toasted

1. Drain grapefruit sections, reserving ½ cup juice. Combine reserved juice and next 4 ingredients in a small bowl; set aside.
2. Combine spinach, fennel, onion, and pecans in a large bowl. Add dressing; toss well to coat. Add grapefruit sections and toss gently to combine. YIELD: 8 servings (serving size: 1¼ cups).

POINTS value: 1; **Exchanges:** ½ Fruit, 1½ Vegetable, ½ Fat; **Per serving:** CAL 82 (26% from fat); PRO 3.1g; FAT 2.7g (sat 0.3g); CARB 13.9g; FIB 2.4g; CHOL 0mg; IRON 2.7mg; SOD 376mg; CALC 106mg

ROASTED SWEET POTATOES

prep: 10 minutes • cook: 40 minutes

These cubes of roasted sweet potatoes have a wonderful hint of maple.

6   cups cubed peeled sweet potatoes (about 2 pounds)
Cooking spray
2   tablespoons olive oil
½   teaspoon salt
¼   teaspoon freshly ground black pepper
¼   cup pure maple syrup

1. Preheat oven to 450°.
2. Spread potatoes in a single layer on a foil-lined baking sheet coated with cooking spray. Drizzle with olive oil and sprinkle with salt and pepper. Bake at 450° for 25 minutes.
3. Remove potatoes from oven and cool in pan on a wire rack to room temperature.
4. Wrap potatoes in foil from baking sheet. Refrigerate overnight.
5. Preheat oven to 450°.
6. Place foil packet on baking sheet; fold back foil to edges of baking sheet. Brush potatoes with syrup; bake 15 minutes or until potatoes are roasted. YIELD: 8 servings (serving size: ½ cup).

POINTS value: 2; **Exchanges:** 1½ Starch, ½ Fat; **Per serving:** CAL 119 (25% from fat); PRO 1.3g; FAT 3.4g (sat 0.5g); CARB 21.4g; FIB 2.5g; CHOL 0mg; IRON 0.7mg; SOD 159mg; CALC 32mg

Quick Tip: If you have two ovens, you can roast the sweet potatoes while the quiche cooks.

Off The Grill

Serves 4 • Total **POINTS** value: 12

Molasses-Bourbon Grilled Salmon • Grilled Vegetable Platter
Grilled Caramel-Banana Sundaes • Ginger-Peach Tea

GAME PLAN

1. Marinate **Molasses-Bourbon Grilled Salmon** for about 8 hours.

2. Prepare **Ginger-Peach Tea** and refrigerate.

3. Prepare **Grilled Vegetable Platter**.

4. While vegetables stand, make caramel sauce for **Grilled Caramel-Banana Sundaes;** keep warm.

5. Grill salmon and bananas at the same time.

6. Garnish tea with mint sprigs, if desired.

MOLASSES-BOURBON GRILLED SALMON

prep: 4 minutes • cook: 12 minutes • other: 8 hours

Place the salmon in the marinade before you leave for work. It will be ready to cook as soon as you get home. The combination of bourbon and molasses gives this fish a sweet, glazed flavor. If you prefer, substitute apple juice for the bourbon.

½   cup chopped green onions (about 4)
¼   cup packed brown sugar
1   teaspoon grated peeled fresh ginger
½   teaspoon minced garlic
⅓   cup bourbon
⅓   cup low-sodium soy sauce
⅓   cup Dijon mustard
2   tablespoons molasses
4   (6-ounce) salmon fillets
Cooking spray

1. Combine green onions and next 7 ingredients in a large zip-top plastic bag; add fish and seal. Marinate in refrigerator about 8 hours.
2. Prepare grill.
3. Remove fish from marinade; discard marinade. Place fish on grill rack coated with cooking spray; grill, 6 minutes on each side, or until fish flakes easily when tested with a fork. YIELD: 4 servings (serving size: 1 fillet).

POINTS value: 5; **Exchanges:** 4½ Lean Meat; **Per serving:** CAL 246 (24% from fat); PRO 34.7g; FAT 6.5g (sat 1.0g); CARB 6.8g; FIB 0.2g; CHOL 88mg; IRON 1.8mg; SOD 459mg; CALC 42mg

Quick Tip: Rather than heating up the grill, use a grill pan. It gives the food a grilled appearance and flavor, and it provides nice browning. The cooking time will be about the same time as a regular grill.

GRILLED VEGETABLE PLATTER

prep: 15 minutes • cook: 10 minutes
other: 30 minutes

1 small Japanese eggplant
1 large zucchini, cut lengthwise into 4 (¼-inch-thick) slices
8 asparagus spears
Olive oil-flavored cooking spray
1 (12-ounce) bottle roasted red bell peppers, drained and cut into ½-inch-wide strips
¼ cup fat-free, less-sodium chicken broth
¼ cup red wine vinegar
1 tablespoon chopped fresh basil
1 tablespoon olive oil
1 teaspoon sugar
1 teaspoon Dijon mustard
½ teaspoon minced garlic
¼ teaspoon salt
¼ teaspoon black pepper

1. Prepare grill.
2. Trim eggplant. Cut eggplant into ¼-inch-thick slices.
3. Arrange eggplant, zucchini, and asparagus in a grill basket coated with cooking spray. Grill, covered, 10 to 12 minutes, turning once, or until lightly charred. Place in a shallow dish; stir in roasted red pepper strips.
4. Combine broth and next 8 ingredients in a bowl; stir well with a whisk.
5. Pour dressing over vegetables. Cover and let stand at least 30 minutes. YIELD: 4 servings (serving size: 1 cup vegetables and about 2 tablespoons dressing).

POINTS value: 1; **Exchanges:** 2 Veg, ½ Fat ; **Per serving:** CAL 82 (39% from fat); PRO 2.8g; FAT 3.8g (sat 0.5g); CARB 10.7g; FIB 2.8g; CHOL 0mg; IRON 0.8mg; SOD 77mg; CALC 26m

GRILLED CARAMEL-BANANA SUNDAES

prep: 5 minutes • cook: 19 minutes

To save time, use ½ cup fat-free commercial caramel sauce (such as T. Marzetti's) instead of making your own. Top each sundae with 2 tablespoons sauce for a POINTS value of 5.

½ cup sugar
2 tablespoons water
1 tablespoon butter
⅓ cup evaporated fat-free milk
¼ teaspoon vanilla extract
⅛ teaspoon salt
2 large bananas
2 tablespoons sugar
¼ teaspoon ground cinnamon
¼ cup pineapple-orange juice
Cooking spray
1 cup vanilla low-fat ice cream

1. Combine ½ cup sugar and water in a heavy saucepan; cook over medium heat 6 minutes or until sugar dissolves. Cover, increase heat to medium-high, and boil 1 minute. (Crystals on side of pan will dissolve.) Uncover; boil 5 minutes or until amber or golden (do not stir).
2. Remove from heat; let stand 1 minute. Add butter; stir until melted. Whisk in milk, stirring constantly (mixture will bubble). Stir in vanilla and salt. Pour sauce into a bowl; set aside.
3. Prepare grill.
4. Slice each banana in half lengthwise then cut each piece in half crosswise. Combine 2 tablespoons sugar and cinnamon. Dip banana pieces in juice; coat with sugar mixture. Arrange banana pieces in a grill basket coated with cooking spray. Place grill basket on grill rack; grill 3 to 4 minutes on each side or until bananas are browned.
5. Place 2 banana slices in each of 4 bowls; top with ¼ cup vanilla ice cream. Drizzle with 3 tablespoons caramel sauce. YIELD: 4 servings (serving size: 1 sundae).

POINTS value: 5; **Exchanges:** 2½ Starch, ½ Fruit, ½ Skim Milk; **Per serving:** CAL 280 (13% from fat); PRO 3.6g; FAT 4.0g (sat 2.0g); CARB 59.0g; FIB 2.9g; CHOL 10mg; IRON 0.3mg; SOD 366mg; CALC 123mg

GINGER-PEACH TEA

prep: 5 minutes • cook: 25 minutes
other: 5 minutes

3½ cups water
1 (3-inch) piece peeled fresh ginger, sliced
3 tablespoons sugar
4 regular-sized tea bags
1 cup peach nectar
Mint sprigs (optional)

1. Combine water and ginger in a medium saucepan; bring to a boil over high heat. Reduce heat to medium; simmer, uncovered, 20 minutes. Remove from heat; remove and discard ginger slices. Add sugar, stirring until sugar dissolves. Add tea bags; steep 5 minutes. Remove and discard tea bags; let cool. Stir in peach nectar; cover and chill. Serve over ice. Garnish with mint sprigs, if desired. YIELD: 4 servings (serving size: 1¼ cups).

POINTS value: 1; **Exchange:** 1 Starch; **Per serving:** CAL 70 (0% from fat); PRO 0.2g; FAT 0.0g (sat 0.0g); CARB 18.1g; FIB 0.4g; CHOL 0mg; IRON 0.1mg; SOD 9mg; CALC 7mg

A Taste of Italy

Serves 8 • Total **POINTS** value: 10

"Osso Bucco"-Style Chicken • Polenta with Fontina
Orange Salad with Onions and Olives • Frozen Hazelnut Cappuccino

GAME PLAN

1. Prepare and freeze **Frozen Hazelnut Cappuccino.**

2. Prepare and bake **"Osso Bucco"-Style Chicken.**

3. While chicken bakes, prepare onion and orange mixture in **Orange Salad with Onions and Olives.**

4. Make sauce for chicken.

5. Prepare **Polenta with Fontina.**

6. Prepare salad.

"OSSO BUCCO"-STYLE CHICKEN

prep: 21 minutes • cook: 1 hour and 41 minutes

⅓	cup all-purpose flour
½	teaspoon salt
½	teaspoon pepper
1	pound chicken thighs, skinned (about 4)
1	pound chicken drumsticks, skinned (about 4)
2	teaspoons olive oil, divided
	Cooking spray
1	cup diced carrot
1	cup diced celery
1	cup diced onion
4	garlic cloves, minced
1	cup dry white wine
½	cup fat-free, less-sodium chicken broth
1	(14.5-ounce) can Italian-style diced tomatoes, undrained
1	bay leaf
1	rosemary sprig
2	tablespoons chopped parsley
2	teaspoons grated lemon rind
1	garlic clove, minced

1. Preheat oven to 350°.
2. Combine flour, salt, and pepper in a shallow dish. Dredge chicken pieces in flour mixture, shaking off any excess.

3. Heat 1 teaspoon oil in a Dutch oven coated with cooking spray over medium-high heat. Cook half of chicken, 4 to 5 minutes on each side, or until browned. Remove chicken and set aside. Repeat with remaining oil and chicken.
4. Reduce heat to medium; add carrot and next 4 ingredients. Cook 5 minutes, scraping pan to loosen browned bits. Add broth and next 3 ingredients. Return chicken to pan; stir gently.
5. Bake, covered, at 350° for 1 hour and 15 minutes or until chicken is no longer pink. Remove and discard bay leaf and rosemary sprig. Transfer chicken to a platter; keep warm.
6. Place pan over medium-high heat. Bring broth to a boil. Reduce heat; simmer, uncovered, 5 minutes or until mixture thickens. Remove from heat; stir in parsley, lemon rind, and garlic. Spoon sauce over chicken. YIELD: 8 servings (serving size: 4 ounces chicken and ½ cup sauce).

POINTS value: 4; **Exchanges:** 1½ Vegetable, 3 Lean Meat; **Per serving:** CAL 201 (25% from fat); PRO 24.7g; FAT 5.5g (sat 1.2g); CARB 12.3g; FIB 2.0g; CHOL 91mg; IRON 2.2mg; SOD 377mg; CALC 54mg

POLENTA WITH FONTINA

prep: 3 minutes • cook: 10 minutes

Be sure to use plain cornmeal and not a cornmeal mix. For a flavor variation, substitute ¼ cup grated fresh Parmesan cheese or ¼ cup Asiago cheese for the fontina cheese.

1¼ cups yellow cornmeal
¼ teaspoon salt
⅛ teaspoon black pepper
3¼ cups fat-free, less-sodium chicken broth
¾ cup fat-free milk
½ cup frozen whole-kernel corn, thawed
½ cup (2 ounces) shredded fontina cheese

1. Combine cornmeal, salt, and pepper in a medium saucepan. Gradually add broth and milk, stirring constantly with a whisk. Bring to a boil; reduce heat to low, and stir in corn. Cook 7 minutes, stirring frequently, or until thickened. Remove from heat; add cheese, stirring until cheese melts. Serve immediately. YIELD: 8 servings (serving size: ½ cup).

POINTS value: 2; **Exchanges:** 1 Starch, ½ Medium-Fat Meat; **Per serving:** CAL 119 (21% from fat); PRO 5.6g; FAT 2.9g (sat 1.4g); CARB 18.7g; FIB 1.7g; CHOL 8mg; IRON 0.9mg; SOD 397mg; CALC 60mg

Quick Tip: Use a microplane grater to quickly grate lemon rind or hard cheeses such as Asiago, Parmesan, or Romano.

ORANGE SALAD WITH ONIONS AND OLIVES

prep: 9 minutes • other: 30 minutes

¼ cup orange juice
2 tablespoons white balsamic vinegar
2 teaspoons olive oil
⅛ teaspoon salt
⅛ teaspoon ground red pepper
3 large navel oranges
1 small red onion, thinly sliced
4 cups mixed salad greens
2 tablespoons sliced black olives

1. Combine orange juice and next 4 ingredients; set aside.
2. Peel oranges; slice crosswise into thin slices. Arrange orange and onion in a shallow dish. Pour orange juice mixture over orange and onion. Let stand 30 minutes.
3. Arrange salad greens on 4 individual serving plates. Top with orange and onion. Sprinkle evenly with olives. Drizzle 1 tablespoon orange juice mixture evenly over each serving. YIELD: 8 servings (serving size: ½ cup salad greens, ½ cup orange mixture, and about 2 teaspoons orange juice mixture).

POINTS value: 1; **Exchanges:** 1 Vegetable, ½ Fruit; **Per serving:** CAL 52 (24% from fat); PRO 1.1g; FAT 1.5g (sat 0.2g); CARB 9.8g; FIB 2.0g; CHOL 0mg; IRON 0.6mg; SOD 64mg; CALC 43mg

FROZEN HAZELNUT CAPPUCCINO

prep: 6 minutes • other: 8 hours and 5 minutes

Rather than freezing the cappuccino mixture, fill eight tall glasses with crushed ice and pour the chilled coffee mixture evenly into each glass.

2 cups water
½ cup sugar
¼ cup instant coffee granules
5 cups fat-free milk
1 cup fat-free hazelnut-flavored coffee creamer

1. Combine water and sugar in a small saucepan; cook over high heat, stirring until sugar dissolves. Remove from heat. Stir in coffee granules; chill.
2. Combine chilled coffee mixture, milk, and creamer in a shallow container. Cover and freeze 8 hours or until solid.
3. Let stand 5 minutes, if needed, to soften slightly. Break frozen mixture into chunks. Process in a blender or food processor until smooth, stopping to scrape down sides. Spoon into 8 serving bowls. Serve immediately. YIELD: 8 servings (serving size: ½ cup).

POINTS value: 3; **Exchanges:** 1½ Starch, ½ Skim Milk; **Per serving:** CAL 160 (1% from fat); PRO 5.4g; FAT 0.1g (sat 0.1g); CARB 32.1g; FIB 0.0g; CHOL 3mg; IRON 0.9mg; SOD 75mg; CALC 143mg

Family Holiday Dinner

(pictured on page 1)

Serves 8 • Total **POINTS** value: 12

Holiday Herbed Pork Roast • **Citrus Cran-Apple Relish**
Garlic-Roasted Brussels Sprouts
Brown Sugar-Crusted Sweet Potato Casserole

GAME PLAN

1. Cook sweet potatoes for **Brown Sugar-Crusted Sweet Potato Casserole;** cover and refrigerate overnight.

2. Butterfly, stuff, and tie pork roast for **Holiday Herbed Pork Roast;** refrigerate overnight.

3. Prepare **Citrus Cran-Apple Relish** and chill for 2 hours.

4. Bake pork roast; prepare **Garlic-Roasted Brussels Sprouts.**

5. Bake Brussels sprouts; prepare gravy.

6. Bake sweet potato casserole.

HOLIDAY HERBED PORK ROAST

prep: 25 minutes • cook: 1 hour and 18 minutes • other: 10 minutes

See the "how-to" pictures on page 88 for an example of how to double butterfly and stuff a pork loin.

2	teaspoons olive oil, divided
½	cup minced shallot (about 1 large)
2	tablespoons minced garlic
¼	cup chopped walnuts
1	tablespoon chopped fresh sage
1	tablespoon chopped fresh rosemary
1	tablespoon chopped fresh thyme
1¼	teaspoons salt, divided
¾	teaspoon black pepper, divided
1	(3-pound) boneless top pork loin roast, trimmed
	Cooking spray
1	cup fat-free, less-sodium chicken broth, divided
1	tablespoon all-purpose flour

1. Preheat oven to 450°.

2. Heat 1 teaspoon oil in a nonstick skillet over medium-high heat. Sauté shallot, garlic, and walnuts 2 minutes or until shallot is tender. Remove from pan.

3. Combine sage, rosemary, and thyme in a small bowl. Add half of herb mixture to shallot mixture; set aside. Combine remaining herb mixture with 1 teaspoon olive oil, 1 teaspoon salt, and ½ teaspoon black pepper; stir well and set aside.

4. Starting off-center, slice pork lengthwise, cutting to, but not through, other side. Open butterflied portions, laying pork flat. Turning knife blade parallel to surface of cutting board, slice larger portion of pork in half horizontally, cutting to, but not through, other side; open flat. Place between 2 sheets of heavy-duty plastic wrap, and flatten to ½-inch thickness, using a meat mallet or rolling pin. Spread shallot mixture over roast. Roll up pork, jelly roll fashion, starting with long side. Secure pork at 2-inch intervals with heavy string.

5. Place pork on a rack coated with cooking spray in a shallow roasting pan. Rub herb mixture over outside of pork. Bake, uncovered, at 450° for 15 minutes.

6. Reduce oven temperature to 350°. Bake at 350° for 55 minutes or until thermometer inserted into thickest portion of pork registers 155°. Remove from oven. Cover pork with foil; let stand 10 minutes or until thermometer registers 160° (slightly pink). Remove pork and rack from pan, reserving drippings in pan. Place pork on a serving platter; slice evenly into slices. Cover and keep warm.

7. Place pan on cooktop over medium heat, and add ½ cup chicken broth. Whisk together flour and ½ cup chicken broth. Add flour mixture to pan and bring to a boil, whisking constantly. Reduce heat, and cook 6 minutes or until mixture thickens, whisking constantly. Stir in ¼ teaspoon salt and ¼ teaspoon pepper. Serve gravy over pork. YIELD: 8 servings (serving size: 3 ounces pork and about 1½ tablespoons gravy).

POINTS value: 6; **Exchanges:** 5 Lean Meat; **Per serving:** CAL 276 (40% from fat); PRO 35.2g; FAT 11.9g (sat 3.1g); CARB 4.4g; FIB 0.5g; CHOL 84mg; IRON 1.7mg; SOD 517mg; CALC 49mg

CITRUS CRAN-APPLE RELISH

prep: 12 minutes • cook: 3 minutes
other: 2 hours

1   (12-ounce) package fresh
    cranberries
1   Granny Smith apple, peeled
    and coarsely chopped
⅓   cup orange sections
½   cup sugar
1   teaspoon grated orange
    rind
⅓   cup walnuts, toasted

1. Combine first 5 ingredients in a food processor; pulse until coarsely chopped. Place mixture in a bowl; stir in walnuts. Cover and chill 2 hours. YIELD: 8 servings (serving size: ⅓ cup).

POINTS value: 2; **Exchanges:** 1 Starch, ½ Fruit; **Per serving:** CAL 111 (22% from fat); PRO 0.8g; FAT 2.7g (sat 0.3g); CARB 21.6g; FIB 2.4g; CHOL 0mg; IRON 0.2mg; SOD 0mg; CALC 9mg

GARLIC-ROASTED BRUSSELS SPROUTS

prep: 9 minutes • cook: 20 minutes

4   cups trimmed Brussels
    sprouts, halved (about 2
    pounds)
3   garlic cloves, thinly sliced
2   teaspoons olive oil
½   teaspoon salt
¼   teaspoon black pepper
Cooking spray

1. Preheat oven to 450°.
2. Combine first 5 ingredients in a bowl; toss gently. Place Brussels sprouts on a baking sheet coated with cooking spray. Bake at 450° for 20 to 25 minutes or until tender; serve immediately. YIELD: 8 servings (serving size: ½ cup).

POINTS value: 1; **Exchanges:** 2 Vegetable, ½ Fat; **Per serving:** CAL 71 (32% from fat); PRO 2.8g; FAT 2.4g (sat 0.2g); CARB 8.5g; FIB 4.1g; CHOL 0mg; IRON 0.1mg; SOD 182mg; CALC 29mg

BROWN SUGAR-CRUSTED SWEET POTATO CASSEROLE

prep: 14 minutes • cook: 34 minutes
other: 5 minutes

With its brown sugar brûlée topping, this side is sweet enough to serve as dessert.

3   pounds sweet potatoes
    (about 3 large)
2   tablespoons butter, melted
2   teaspoons grated orange
    rind
2   tablespoons fresh orange
    juice
1   teaspoon ground cinnamon
¾   teaspoon salt
¼   teaspoon pumpkin pie spice
Cooking spray
½   cup packed light brown
    sugar

1. Cut each potato into 3 large chunks. Place in a Dutch oven; fill with water to cover. Bring to a boil, and cook 25 to 30 minutes or until potatoes are tender. Drain, peel, and mash.
2. Preheat broiler.
3. Combine potato and next 6 ingredients in a large bowl. Spoon potato mixture into an 11 x 7-inch baking dish coated with cooking spray. Sprinkle brown sugar evenly over top. Broil 4 minutes or until sugar melts. Let stand 5 minutes or until melted sugar hardens. YIELD: 8 servings (serving size: ½ cup).

POINTS value: 3; **Exchanges:** 1½ Starch; **Per serving:** CAL 173 (15% from fat); PRO 2.2g; FAT 3.0g (sat 1.5g); CARB 35.5g; FIB 3.0g; CHOL 8mg; IRON 1.0mg; SOD 284mg; CALC 56mg

One day's menu provides at least two servings of milk and at least five servings of fruits and/or vegetables.

	MONDAY	TUESDAY	WEDNESDAY	THURSDAY
BREAKFAST	**Breakfast Sandwich** (Split an English Muffin in half; toast. Layer 1 oz lean ham, 1 scrambled egg, and 2 tbsp shredded reduced-fat, Cheddar cheese on bottom half of bread. Top with other half - **POINTS value: 6**) **blueberries**, ½ cup **fat-free milk**, 1 cup **TOTAL *POINTS* value: 9**	**whole wheat bagel**, 1 small, split and toasted **light cream cheese**, 1 tablespoon **strawberries**, 1 cup **TOTAL *POINTS* value: 5**	**Strawberry Smoothie** (Combine ½ cup strawberries, ½ cup whipped topping, and 2 oz lemon yogurt in a blender. Add ice to reach 1 cup level. Process until smooth - **POINTS value: 2**) **whole wheat toast**, 2 slices **light butter**, 1 tablespoon **TOTAL *POINTS* value: 5**	**bran flakes**, ¾ cup **fat-free milk**, 1 cup **banana**, 1 medium **TOTAL *POINTS* value: 5**
LUNCH	**Blue Cheese and Steak Quesadilla** (Heat a nonstick skillet coated with cooking spray over medium heat. Place a low-fat tortilla, coated with cooking spray, in pan; add 2 oz cooked flank steak, cut into strips, and ½ cup torn spinach leaves. Add ¼ cup blue cheese. Fold half of tortilla over; cook until slightly browned, turning once. Cut into 2 wedges - **POINTS value: 6**) **red seedless grapes**, 15 **TOTAL *POINTS* value: 7**	**Apple Slaw and Ham Sandwiches**, page 131, 1 serving **Chive-Parmesan Potato Chips**, page 16, 1 serving **celery sticks**, 1 cup **fat-free milk**, 1 cup **TOTAL *POINTS* value: 8**	**Salmon Salad**, page 123, 1 serving **sliced tomato**, 1 (sprinkle with basil and black pepper) **Watermelon with Mint Syrup** (Combine 1 tbsp water and 1 tbsp sugar in a small saucepan; bring to a boil, stirring to dissolve sugar. Pour mixture into a small bowl; stir in ½ tbsp chopped fresh mint. Cover and chill. Toss 1 cup cubed watermelon with syrup before serving - **POINTS value: 2**) **TOTAL *POINTS* value: 6**	**hamburger**, 1 fast food **side salad**, 1 fast food **fat-free Italian dressing**, 2 tablespoons **diet soft drink**, 8 ounces **TOTAL *POINTS* value: 7**
DINNER	**Fresh Tuna Burgers with Mango-Jalapeño Jam**, page 125, 1 serving **spinach salad**, 1 cup **fat-free raspberry vinaigrette**, 2 tablespoons **pear**, 1 medium **TOTAL *POINTS* value: 6**	**Veal Cutlets with Wine-Braised Mushrooms**, page 86, 1 serving **Maple-Pecan Sweet Potatoes**, page 147, 1 serving **mixed greens salad**, 1 cup **fat-free Italian dressing**, 2 tablespoons **TOTAL *POINTS* value: 8**	**Pork with Grapefruit-Mint Salsa**, page 93, 1 serving **brown rice**, ¾ cup **steamed green beans**, 1 cup **fat-free milk**, 1 cup **TOTAL *POINTS* value: 8**	**baked chicken breast**, 3 ounces **Roasted Green Beans** (Preheat oven to 425°. Combine ½ cup beans, ½ tsp olive oil, and ⅛ tsp salt in a large bowl. Place beans on a baking sheet; sprinkle with 1 tsp sesame seeds. Roast 10 minutes or until beans are tender, stirring once - **POINTS value: 1**) **Oven-Roasted Potato Wedges**, page 146, 1 serving **TOTAL *POINTS* value: 6**
SNACK	**Triple Chocolate Mocha Latte**, page 19, 1 serving **TOTAL *POINTS* value: 2**	**raspberry fat-free yogurt**, 8 ounces **gingersnaps**, 2 **TOTAL *POINTS* value: 3**	**part-skim mozzarella string cheese**, 1 stick **apple**, 1 small **TOTAL *POINTS* value: 3**	**Glazed Apricot Scones**, page 27, 1 serving **fat-free milk**, 1 cup **TOTAL *POINTS* value: 6**
POINTS VALUE	***POINTS* value for the day: 24**	***POINTS* value for the day: 24**	***POINTS* value for the day: 22**	***POINTS* value for the day: 24**

	FRIDAY	SATURDAY	SUNDAY
BREAKFAST	**cooked oatmeal,** 1 cup **honey,** 1 tablespoon **peach fat-free yogurt,** 8 ounces **orange juice,** ½ cup **TOTAL *POINTS* value: 6**	**fat-free cereal bar,** 1 (1½-ounce) **fat-free vanilla yogurt,** 8 ounces **cantaloupe chunks,** 1 cup **TOTAL *POINTS* value: 6**	**Cornmeal Pancakes, page 27,** 3 servings **sugar-free maple syrup,** 2 tablespoons **raspberries,** 1 cup **fat-free milk,** 1 cup **TOTAL *POINTS* value: 9**
LUNCH	**Creamy Tomato Soup with Roasted Garlic and Basil, page 161,** 1 serving **Grilled Double Cheese and Tomato Sandwiches, page 126,** 1 serving **fat-free milk,** 1 cup **TOTAL *POINTS* value: 8**	**Roast Beef and Blue Cheese Salad** (Top 2 cups shredded Romaine lettuce with 2 oz lean deli roast beef, 5 cherry tomatoes, 2 tbsp crumbled blue cheese, and 2 tbsp fat-free raspberry vinaigrette - ***POINTS* value: 5)** **saltine crackers,** 6 **TOTAL *POINTS* value: 6**	**Greek Pasta Salad** (Combine ½ cup each of cannellini beans, chopped tomato, shredded romaine lettuce, and hot cooked penne pasta. Stir in 1 tsp olive oil and top with 1 tbsp Parmesan cheese - ***POINTS* value: 5)** **Strawberry Chiller, page 20,** 1 serving **TOTAL *POINTS* value: 6**
DINNER	**Cajun Catfish** (Brush both sides of a 6-oz catfish fillet with 1 tsp lemon juice; sprinkle with 1 tsp Cajun seasoning. Place fish on a broiler pan coated with cooking spray. Broil 5 minutes on each side or until fish flakes easily when tested with a fork - ***POINTS* value: 4)** **steamed asparagus,** 12 spears **wild rice,** 1 cup **TOTAL *POINTS* value: 7**	**"A Taste of Italy" menu,** **pages 170-171** **"Osso-Bucco"-Style Chicken,** 1 serving **Polenta with Fontina,** 1 serving **Orange Salad with Onions and Olives,** 1 serving **Frozen Hazelnut Cappuccino,** 1 serving **TOTAL *POINTS* value: 10**	**Korean Beef with Spicy Cabbage, page 84,** 1 serving **nectarine,** 1 medium **fat-free milk,** 1 cup **TOTAL *POINTS* value: 6**
SNACK	**baby carrots,** 1 cup **reduced-fat ranch dressing,** 2 tablespoons **TOTAL *POINTS* value: 2**	**celery sticks,** 1 cup **fat-free milk,** 1 cup **TOTAL *POINTS* value: 2**	**Triple Chocolate Sundae** (Top ½ cup chocolate low-fat ice cream with 1 tbsp chocolate sauce and 1 tsp chocolate sprinkles - ***POINTS* value: 3)** **TOTAL *POINTS* value: 3**
POINTS VALUE	***POINTS* value for the day: 23**	***POINTS* value for the day: 24**	***POINTS* value for the day: 24**

One day's menu provides at least two servings of milk and at least five servings of fruits and/or vegetables.

	MONDAY	TUESDAY	WEDNESDAY	THURSDAY
BREAKFAST	**Peaches and Cream Oatmeal** (Stir 2 tbsp fat-free milk and 1 tbsp brown sugar into 1 cup cooked oatmeal. Top with ½ cup peach slices - *POINTS* value: 4) **fat-free milk**, 1 cup TOTAL *POINTS* value: 6	**fat-free frozen waffles**, 2 **sugar-free maple syrup,** 1 tablespoon **blueberries**, ½ cup **fat-free milk**, 1 cup TOTAL *POINTS* value: 6	**poached egg**, 1 large egg **meatless breakfast patty**, 1 **fat-free milk**, 1 cup TOTAL *POINTS* value: 5	**Toasted Coconut Banana Muffins,** page 26, 1 serving **fat-free milk**, 1 cup TOTAL *POINTS* value: 6
LUNCH	**Fresh Vegetable Po'Boy,** page 127, 1 serving **celery sticks**, 1 cup TOTAL *POINTS* value: 5	**Oat Grain-Feta Salad, page 122,** 1 serving **strawberries with fresh mint**, 1 cup **whole wheat pita bread**, ½ pita **grape tomatoes**, 1 cup TOTAL *POINTS* value: 8	**Beef Minestrone, page 162,** 1 serving **Caesar Salad** (Combine 2 cups torn romaine lettuce with 2 tbsp light Caesar dressing. Top with 1 tbsp grated fresh Parmesan cheese and ¼ cup commercial croutons. - *POINTS* value: 3) **unsweetened iced tea**, 8 ounces TOTAL *POINTS* value: 7	**Chicken and Vegetable Garden Wraps, page 131,** 1 serving **orange**, 1 medium TOTAL *POINTS* value: 7
DINNER	**Roasted Italian Pork Tenderloin,** page 94, 1 serving **Fresh Lemon and Pepper Linguine** (Combine ¾ cup hot cooked linguine, ½ tsp freshly ground black pepper, 1 tsp fresh lemon juice, and 1 tsp olive oil. Toss well - *POINTS* value: 4) **steamed broccoli florets**, 1 cup TOTAL *POINTS* value: 7	**grilled chicken breast**, 4 ounces **steamed zucchini and yellow squash**, 1 cup **Cranberry Rice Salad, page 123,** 1 serving TOTAL *POINTS* value: 6	**Skillet Ham with Pineapple-Ginger Salsa, page 94,** 1 serving **baked sweet potato**, 1 medium **steamed green beans**, 1 cup **fat-free milk**, 1 cup TOTAL *POINTS* value: 8	**Broiled Shrimp Skewers** (Thread 12 large peeled shrimp onto 2 [10-inch] skewers. Brush with ½ tsp olive oil, and sprinkle with ⅛ tsp salt. Broil about 3 minutes, turning once - *POINTS* value: 2) **Carrot-Edamame Sauté, page 144,** 1 serving **spinach salad**, 1 cup **fat-free balsamic vinaigrette,** 2 tablespoons **fat-free milk**, 1 cup TOTAL *POINTS* value: 6
SNACK	**apple**, 1 medium **peanut butter**, 1 tablespoon **fat-free milk**, 1 cup TOTAL *POINTS* value: 5	**low-fat granola**, ¼ cup **blueberry fat-free yogurt**, 8 ounces TOTAL *POINTS* value: 3	**Fresh Fruit Salad with Ginger-Lime Syrup, page 118,** 1 serving **graham crackers**, 4 squares TOTAL *POINTS* value: 3	**Tiramisu, page 40,** 1 serving **decaffeinated coffee**, 6 ounces TOTAL *POINTS* value: 4
POINTS VALUE	*POINTS* value for the day: 23	*POINTS* value for the day: 23	*POINTS* value for the day: 23	*POINTS* value for the day: 23

	FRIDAY	SATURDAY	SUNDAY	
BREAKFAST	**Classic Mushroom and Cheese Omelet, page 73,** 1 serving **fat-free milk,** 1 cup **TOTAL *POINTS* value: 6**	**bran flakes,** ¾ cup **banana,** 1 medium **fat-free milk,** 1 cup **TOTAL *POINTS* value: 5**	**Overnight Caramel-Pecan Bread, page 28,** 2 servings **fat-free milk,** 1 cup **TOTAL *POINTS* value: 8**	
LUNCH	**Mushroom and Onion Quesadillas, page 64,** 1 serving **salsa,** ½ cup **mixed greens salad,** 1 cup **fat-free Italian dressing,** 2 tablespoons **papaya chunks,** 1 cup **TOTAL *POINTS* value: 5**	**Southwestern Turkey Burger, page 132,** 1 serving **Simple Black-Eyed Pea and Corn Salad** (Combine ½ cup chopped tomato, ¼ cup each of canned black-eyed peas, canned corn kernels, and chopped green bell pepper; 1 tbsp each of chopped onion and chopped fresh cilantro; and 1 tsp chopped seeded jalapeño pepper. Cover and chill - *POINTS* value: **2**) **watermelon chunks,** 1 cup **TOTAL *POINTS* value: 8**	**Lemon Grass Vegetable Stew, page 152,** 1 serving **saltine crackers,** 6 **apple,** 1 medium **fat-free milk,** 1 cup **TOTAL *POINTS* value: 7**	
DINNER	**"Easy Weeknight Suppers" menu, pages 164-165** **Spaghetti Pie,** 1 serving **Creamy Veggie Dip,** 1 serving **Parmesan-Herb Bread,** 1 serving **Root Beer Floats,** 1 serving **zucchini sticks,** 1 cup **TOTAL *POINTS* value: 11**	**broiled halibut fillet,** 4 ounces **Creamed Spinach** (Coat a large non-stick skillet with cooking spray; add ¼ cup chopped onion. Sauté over medium-high heat 3 minutes or until tender. Stir in 1 [10-oz] package thawed frozen chopped spinach; cook 1 minute. Stir in ¼ cup light spreadable cheese with garlic and herbs (such as Alouette); sprinkle with 1 tbsp grated fresh Parmesan cheese *POINTS* value: **3**) **dinner roll,** 1 **TOTAL *POINTS* value: 9**	**Cumin Lamb Chops with Pear Chutney, page 87,** 1 serving **couscous,** 1 cup **mixed greens salad,** 1 cup **fat-free Italian dressing,** 2 tablespoons **TOTAL *POINTS* value: 8**	
SNACK	**reduced-fat American cheese,** 1 slice **whole wheat toast,** 1 slice **TOTAL *POINTS* value: 2**	**peach fat-free yogurt,** 8 ounces **TOTAL *POINTS* value: 2**	**sugar-free strawberry-flavored gelatin,** 1 cup **reduced-calorie whipped topping,** ¼ cup **TOTAL *POINTS* value: 1**	
POINTS VALUE	*POINTS* value for the day: 24	*POINTS* value for the day: 24	*POINTS* value for the day: 24	

One day's menu provides at least two servings of milk and at least five servings of fruits and/or vegetables.

	MONDAY	TUESDAY	WEDNESDAY	THURSDAY
BREAKFAST	**Greek Frittata, page 74,** 1 serving **fat-free milk,** 1 cup TOTAL *POINTS* value: 7	**cooked grits,** 1 cup **lean Canadian bacon,** 1 slice **fat-free milk,** 1 cup TOTAL *POINTS* value: 5	**Banana Breakfast Smoothie, page 20,** 1 serving **whole wheat toast,** 1 slice **reduced-fat American cheese,** 1 slice TOTAL *POINTS* value: 6	**Smoked Salmon Omelet** (Heat a small nonstick skillet coated with cooking spray over medium heat. Add ½ cup egg substitute; cook 2 minutes or until set. Spread 1 tbsp fat-free cream cheese over half of omelet; top with 2 oz thinly sliced smoked salmon and 1 tbsp chopped green onions. Fold in half - *POINTS* value: **3**) **fat-free milk,** 1 cup TOTAL *POINTS* value: 5
LUNCH	**Tofu and Chickpea Patties with Cucumber-Mint Relish, page 79,** 1 serving **whole wheat pita crisps,** 1 ounce (see text box on page 12 for cooking instructions) **pineapple chunks,** 1 cup TOTAL *POINTS* value: 7	**Pork and Garbanzo Bean Chili, page 162,** 1 serving **oyster crackers,** ½ cup **carrot and celery sticks,** 1 cup **pear,** 1 medium TOTAL *POINTS* value: 9	**Bacon-Egg-Arugula Sandwich, page 130,** 1 serving **Salt and Vinegar Potato Chips, page 15,** 1 serving **fresh fruit salad,** 1 cup TOTAL *POINTS* value: 6	**Margherita Pizza, page 62,** 1 serving **spinach salad,** 1 cup **fat-free Italian dressing,** 2 tablespoons **Brown Sugar-Balsamic Marinated Strawberries** (Combine 1 cup halved strawberries, 1 tsp brown sugar, and 1 tsp balsamic vinegar. Cover and let stand 30 minutes. Toss well before serving - *POINTS* value: **2**) TOTAL *POINTS* value: 7
DINNER	**Grilled Grouper Tacos, page 54,** 1 serving **Jicama-Orange Salad** (Combine ½ cup julienne-cut peeled jicama, ½ cup orange sections, 1 tbsp chopped green onions, and 2 tsp bottled low-fat vinaigrette. Cover and chill - *POINTS* value: **1**) TOTAL *POINTS* value: 5	**Marsala-Style Chicken, page 99,** 1 serving **wide egg noodles,** ¾ cup **Marinated Tomato and Cucumber Salad** (Combine ½ of a large cucumber, sliced, and ½ of a tomato, sliced, with 2 tbsp fat-free Italian dressing. Chill for 2 hours - *POINTS* value: **0**) TOTAL *POINTS* value: 7	**Salad Primavera, page 119,** 1 serving **Baked Vegetable Penne, page 75,** 1 serving **crusty French bread,** 1 ounce TOTAL *POINTS* value: 9	**grilled tenderloin steak,** 3 ounces **Cheesy Cheddar Mashed Potatoes** (Combine ¾ cup mashed cooked peeled baking potato; 2 tbsp each of reduced-fat sour cream, fat-free milk, and reduced-fat Cheddar cheese; and a dash each of salt and pepper. Mix well - *POINTS* value: **3**) **steamed asparagus,** 12 spears TOTAL *POINTS* value: 7
SNACK	**apple,** 1 medium **peanut butter,** 1 tablespoon **fat-free milk,** 1 cup TOTAL *POINTS* value: 5	**Creamy Rice Pudding with Dried Cherries, page 40,** 1 serving TOTAL *POINTS* value: 3	**Fresh Green Veggie Salsa, page 13,** 1 serving **baked low-fat tortilla chips,** 1 ounce TOTAL *POINTS* value: 3	**Peach Shortcake** (Top a 1-oz slice of angel food cake with ¾ cup sliced peaches and ¼ cup reduced-calorie whipped topping- *POINTS* value: **2**) **fat-free milk,** 1 cup TOTAL *POINTS* value: 4
POINTS VALUE	*POINTS* value for the day: 24	*POINTS* value for the day: 24	*POINTS* value for the day: 24	*POINTS* value for the day: 23

	FRIDAY	SATURDAY	SUNDAY	
BREAKFAST	**Cherry-Almond Biscotti, page 33,** 1 serving **blackberries,** 1 cup **decaffeinated coffee,** 6 ounces TOTAL *POINTS* value: 3	**cinnamon-raisin toast,** 1 slice **light butter,** 2 teaspoons **fat-free milk,** 1 cup TOTAL *POINTS* value: 5	**blueberry fat-free yogurt,** 8 ounces **low-fat granola,** ¼ cup TOTAL *POINTS* value: 3	
LUNCH	**grilled hamburger patty,** 3 ounces **whole wheat bun,** 1 **Baked French Fries** (Slice 4 oz red potatoes into ¼-inch cubed strips; place strips in a large zip-top plastic bag. Add 1 tsp olive oil and ⅛ tsp salt; toss well. Arrange on a baking sheet; bake at 450° for 15 minutes, turning once - *POINTS* value: **2**) **sliced tomato,** 1 (sprinkle with basil and black pepper) **fat-free milk,** 1 cup TOTAL *POINTS* value: 10	**Chicken and Black Bean Taco Salad with Chipotle Dressing, page 124,** 1 serving **mango chunks,** 1 cup TOTAL *POINTS* value: 8	**"Simple Sunday Brunch" menu, pages 166-167** **Mushroom Quiche,** 1 serving **Turkey Sausage Patties,** 1 serving **Spinach Salad with Grapefruit and Fennel,** 1 serving **Roasted Sweet Potatoes,** 1 serving TOTAL *POINTS* value: 12	
DINNER	**Pesto-Crusted Flounder** (Combine 2 tsp pesto, 2 tbsp breadcrumbs, and ⅛ tsp pepper in a shallow dish. Dredge a 6-oz flounder fillet in breadcrumb mxture and place in an 11 x 7-inch baking dish coated with cooking spray. Coat fillet with cooking spray. Bake at 400° for 15 minutes or until fish flakes easily when tested with a fork - *POINTS* value: **4**) **Sautéed Grape Tomatoes, page 148,** 1 serving **steamed carrots,** 1 cup **white rice,** ½ cup TOTAL *POINTS* value: 8	**Scallop Vermicelli with Spinach, page 59,** 1 serving **spinach salad,** 1 cup **fat-free balsamic vinaigrette,** 2 tablespoons **dinner roll,** 1 TOTAL *POINTS* value: 9	**Skillet Sausage Casserole, page 94,** 1 serving **steamed green beans,** 1 cup TOTAL *POINTS* value: 7	
SNACK	**raspberry fat-free yogurt,** 8 ounces **pineapple chunks,** 1 cup TOTAL *POINTS* value: 3	**fat-free chocolate pudding snack cup,** 1 TOTAL *POINTS* value: 2	**reduced-fat American cheese slice,** 1 **apple,** 1 small TOTAL POINTS value: 2	
POINTS VALUE	*POINTS* value for the day: 24	*POINTS* value for the day: 24	*POINTS* value for the day: 24	

One day's menu provides at least two servings of milk and at least five servings of fruits and/or vegetables.

	MONDAY	TUESDAY	WEDNESDAY	THURSDAY
BREAKFAST	**1% low-fat cottage cheese,** 1 cup **cantaloupe chunks,** 1 cup **orange juice,** 1 cup **TOTAL** *POINTS* value: 6	**Cranberry-Pecan Buns, page 30,** 1 serving **blueberries,** 1 cup **fat-free milk,** 1 cup **TOTAL** *POINTS* value: 7	**scrambled egg,** 1 large **bagel,** 1 small, split and toasted **reduced-fat American cheese slice,** 1 **strawberries,** 1 cup **TOTAL** *POINTS* value: 7	**oven-toasted rice cereal** (such as **Rice Krispies),** 1½ cups **banana,** 1 medium **fat-free milk,** 1 cup **TOTAL** *POINTS* value: 6
LUNCH	**Strawberry-Romaine Salad** (Combine ½ cup halved strawberries, ¼ cup grapefruit sections, 1 tsp honey, ½ tsp olive oil, and ⅛ tsp cinnamon in a bowl; let stand 30 minutes. Add 1 cup sliced romaine lettuce; toss well - *POINTS* value: 1) **Provolone Panini Sandwiches, page 127,** 1 serving **TOTAL** *POINTS* value: 7	**Asian-Style Crab Cakes, page 58,** 1 serving **spinach salad,** 1 cup **fat-free balsamic vinaigrette,** 2 tablespoons **fat-free milk,** 1 cup **TOTAL** *POINTS* value: 6	**Bow Tie Pasta and Kalamata Olive Toss, page 74,** 1 serving **Herbed Tomato-Mozzarella Salad** (Combine ½ cup halved grape tomatoes and ⅓ cup cubed fresh mozzarella cheese in a large bowl. Combine 1 tsp white balsamic vinegar, ¼ tsp olive oil, and dash each of salt, dried basil, and dried oregano in a small bowl. Stir well. Pour dressing over salad; toss well. Serve chilled - *POINTS* value: 1) **TOTAL** *POINTS* value: 6	**Ham and Cheese Grill** (Combine 2 tsp apricot preserves and 2 tsp light cream cheese. Spread over 1 slice of reduced-calorie rye bread. Top with 2 oz lean ham, 1 [¾-oz] slice fat-free Swiss cheese, and 1 slice of reduced-calorie rye bread. Melt ½ tsp butter in a skillet; add sandwich. Cook 2 minutes on each side or until golden - *POINTS* value: 4) **Gingered Butternut Squash Soup, page 156,** 1 serving **TOTAL** *POINTS* value: 7
DINNER	**Asian Burgers** (Combine 2 tbsp hoisin sauce, ¼ tsp garlic powder, ⅛ tsp ground ginger, and 6 oz ground turkey breast. Shape into a ¾-inch-thick patty. Grill or broil 5 minutes on each side or until done. Serve on a light whole wheat bun with lettuce and tomatoes - *POINTS* value: 4) **Asian Slaw with Roasted Peanuts, page 120,** 1 serving **apple,** 1 small **TOTAL** *POINTS* value: 8	**grilled pork tenderloin,** 3 ounces **Grapefruit and Avocado Salad** (Combine 1 cup torn romaine lettuce, ½ cup grapefruit sections, and ¼ cup sliced peeled avocado in a large bowl. Combine 2 tsp honey, 2 tsp white balsamic vinegar, ½ tsp Dijon mustard, and ½ tsp olive oil in a small bowl; drizzle over salad, and toss well - *POINTS* value: 3) **dinner roll,** 1 **TOTAL** *POINTS* value: 9	**Poached Salmon with Spring Vegetables, page 57,** 1 serving **crusty French bread,** 1 ounce **mixed greens salad,** 1 cup **fat-free Italian dressing,** 2 tablespoons **TOTAL** *POINTS* value: 7	**Skillet Turkey Parmesan, page 106,** 1 serving **Italian Vegetable Salad** (Combine ½ cup sliced zucchini, ½ cup quartered artichoke hearts, ¼ cup sliced carrot, and 1 tsp capers. Add 1 tbsp fat-free Italian dressing; toss to coat - *POINTS* value: 1) **fat-free milk,** 1 cup **TOTAL** *POINTS* value: 9
SNACK	**Maple-Pecan Grapefruit** (Place ½ grapefruit, cut side up, on a broiler pan. Combine 2 tsp maple syrup and ⅛ tsp vanilla extract; brush over grapefruit. Sprinkle with 1 tsp chopped pecans. Broil 5 minutes - *POINTS* value: 2) **TOTAL** *POINTS* value: 2	**Rosemary-White Bean Hummus, page 12,** 1 serving **cucumber slices,** 1 cup **TOTAL** *POINTS* value: 1	**Berry and Mousse Pastries, page 34,** 1 serving **TOTAL** *POINTS* value: 3	**angel food cake,** 2 ounces **fat-free whipped topping,** 2 tablespoons **TOTAL** *POINTS* value: 2
POINTS VALUE	*POINTS* value for the day: 23	*POINTS* value for the day: 23	*POINTS* value for the day: 23	*POINTS* value for the day: 24

	FRIDAY	SATURDAY	SUNDAY	
BREAKFAST	**cooked oatmeal,** 1 cup (sprinkle with cinnamon) **fat-free milk,** 1 cup **TOTAL *POINTS* value: 4**	**whole wheat English muffin,** 1 **light butter,** 2 tablespoons **vanilla fat-free yogurt,** 8 ounces **TOTAL *POINTS* value: 5**	**cooked cream of wheat,** 1 cup **honey,** 1 tablespoon **blueberries,** 1 cup **fat-free milk,** 1 cup **TOTAL *POINTS* value: 6**	
LUNCH	**Pecan-Crusted Chicken Fingers with Dijon-Maple Sauce, page 98,** 1 serving **spinach salad,** 1 cup **sliced tomato,** 1 **fat-free Italian dressing,** 2 tablespoons **TOTAL *POINTS* value: 6**	**Curried Pumpkin Stew with Roasted Pepitas, page 156,** 1 serving **Apricot Greens and Swiss with Ginger Vinaigrette, page 118,** 1 serving **saltine crackers,** 6 **TOTAL *POINTS* value: 10**	**Risotto with Spinach and Shrimp, page 60,** 1 serving **sliced fresh tomatoes and cucumbers,** 1 cup **fat-free Italian dressing,** 2 tablespoons **TOTAL *POINTS* value: 5**	
DINNER	**"Off the Grill" menu, pages 168-169** **Molasses-Bourbon Grilled Salmon,** 1 serving **Grilled Vegetable Platter,** 1 serving **Grilled Bananas with Ice Cream and Caramel Sauce,** 1 serving **Ginger Peach Tea,** 1 serving **TOTAL *POINTS* value: 12**	**Dijon Steak with Orange Balsamic Sauce, page 85,** 1 serving **Citrus Roasted Brussels Sprouts, page 144,** 1 serving **wild rice,** ¾ cup **TOTAL *POINTS* value: 7**	**Lemon-Caper Chicken** (Cook 1 (6-oz) chicken breast half in a nonstick skillet coated with cooking spray over medium-high heat 6 minutes on each side. Remove from pan. Melt 1 tsp butter in pan; stir in 1 tbsp brown sugar, 1 tbsp lemon juice, 1 tsp capers, ¼ tsp dry mustard, ⅛ tsp salt, and ⅛ tsp pepper. Combine 1 tsp cornstarch and 2 tbsp water; add to pan. Cook 1 minute or until thick; stir constantly. Spoon over chicken - ***POINTS* value: 6)** **wide egg noodles,** 1 cup **steamed broccoli,** 1 cup **TOTAL *POINTS* value: 9**	
SNACK	**fat-free chocolate pudding snack cup,** 1 **TOTAL *POINTS* value: 2**	**reduced-fat American cheese,** 1 slice **apple,** 1 small **TOTAL *POINTS* value: 2**	**vanilla low-fat ice cream,** ½ cup **sliced strawberries,** ½ cup **fat-free chocolate sauce,** 1 tablespoon **TOTAL *POINTS* value: 4**	
POINTS VALUE	***POINTS* value for the day: 24**	***POINTS* value for the day: 24**	***POINTS* value for the day: 24**	

181

General Recipe Index

Almond Biscotti, Cherry-, 33
Ambrosia, Island, 118
Appetizers. *See also* **Snacks**.
  Bruschetta, Charred
    Tomato, 16
  Crostini, Roasted Red Pepper
    and Escarole, 16
  Dips
      Hummus, Lentil, 12
      Hummus, Rosemary-White
        Bean, 12
      Hummus with Avocado and
        Lime, 12
      Spinach and Sundried Tomato
        Cheese Dip, 14
      Veggie Dip,
        Creamy, 165
  Empanadas, Picadillo, 17
  Kalamata-Herb Cream
    Cheese, 14
  Quesadillas, Roasted Corn and
    Chicken, 18
  Spread, Black Bean and Goat
    Cheese, 14
Apples
  Crisp, Apple Cider, 34
  Pork Loin with Maple-Mustard
    Sauce, Apple-Stuffed, 88
  Relish, Citrus Cran-Apple, 173
  Slaw and Ham Sandwiches,
    Apple, 131
  Strudel, Apple, 34
Apricot Greens and Swiss with
    Ginger Vinaigrette, 118
Apricot Scones, Glazed, 27
Artichokes
  Calzones, Artichoke, Mushroom,
    and Prosciutto, 130
  Pizza with Chicken, Artichokes,
    and Basil, 96
  Risotto, Lemon
    Artichoke, 150
  Salad, Artichoke-Pepperoncini
    Pasta, 123
Asparagus and Eggs, Fried Rice
    with, 78
Asparagus Spears with
    Lemon-Tarragon Butter, 142
Avocado and Lime, Hummus
    with, 12
Avocado Salad, Grapefruit
    and, 180

Bacon
  Brussels Sprouts with Tomato,
    Olives, and Bacon, 143
  Salad, Pan-Seared Scallops and
    Bacon, 124
  Sandwiches, Bacon-Egg-
    Arugula, 130
Bananas
  Cupcakes, Banana Pudding Ice
    Cream, 50
  Grilled Caramel-Banana
    Sundaes, 169
  Muffins, Toasted Coconut
    Banana, 26
  Smoothie, Banana Breakfast, 20
Barley
  Black Beans and Barley, 149
  Brussels Sprouts, Barley and, 149
  Salad, Barley and Vegetable
    Chopped, 122
Beans
  Baby Lima Bean Soup with Crispy
    Sage, 153
  Black
      Barley, Black Beans and, 149
      Black Bean and Couscous Salad
        with Jalapeño-Lemon
        Dressing, 121
      Salad with Chipotle Dressing,
        Chicken and Black Bean
        Taco, 124
      Salsa, Black Bean and
        Tomatillo, 93
      Spread, Black Bean and Goat
        Cheese, 14
  Burritos, Bean and Roasted
    Vegetable, 64
  Chickpea Patties with Cucumber
    Mint Relish, Tofu and, 79
  Enchiladas, Turkey and Bean, 105
  Garbanzo Bean Chili, Pork and, 162
  Green
      Casserole, Green Bean, 142
      Roasted Green Beans, 174
      Salad with Caramelized
        Onions, Green Bean, 120
  Pizza, Vegetarian Tortilla, 63
  White
      Chicken with White Beans,
        Rosemary, 101
      Hummus, Rosemary-White
        Bean, 12

  Oreganata, White Beans, 79
  Soup, Roasted Vegetable and
    White Bean, 161
  Tomatoes, Zesty White Beans
    and, 143
Beef. *See also* **Beef, Ground**.
  Salad, Roast Beef and Blue
    Cheese, 175
  Sandwiches, Roast Beef on
    Rye, 129
  Steaks
      Dijon Steak with Orange-
        Balsamic Sauce, 85
      Filet Mignon with Rosemary-
        Port Sauce, 85
      Filet Mignon with Sherry-
        Mushroom Sauce, 86
      Flank Steak, Lime-
        Marinated, 83
      Korean Beef with Spicy
        Cabbage, 84
      Quesadilla, Blue Cheese and
        Steak, 174
      Tenderloin Steak with
        Cherry-Port Sauce, Beef, 84
Beef, Ground
  Cinnamon Beef over Couscous, 83
  Minestrone, Beef, 162
  Pastitsio, 82
  Pie, Spaghetti, 164
  Sandwiches, Loose Meat, 130
  Spaghetti with Fresh Basil Meat
    Sauce, 83
Beverages
  Chiller, Strawberry, 20
  Floats, Root Beer, 165
  Hot Chocolate, Orange-
    Flavored, 19
  Latte, Triple Chocolate
    Mocha, 19
  Melon Agua Fresca, 20
  Smoothie, Banana Breakfast, 20
  Smoothie, Strawberry, 174
Biscuits, Dijon-Cracked Pepper
    Drop, 26
Biscuits, Skillet Chicken and, 97
Breads *See also* **specific types**.
  Focaccia, Rosemary and
    Kalamata, 28
  Herb Bread, Buttery, 26
  Overnight Caramel-Pecan
    Bread, 28

Parmesan-Herb Bread, 165
Popovers with Lemon Butter,
    Rosemary, 27
Scones, Glazed Apricot, 27
Spoonbread, Sweet Corn, 28
Walnut Bread, Pear and Creamy
    Swiss Cheese on, 126
Yeast
    Cranberry Pecan Buns, 30
    Dill and Cheddar Loaf, 29
    Parmesan Twist, 29
    White Bread, Basic, 29
    Whole Wheat Bread,
        Caraway-Raisin, 30
Broccoli, Lemon, 143
Brussels Sprouts
Barley and Brussels Sprouts, 149
Roasted Brussels Sprouts,
    Citrus, 144
Roasted Brussels Sprouts,
    Garlic-, 173
Tomato, Olives, and Bacon, Brussels
    Sprouts with, 143
Burritos, Bean and Roasted
    Vegetable, 64
Butter
Lemon Butter, Mixed Seafood Grill
    with, 58
Lemon Butter, Rosemary Popovers
    with, 27
Lemon-Tarragon Butter, Asparagus
    Spears with, 142

Cabbage
Spicy Cabbage, 84
Spicy Cabbage, Korean Beef
    with, 84
Toss, Cabbage, Onion, and
    Pepper, 144
Cakes
Carrot Cake with Cream Cheese
    Frosting, 38
Cheesecake, Pumpkin, 37
Chocolate-Toffee Pudding
    Cake, 39
Cupcakes, Banana Pudding Ice
    Cream, 50
Dark Chocolate and Raspberry
    Layer Cake, 37
Pound Cake, Peach Preserves, 39
Shortcake, Peach, 178
Upside-Down Cake with Pecans,
    Pear, 38
Caramel-Pecan Bread, Overnight, 28
Caramel-Banana Sundaes,
    Grilled , 169

Carrots
Cake with Cream Cheese Frosting,
    Carrot, 38
Moroccan Carrots, 145
Sauté, Carrot-Edamame, 144
Soup, Spiced Carrot, 152
Casseroles
Enchiladas, Chicken and Rice, 97
Green Bean Casserole, 142
Pastitsio, 82
Roasted Poblano and Potato
    Gratin, 146
Sausage Casserole, Skillet, 94
Shells with Three Cheeses, Baked, 75
Turkey Sausage and Pasta Bake, 107
Vegetable
    Sweet Potato Casserole, Brown
        Sugar-Crusted, 173
Cauliflower, Garlicky, 145
Cheese
Breads
    Dill and Cheddar Loaf, 29
    Parmesan-Herb Bread, 165
    Twist, Parmesan, 29
Dip, Spinach and Sundried Tomato
    Cheese, 14
Frosting, Carrot Cake with Cream
    Cheese, 38
Greens and Swiss with Ginger
    Vinaigrette, Apricot, 118
Kalamata-Herb Cream Cheese, 14
Mashed Potatoes, Gorgonzola and
    Chive, 147
Oat Grain-Feta Salad, 122
Omelets, Classic Mushroom and
    Cheese, 73
Pizza, Grilled Provolone and
    Vegetable, 62
Polenta, Parmesan, 150
Polenta with Fontina, 171
Potato Chips, Chive-Parmesan, 15
Quesadilla, Blue Cheese and
    Steak, 174
Salad, Herbed Tomato-
    Mozzarella, 180
Salad, Roast Beef and Blue
    Cheese, 175
Sandwiches
    Grilled Double Cheese and
        Tomato Sandwiches, 126
    Grilled Mozzarella Chicken
        Sandwiches, 132
    Grill, Ham and Cheese, 180
    Panini Sandwiches,
        Provolone, 127
    Swiss Cheese on Walnut Bread,
        Pear and Creamy, 126

Shells with Three Cheeses,
    Baked, 75
Spread, Black Bean and Goat
    Cheese, 14
Tiramisu, 40
Turkey Parmesan, Skillet, 106
Vegetables
    Baked Potatoes, Cheddar and
        Blue Cheese Twice-, 77
    Mashed Potatoes, Cheesy
        Cheddar, 178
    Spinach, Creamed, 177
    Zucchini, Parmesan-Herb, 149
Cherries
Biscotti, Cherry-Almond, 33
Pudding with Dried Cherries,
    Creamy Rice, 40
Sauce, Beef Tenderloin Steak with
    Cherry-Port, 84
Chicken
Balsamic Chicken and Rice
    Skillet, 103
Cajun Chicken, 100
Cranberry-Orange Chicken, 102
Creamed Chicken with
    Noodles, 98
Dumplings, Hearty Chicken
    and, 104
Enchiladas, Chicken and Rice, 97
Fingers with Dijon-Maple Sauce,
    Pecan-Crusted Chicken, 98
Herbed Roasted Chicken, 104
Lemon-Caper Chicken, 181
Marsala-Style Chicken, 99
Mexican-Style Chicken, 102
"Osso Bucco"-Style Chicken, 170
Pizza, Chicken and Spinach, 96
Pizza, Southwest Chicken, 96
Pizza with Chicken, Artichokes, and
    Basil, 96
Quesadillas, Roasted Corn and
    Chicken, 18
Rosemary Chicken with White
    Beans, 100
Salad with Chipotle Dressing,
    Chicken and Black Bean
    Taco, 124
Sandwiches
    Grilled Mozzarella Chicken
        Sandwiches, 132
    Pita, Greek Chicken Salad, 132
    Wraps, Chicken and Vegetable
        Garden, 131
Satay with Peanut Dipping Sauces,
    Chicken Tenders, 18
Skillet Chicken and Biscuits, 97
Soup, Chicken Wonton, 163

Chicken *(continued)*

Stuffed Chicken Breasts, Tomato-Basil-, 101
Stuffed Chicken Breasts with Marsala Cream Sauce, 101
Thighs Piccata-Style, Chicken, 103
Tortillas, Spicy Chicken, 99
Yellow Pepper Chipotle Chicken, 102
Chili, Pork and Garbanzo Bean, 162

Chocolate
Brownies, Mocha-Dark Chocolate Chunk, 32
Cake, Chocolate-Toffee Pudding, 39
Cake, Dark Chocolate and Raspberry Layer, 37
Crème Brûlée, Dark Chocolate, 49
Drops, Brownie Oatmeal, 32
Hot Chocolate, Orange-Flavored, 19
Ice Cream Bars, Mint Brownie, 50
Latte, Triple Chocolate Mocha, 19
Sundae, Triple Chocolate, 175
Chowder, Roasted Pepper and Corn, 154
Chowder, Two Potato, 155
Chutney, Pear, 87

Coconut
Muffins, Toasted Coconut Banana, 26
Rice, Coconut, 80
Shrimp, Creamy Coconut, 60

Coffee
Cappuccino, Frozen Hazelnut, 171
Mocha-Dark Chocolate Chunk Brownies, 32
Mocha Latte, Triple Chocolate, 19
Tiramisu, 40

Cookies
Bars, Ginger-Lime, 32
Biscotti, Cherry-Almond, 33
Brownies, Mocha-Dark Chocolate Chunk, 32
Drops, Brownie Oatmeal, 32
Sugar Cookies, Lemon-Glazed, 33

Corn
Chowder, Roasted Pepper and Corn, 154
Pilaf, Corn and Pecan, 145
Roasted Corn and Chicken Quesadillas, 18
Roasted Corn Salsa, 13
Salad, Simple Black-Eyed Pea and Corn, 177
Spoonbread, Sweet Corn, 28
Tomatoes, Summer Corn and, 146

Cornish Hens
Oriental Hens, 108

Couscous
Beef over Couscous, Cinnamon, 83
Black Bean and Couscous Salad with Jalapeño-Lemon Dressing, 121
Orange Couscous, Butternut Squash Stuffed with, 77
Salad, Mediterranean Couscous and Lentil, 122
Crab Cakes, Asian-Style, 58

Cranberries
Buns, Cranberry Pecan, 30
Chicken, Cranberry-Orange, 102
Custard with Maple Cream, Pumpkin-Cranberry, 49
Jelly, Cranberry-Spiced Pepper, 15
Relish, Citrus Cran-Apple, 173
Salad, Cranberry Rice, 123
Sauce, Turkey Scaloppine in Cranberry-Port, 106
Cucumber Mint Relish, 79
Cucumber Salad, Marinated Tomato and, 178

Curry
Mussels, Curried, 59
Red Curry Peanut Sauce, 19
Red Curry Tofu Stir-Fry, 80
Shrimp, Thai Curry, 60
Stew with Roasted Pepitas, Curried Pumpkin, 156

Desserts. *See also* **specific types**.
Caramel-Banana Sundaes, Grilled, 169
Cream, Maple, 49
Crème Brûlée, Dark Chocolate, 49
Custard with Maple Cream, Pumpkin-Cranberry, 49

Frozen
Frozen Hazelnut Cappuccino, 171
Ice Cream Bars, Mint Brownie, 50
Ice Cream Cupcakes, Banana Pudding, 50
Sorbet, Raspberry Lemonade, 50
Sundae, Triple Chocolate, 175
Tiramisu, 40
Dumplings, Hearty Chicken and, 104

Edamame Salad, 120
Edamame Sauté, Carrot-, 144

Eggplant
Frittata, Greek, 74
Sandwiches, Open-Faced Eggplant-Olive, 126

Eggs
Fried Rice with Asparagus and Eggs, 78
Frittata, Greek, 74
Frittata with Whole Wheat Spaghetti and Spinach, 73
Omelet, Classic Mushroom and Cheese, 73
Omelet, Smoked Salmon, 178
Sandwich, Breakfast, 174
Sandwiches, Bacon-Egg-Arugula, 130
Enchiladas, Chicken and Rice, 97
Enchiladas, Turkey and Bean, 105

Fish. *See also* **specific types; Seafood**.
Amberjack Skewers, Teriyaki, 52
Catfish, Cajun, 175
Catfish, Cornmeal- and Pecan-Crusted, 53
Flounder, Pan-Fried, 53
Flounder, Pesto-Crusted, 179
Grouper Tacos, Grilled, 54
Grouper with Tomato-Dill Sauce, Lemon, 54
Halibut, Oven-Roasted, 55
Halibut with Warm Scallions, Mustard-Glazed, 55
Mahimahi Fingers with Creamy Dill Tartar Sauce, 56
Seared Fish with Tomato-Tarragon Salsa, 52
Snapper with Garlic-Herb Vinaigrette, Pan-Seared, 57
Striped Bass en Papillote, 52
Tilapia, Southwestern, 58
Frittata, Greek, 74
Frittata with Whole Wheat Spaghetti and Spinach, 73

Fruit. *See also* **specific type**.
Pastries, Berry and Mousse, 34
Salads
Ambrosia, Island, 118
Cantaloupe-Pineapple-Ginger Fruit Salad, 118
Fresh Fruit Salad with Lime-Ginger Syrup, 118
Greens with Fresh Berries, Crunchy Pecan, 119
Salsa, Ginger Fruit, 13
Soup, Gingered Peach Fruit, 152

Garlic

Carrots, Moroccan, 145
Cauliflower, Garlicky, 145
Chicken, "Osso Bucco"-Style, 170
Chicken, Yellow Pepper Chipotle, 102
Garlic-Roasted Brussels Sprouts, 173
Minestrone, Beef, 162
Oreganata, White Beans, 79
Pizza, Margherita, 62
Po' Boys, Fresh Vegetable, 127
Risotto with Spinach and Shrimp, 60
Roasted Garlic and Basil, Creamy Tomato Soup with, 161
Soup with Crispy Sage, Baby Lima Bean, 153

Grapefruit

Maple-Pecan Grapefruit, 180
Salad, Grapefruit and Avocado, 180
Salad with Grapefruit and Fennel, Spinach, 167
Salsa, Pork with Grapefruit-Mint, 93

Grilled

Caramel-Banana Sundaes, Grilled, 169
Chicken Sandwiches, Grilled Mozzarella, 132
Chicken Tenders Satay with Peanut Dipping Sauces, 18
Fish and Shellfish
    Amberjack Skewers, Teriyaki, 52
    Grouper Tacos, Grilled, 54
    Salmon, Molasses-Bourbon Grilled, 168
    Seafood Grill with Lemon Butter, Mixed, 58
    Tuna Burgers with Mango-Jalapeño Jam, Fresh, 129
Flank Steak, Lime-Marinated, 83
Pizza, Grilled Provolone and Vegetable, 62
Pork Chops with Orange-Olive Relish, Grilled, 87
Portobello Mushrooms, Grilled, 147
Turkey Kabobs, Caribbean Grilled, 107
Vegetable Platter, Grilled, 169

Ham. *See also* **Bacon, Pork**.

Prosciutto, and Pine Nut Salad, Pear, 119
Sandwiches
    Apple Slaw and Ham Sandwiches, 131

Calzones, Artichoke, Mushroom, and Prosciutto, 130
Grill, Ham and Cheese, 180
Skillet Ham with Pineapple-Ginger Salsa, 94
Hummus, Lentil, 12
Hummus, Rosemary-White Bean, 12

Jam, Mango-Jalapeño, 129

Jelly, Cranberry-Spiced Pepper, 15
Jicama-Orange Salad, 178

Kabobs

Amberjack Skewers, Teriyaki, 52
Chicken Tenders Satay with Peanut Dipping Sauces, 18
Seafood Grill with Lemon Butter, Mixed, 58
Shrimp Skewers, Broiled, 176
Turkey Kabobs, Caribbean Grilled, 107

Lamb Chops with Pear Chutney, Cumin, 86

Lemon

Broccoli, Lemon, 143
Butter, Asparagus Spears with Lemon-Tarragon, 142
Butter, Mixed Seafood Grill with Lemon, 58
Butter, Rosemary Popovers with Lemon, 27
Chicken, Lemon-Caper, 181
Chicken Thighs Piccata-Style, 103
Cookies, Lemon-Glazed Sugar, 33
Greens on Red Pepper Focaccia, Fresh Lemon, 128
Grouper with Tomato-Dill Sauce, Lemon, 54
Linguine, Fresh Lemon and Pepper, 176
Pie in Biscotti Crust, Lemonade Pudding, 36
Risotto, Lemon Artichoke, 150
Salad, Lemon-Dill Potato, 121
Sorbet, Raspberry Lemonade, 50
Lentil Hummus, 12
Lentil Salad, Mediterranean Couscous and, 122

Lime

Bars, Ginger-Lime, 32
Flank Steak, Lime-Marinated, 83

Hummus with Avocado and Lime, 12
Syrup, Fresh Fruit Salad with Lime-Ginger, 118
Linguine, Fresh Lemon and Pepper, 176

Mango-Jalapeño Jam, 129

Meat Loaf with Roasted Red Bell Pepper Sauce, Turkey, 105

Melons

Agua Fresca, Melon, 20
Cantaloupe-Pineapple-Ginger Fruit Salad, 118
Watermelon with Mint Syrup, 174

Microwave

Dip, Spinach and Sundried Tomato Cheese, 14
Drops, Brownie Oatmeal, 32
Pork Loin with Maple-Mustard Sauce, Apple-Stuffed, 88
Pudding with Dried Cherries, Creamy Rice, 40
Vegetables
    Brussels Sprouts with Tomato, Olives, and Bacon, 143
    Green Bean Casserole, 142
    Poblano and Potato Gratin, Roasted, 146
    Potatoes, Cheddar and Blue Cheese Twice-Baked, 77
    Potatoes, Stuffed New, 16
Muffins, Toasted Coconut Banana, 26

Mushrooms

Alfredo, Creamy Spinach and Mushroom, 74
Calzones, Artichoke, Mushroom, and Prosciutto, 130
Omelets, Classic Mushroom and Cheese, 73
Portobello Mushrooms, Grilled, 147
Quesadillas, Mushroom and Onion, 64
Quiche, Mushroom, 166
Risotto with Spinach and Mushrooms, 76
Sauce, Filet Mignon with Sherry-Mushroom, 86
Sauce, Stuffed Pasta Shells with Tofu Mushroom, 76
Veal Cutlets with Wine-Braised Mushrooms, 86
Mussels, Curried, 59
Mustard Sauce, Maple-, 88

Noodles, Creamed Chicken with, 98

Oat Grain-Feta Salad, 122
Oatmeal Drops, Brownie, 32
Oatmeal, Peaches and Cream, 176
Olives
    Brussels Sprouts with Tomato,
        Olives, and Bacon, 143
    Kalamata Focaccia, Rosemary
        and, 28
    Kalamata-Herb Cream Cheese, 14
    Kalamata Olive Toss, Bow Tie Pasta
        and, 74
    Relish, Orange-Olive, 87
    Salad with Onions and Olives,
        Orange, 171
    Sandwiches, Open-Faced Eggplant-
        Olive, 126
Omelets, Classic Mushroom and
    Cheese, 73
Omelet, Smoked Salmon, 178
Onions
    Caramelized Onions, Green Bean
        Salad with, 120
    Quesadillas, Mushroom and
        Onion, 64
    Salad with Onions and Olives,
        Orange, 171
    Sauce, Baked Salmon with Creamy
        Onion, 56
    Scallions, Mustard-Glazed Halibut
        with Warm, 55
    Soup, Classic French Onion, 154
    Toss, Cabbage, Onion, and
        Pepper, 144
Oranges
    Berry Pilaf, Orange-Kissed, 150
    Chicken, Cranberry-Orange, 102
    Couscous, Butternut Squash Stuffed
        with Orange, 77
    Hot Chocolate, Orange-
        Flavored, 19
    Relish, Orange-Olive, 87
    Salad, Jicama-Orange, 178
    Salad with Onions and Olives,
        Orange, 171
    Sauce, Dijon Steak with Orange-
        Balsamic, 85

Pancakes, Cornmeal, 27
Pastas. *See also* **specific types**.
    Bake, Turkey Sausage and Pasta, 107
    Bow Tie Pasta and Kalamata Olive
        Toss, 74
    Pastitsio, 82

Penne, Baked Vegetable, 75
Salad, Artichoke-Pepperoncini
    Pasta, 123
Salad, Greek Pasta, 175
Shells with Three Cheeses,
    Baked, 75
Shells with Tofu Mushroom Sauce,
    Stuffed Pasta, 76
Vermicelli with Spinach, Scallop, 59
Pastitsio, 82
Peaches
    Oatmeal, Peaches and Cream, 176
    Pies, Quick Peach and
        Raspberry, 36
    Pound Cake, Peach Preserves, 39
    Shortcake, Peach, 178
    Soup, Gingered Peach Fruit, 152
    Tea, Ginger-Peach, 169
Peanut Butter
    Sauce, Peanut Dipping, 19
    Sauce, Red Curry Peanut, 19
Peanuts, Asian Slaw with Roasted, 120
Pears
    Chutney, Pear, 87
    Salad, Pear, Prosciutto, and Pine
        Nut, 119
    Upside-Down Cake with Pecans,
        Pear, 38
    Walnut Bread, Pear and Creamy
        Swiss Cheese on, 126
Pea and Corn Salad, Simple
    Black-Eyed, 177
Pecans
    Bread, Overnight Caramel-Pecan, 28
    Buns, Cranberry Pecan, 30
    Cake with Pecans, Pear Upside-
        Down, 38
    Catfish, Cornmeal- and
        Pecan-Crusted, 53
    Chicken Fingers with Dijon-Maple
        Sauce, Pecan-Crusted, 98
    Grapefruit, Maple-Pecan, 180
    Greens with Fresh Berries, Crunchy
        Pecan, 119
    Pilaf, Corn and Pecan, 145
    Sweet Potatoes, Maple-Pecan, 147
Peppers
    Cabbage, Spicy, 84
    Chicken, Mexican-Style, 102
    Chile
        Chipotle Red Pepper
            Soup, 154
        Chipotle Shrimp Bisque,
            Creamy, 162
        Poblano and Potato Gratin,
            Roasted, 146
    Jalapeño Jam, Mango-, 129

Red
    Focaccia, Fresh Lemon Greens
        on Red Pepper, 128
    Roasted Red Bell Pepper
        Sauce, 105
    Roasted Red Pepper and
        Escarole Crostini, 16
    Roasted Pepper and Corn
        Chowder, 154
    Salad, Artichoke-Pepperoncini
        Pasta, 123
    Toss, Cabbage, Onion, and
        Pepper, 144
    Yellow Pepper Chipotle
        Chicken, 102
Pies and Pastries
    Crisp, Apple Cider, 34
    Lemonade Pudding Pie in Biscotti
        Crust, 36
    Pastries
        Berry and Mousse
            Pastries, 34
        Empanadas, Picadillo, 17
        Strudel, Apple, 34
    Peach and Raspberry Pies,
        Quick, 36
    Spaghetti Pie, 164
Pilaf, Orange-Kissed Berry, 150
Pineapple-Ginger Fruit Salad,
    Cantaloupe-, 118
Pineapple-Ginger Salsa, Skillet
    Ham with, 94
Pizza
    Chicken and Spinach Pizza, 96
    Chicken, Artichokes, and Basil,
        Pizza with, 96
    Chicken Pizza, Southwest, 96
    Grilled Provolone and Vegetable
        Pizza, 62
    Margherita Pizza, 62
    Mediterranean Pizza with Whole
        Wheat Crust, 63
    Vegetarian Tortilla Pizza, 63
Polenta
    Fontina, Polenta with, 171
    Pan-Seared Polenta with
        Mediterranean Vegetables, 78
    Parmesan Polenta, 150
Pork
    Chili, Pork and Garbanzo
        Bean, 162
    Chops with Orange-Olive Relish,
        Grilled Pork, 87
    Loin with Maple-Mustard Sauce,
        Apple-Stuffed Pork, 88
    Roast, Holiday Herbed
        Pork, 172

Tenderloin
    Grapefruit-Mint Salsa, Pork
       with, 93
    Roasted Italian Pork
       Tenderloin, 94
    Spicy Pork with Black Bean
       and Tomatillo Salsa, 93

Potatoes. *See also* **Sweet Potatoes**.
    Baked Potatoes, Cheddar and Blue
       Cheese Twice-, 77
    Chips, Chive-Parmesan Potato, 15
    Chowder, Two Potato, 155
    French Fries, Baked, 179
    Gratin, Roasted Poblano and
       Potato, 146
    Mashed Potatoes, Cheesy
       Cheddar, 178
    Mashed Potatoes, Gorgonzola and
       Chive, 147
    New Potatoes, Stuffed, 16
    Oven-Roasted Potato Wedges, 146
    Salad, Lemon-Dill Potato, 121
    Salad, Warm Potato and
       Sausage, 121
    Pudding Ice Cream Cupcakes,
       Banana, 50
    Pudding with Dried Cherries, Creamy
       Rice, 40

Pumpkin
    Cheesecake, Pumpkin, 37
    Custard with Maple Cream,
       Pumpkin-Cranberry, 49
    Stew with Roasted Pepitas, Curried
       Pumpkin, 156

Quesadillas
    Blue Cheese and Steak
       Quesadilla, 174
    Mushroom and Onion
       Quesadillas, 64
    Roasted Corn and Chicken
       Quesadillas, 18
Quiche, Mushroom, 166

Raisin Whole Wheat Bread,
    Caraway-, 30
Raspberries
    Cake, Dark Chocolate and
       Raspberry Layer, 37
    Pies, Quick Peach and Raspberry, 36
    Sorbet, Raspberry Lemonade, 50
Relishes
    Cran-Apple Relish, Citrus, 173
    Cucumber Mint Relish, 79
    Orange-Olive Relish, 87

Rice
    Chicken and Rice Skillet,
       Balsamic, 103
    Coconut Rice, 80
    Enchiladas, Chicken and Rice, 97
    Fried Rice with Asparagus and
       Eggs, 78
    Pilaf, Corn and Pecan, 145
    Pudding with Dried Cherries,
       Creamy Rice, 40
    Risotto, Lemon Artichoke, 150
    Risotto with Spinach and
       Mushrooms, 76
    Risotto with Spinach and Shrimp, 60
    Salad, Cranberry Rice, 123
    Yellow Squash Rice, 148

Salads and Salad Dressings
    Ambrosia, Island, 118
    Artichoke-Pepperoncini Pasta
       Salad, 123
    Barley and Vegetable Chopped
       Salad, 122
    Black Bean and Couscous Salad
       with Jalapeño-Lemon
       Dressing, 121
    Black-Eyed Pea and Corn Salad,
       Simple, 177
    Caesar Salad, 176
    Cantaloupe-Pineapple-Ginger Fruit
       Salad, 118
    Chicken Salad Pita, Greek, 132
    Couscous and Lentil Salad,
       Mediterranean, 122
    Edamame Salad, 120
    Fruit Salad with Lime-Ginger
       Syrup, Fresh, 118
    Grapefruit and Avocado
       Salad, 180
    Green Bean Salad with Caramelized
       Onions, 120
    Greens and Swiss with Ginger
       Vinaigrette, Apricot, 118
    Greens on Red Pepper Focaccia,
       Fresh Lemon, 128
    Greens with Fresh Berries, Crunchy
       Pecan, 119
    Jicama-Orange Salad, 178
    Marinated Tomato and Cucumber
       Salad, 178
    Oat Grain-Feta Salad, 122
    Orange Salad with Onions and
       Olives, 171
    Pasta Salad, Greek, 175
    Pear, Prosciutto, and Pine Nut
       Salad, 119

Potato and Sausage Salad,
    Warm, 121
Potato Salad, Lemon-Dill, 121
Primavera, Salad, 119
Rice Salad, Cranberry, 123
Roast Beef and Blue Cheese
    Salad, 175
Salmon Salad, 123
Salmon Salad Sandwiches, Open-
    Faced, 128
Scallops and Bacon Salad, Pan-
    Seared, 124
Slaw with Roasted Peanuts,
    Asian, 120
Spinach Salad with Grapefruit and
    Fennel, 167
Strawberry-Romaine Salad, 180
Taco Salad with Chipotle Dressing,
    Chicken and Black Bean, 124
Tomato-Mozzarella Salad,
    Herbed, 180
Vegetable Salad, Italian, 180

Salmon
    Baked Salmon with Creamy Onion
       Sauce, 56
    Grilled Salmon, Molasses-
       Bourbon, 168
    Pan-Seared Salmon with Honey-
       Balsamic Sauce, 56
    Poached Salmon with Spring
       Vegetables, 57
    Salad, Salmon, 123
    Salad Sandwiches, Open-Faced
       Salmon, 128
    Smoked Salmon Omelet, 178

Salsas. *See also* **Sauces**.
    Black Bean and Tomatillo
       Salsa, 93
    Fruit Salsa, Ginger, 13
    Grapefruit-Mint Salsa, Pork
       with, 93
    Green Veggie Salsa, Fresh, 13
    Pineapple-Ginger Salsa, Skillet Ham
       with, 94
    Roasted Corn Salsa, 13
    Soup, Chilled Mexican-Style
       Salsa, 152
    Tomato-Tarragon Salsa, Seared Fish
       with, 52

Sandwiches
    Apple Slaw and Ham
       Sandwiches, 131
    Bacon-Egg-Arugula
       Sandwiches, 130
    Breakfast Sandwich, 174
    Burgers, Asian, 180
    Burgers, Southwestern Turkey, 132

Sandwiches *(continued)*

Burgers with Mango-Jalapeño Jam, Fresh Tuna, 129
Calzones, Artichoke, Mushroom, and Prosciutto, 130
Focaccia, Fresh Lemon Greens on Red Pepper, 128
Grilled Double Cheese and Tomato Sandwiches, 126
Grilled Mozzarella Chicken Sandwiches, 132
Ham and Cheese Grill, 180
Meat Sandwiches, Loose, 130
Open-Faced Eggplant-Olive Sandwiches, 126
Open-Faced Salmon Salad Sandwiches, 128
Panini Sandwiches, Provolone, 127
Pear and Creamy Swiss Cheese on Walnut Bread, 126
Pita, Greek Chicken Salad, 132
Po' Boys, Fresh Vegetable, 127
Po'Boys, Shrimp, 128
Roast Beef on Rye Sandwiches, 129
Wraps, Chicken and Vegetable Garden, 131

Sauces. *See also* **Salsas**.

Basil Meat Sauce, Spaghetti with Fresh, 83
Cherry-Port Sauce, Beef Tenderloin Steak with, 84
Cranberry-Port Sauce, Turkey Scaloppine in, 106
Dijon-Maple Sauce, Pecan-Crusted Chicken Fingers with, 98
Dill Tartar Sauce, Mahimahi Fingers with Creamy, 56
Garlic-Herb Vinaigrette, Pan-Seared Snapper with, 57
Ginger Sauce, Scallops with Mild Creamy, 59
Honey-Balsamic Sauce, Pan-Seared Salmon with, 56
Maple Cream, 49
Maple-Mustard Sauce, 88
Marsala Cream Sauce, Stuffed Chicken Breasts with, 101
Onion Sauce, Baked Salmon with Creamy, 56
Orange-Balsamic Sauce, Dijon Steak with, 85
Peanut Dipping Sauce, 19
Puttanesca Sauce, Turkey Cutlets with, 108

Red Curry Peanut Sauce, 19
Roasted Red Bell Pepper Sauce, 105
Rosemary-Port Sauce, Filet Mignon with, 85
Sherry-Mushroom Sauce, Filet Mignon with, 86
Tofu Mushroom Sauce, Stuffed Pasta Shells with, 76
Tomato-Dill Sauce, Lemon Grouper with, 54

Sausage

Andouille Posole, Spicy, 163
Casserole, Skillet Sausage, 94
Patties, Turkey Sausage, 167
Salad, Warm Potato and Sausage, 121
Turkey Sausage and Pasta Bake, 107

Scallops

Ginger Sauce, Scallops with Mild Creamy, 59
Pan-Seared Scallops and Bacon Salad, 124
Vermicelli with Spinach, Scallop, 59

Seafood. *See also* **specific types; Fish**.

Grill with Lemon Butter, Mixed Seafood, 58

Shrimp

Bisque, Creamy Chipotle Shrimp, 162
Broiled Shrimp Skewers, 176
Coconut Shrimp, Creamy, 60
Curry Shrimp, Thai, 60
Po'Boys, Shrimp, 128
Risotto with Spinach and Shrimp, 60

Snacks

Chips, Chive-Parmesan Potato, 15
Chips, Salt and Vinegar Pita, 15

Soups. *See also* **Chili, Chowder, Stews**.

Baby Lima Bean Soup with Crispy Sage, 153
Bisque, Creamy Chipotle Shrimp, 162
Butternut Squash Soup, Gingered, 156
Carrot Soup, Spiced, 152
Chicken Wonton Soup, 163
Chipotle Red Pepper Soup, 154
Fruit Soup, Gingered Peach, 152
Onion Soup, Classic French, 154
Roasted Vegetable and White Bean Soup, 161

Salsa Soup, Chilled Mexican-Style, 152
Tomato Soup with Roasted Garlic and Basil, Creamy, 161

Spaghetti

Basil Meat Sauce, Spaghetti with Fresh, 83
Pie, Spaghetti, 164
Whole Wheat Spaghetti and Spinach, Frittata with, 73

Spinach

Alfredo, Creamy Spinach and Mushroom, 74
Creamed Spinach, 177
Dip, Spinach and Sundried Tomato Cheese, 14
Frittata with Whole Wheat Spaghetti and Spinach, 73
Pizza, Chicken and Spinach, 96
Risotto with Spinach and Mushrooms, 76
Risotto with Spinach and Shrimp, 60
Salad with Grapefruit and Fennel, Spinach, 167
Sautéed Spinach, Mediterranean, 148
Scallop Vermicelli with Spinach, 59

Spreads

Black Bean and Goat Cheese Spread, 14
Kalamata-Herb Cream Cheese, 14

Squash. *See also* **Zucchini**.

Butternut Squash Soup, Gingered, 156
Butternut Squash Stuffed with Orange Couscous, 77
Yellow Squash Rice, 148

Stews. *See also* **Chili, Chowder, Soups**.

Pumpkin Stew with Roasted Pepitas, Curried, 156
Vegetable Stew, Lemon Grass, 153

Strawberries

Brown Sugar-Balsamic Marinated Strawberries, 178
Chiller, Strawberry, 20
Salad, Strawberry-Romaine, 180
Smoothie, Strawberry, 174

Sweet Potatoes

Casserole, Brown Sugar-Crusted Sweet Potato, 173
Maple-Pecan Sweet Potatoes, 147
Roasted Sweet Potatoes, 167
Syrup, Fresh Fruit Salad with Lime-Ginger, 118
Syrup, Watermelon with Mint, 174

Tacos, Grilled Grouper, 54
Tea, Ginger-Peach, 169
Tips on Food and Nutrition
    Avocado Advice, 13
    Baking Soda Basics, 38
    Balsamic Vinegar, 106
    Chicken Breast Half, How to
        Make a Pocket in a, 100
    Chicken, Shortcuts to
        Cooked, 97
    Chipotle Chiles in Adobo
        Sauce, 161
    Cider Vinegar, 99
    Cocoa vs. Chocolate, 32
    Cooking Temperatures, 85
    Corn Kernels from the Cob,
        How to Cut, 18
    Dairy, Daily, 152
    Dippers, 12
    Edamame, 120
    Eggs, How to Make
        Hard-Cooked, 131
    Empanadas, How to Make, 17
    En Papillote, 53
    Expandable Spatulas, 64
    Extravirgin Olive Oil: It's Well
        Worth the Price, 26
    Fire Up the Coals, 55
    Food Safety, 103
    Herbs, Cooking with
        Fresh, 62
    Hominy, 163
    Knives, Serrated, 127
    Kosher Salt, 15
    Measuring Flour, 39
    Nuts, Toasting, 78
    Omelets and Frittatas, 73
    Pasta Every Time, Perfect, 107
    Phyllo Cups, How to Make, 35
    Pork Loin, How to Double
        Butterfly and Stuff a, 88
    Portobello Mushrooms, 147
    Refrigerated Pie Dough, 36
    Safe Cooking Temperatures, 85
    Salmon, 57
    Sodium Solutions, 129
    Spinach, 76
    Turkey Meat Loaf, 105
    Vanilla Beans, 40
    Wheat Berries, 150
    White Sauce, How to Make a, 82
    Yukon Gold Potatoes, 155
Tofu
    Pan-Fried Tofu with Coconut
        Rice, 80
    Patties with Cucumber Mint
        Relish, Tofu and Chickpea, 79

Sauce, Stuffed Pasta Shells with Tofu
    Mushroom, 76
Stir-Fry, Red Curry
    Tofu, 80
Tomatillo Salsa, Black Bean
    and, 93
Tomatoes
    Bruschetta, Charred Tomato, 16
    Brussels Sprouts with Tomato,
        Olives, and Bacon, 143
    Chicken Breasts, Tomato-Basil-
        Stuffed, 101
    Corn and Tomatoes,
        Summer, 146
    Grape Tomatoes, Sautéed, 148
    Salad, Herbed Tomato-
        Mozzarella, 180
    Salad, Marinated Tomato and
        Cucumber, 178
    Salsa, Seared Fish with
        Tomato-Tarragon, 52
    Sandwiches, Grilled Double
        Cheese and Tomato, 126
    Sauce, Lemon Grouper with
        Tomato-Dill, 54
    Soup with Roasted Garlic and
        Basil, Creamy Tomato, 161
    Sundried Tomato Cheese Dip,
        Spinach and, 14
    Turkey Cutlets with Puttanesca
        Sauce, 108
    White Beans and Tomatoes,
        Zesty, 143
Tortillas. *See also* **Enchiladas**;
    Sandwiches/Wraps.
    Chicken Tortillas, Spicy, 99
    Pizza, Vegetarian Tortilla, 63
Tuna Burgers with Mango-Jalapeño
    Jam, Fresh, 129
Turkey
    Burgers, Asian, 180
    Burgers, Southwestern
        Turkey, 132
    Cutlets with Puttanesca Sauce,
        Turkey, 108
    Enchiladas, Turkey and
        Bean, 105
    Kabobs, Caribbean Grilled
        Turkey, 107
    Meat Loaf with Roasted Red
        Bell Pepper Sauce, Turkey, 105
    Patties, Turkey Sausage, 167
    Sausage and Pasta Bake with
        Turkey, 107
    Scaloppine in Cranberry-Port
        Sauce, Turkey, 106
    Skillet Turkey Parmesan, 106

Veal Cutlets with Wine-Braised
    Mushrooms, 86
Vegetables. *See also* **specific types**.
    Burritos, Bean and Roasted
        Vegetable, 64
    Dip, Creamy Veggie, 165
    Grilled Vegetable Platter, 169
    Mediterranean Vegetables,
        Pan-Seared Polenta with, 78
    Penne, Baked Vegetable, 75
    Pizza, Grilled Provolone and
        Vegetable, 62
    Pizza with Whole Wheat Crust,
        Mediterranean, 63
    Po' Boys, Fresh Vegetable, 127
    Salad, Barley and Vegetable
        Chopped, 122
    Salad, Italian Vegetable, 180
    Salad Primavera, 119
    Salsa, Fresh Green Veggie, 13
    Soups
        Minestrone, Beef, 162
        Roasted Vegetable and White
            Bean Soup, 161
        Salsa Soup, Chilled
            Mexican-Style, 152
    Spring Vegetables, Poached Salmon
        with, 57
    Spring Vegetables, Tarragon, 142
    Stew, Lemon Grass Vegetable, 153
    Wraps, Chicken and Vegetable
        Garden, 131

Walnut Bread, Pear and Creamy Swiss
    Cheese on, 126
Wheat Berries
    Pilaf, Orange-Kissed Berry, 150
Wonton Soup, Chicken, 163

Zucchini, Parmesan-Herb, 149

POINTS Value Recipe Index

0 POINTS value

Asparagus Spears with Lemon-Tarragon Butter, 142
Ginger Fruit Salsa, 13
Marinated Tomato and Cucumber Salad, 178
Orange-Olive Relish, 87
Roasted Red Bell Pepper Sauce, 105

1 POINTS value

Black Bean and Goat Cheese Spread, 14
Black Bean and Tomatillo Salsa, 93
Brownie Oatmeal Drops, 32
Buttery Herb Bread, 26
Cantaloupe-Pineapple-Ginger Fruit Salad, 118
Carrot-Edamame Sauté, 144
Charred Tomato Bruschetta, 16
Chilled Mexican-Style Salsa Soup, 152
Chive-Parmesan Potato Chips, 15
Citrus Roasted Brussels Sprouts, 144
Creamy Tomato Soup with Roasted Garlic and Basil, 161
Fresh Fruit Salad with Lime-Ginger Syrup, 118
Fresh Green Veggie Salsa, 13
Garlicky Cauliflower, 145
Garlic-Roasted Brussels Sprouts, 173
Ginger-Peach Tea, 169
Green Bean Salad with Caramelized Onions, 120
Grilled Portobello Mushrooms, 147
Grilled Vegetable Platter, 169
Herbed Tomato-Mozzarella Salad, 180
Hummus with Avocado and Lime, 12
Island Ambrosia, 118
Italian Vegetable Salad, 180
Jicama-Orange Salad, 178
Lemon Broccoli, 143
Lentil Hummus, 12
Mango-Jalapeño Jam, 129
Maple Cream, 49
Maple-Mustard Sauce, 88

Mediterranean Sautéed Spinach, 148
Moroccan Carrots, 145
Orange Salad with Onions and Olives, 171
Oven-Roasted Potato Wedges, 146
Parmesan-Herb Bread, 165
Parmesan-Herb Zucchini, 149
Peanut Dipping Sauce, 19
Red Curry Peanut Sauce, 19
Roasted Corn and Chicken Quesadillas, 18
Roasted Corn Salsa, 13
Roasted Green Beans, 174
Roasted Red Pepper and Escarole Crostini, 16
Rosemary Popovers with Lemon Butter, 27
Rosemary-White Bean Hummus, 12
Salt and Vinegar Pita Chips, 15
Sautéed Grape Tomatoes, 148
Spiced Carrot Soup, 152
Spicy Cabbage, 84
Spinach and Sundried Tomato Cheese Dip, 14
Spinach Salad with Grapefruit and Fennel, 167
Strawberry Chiller, 20
Strawberry-Romaine Salad, 180
Tarragon Spring Vegetables, 142
Yellow Squash Rice, 148

2 POINTS value

Asian Slaw with Roasted Peanuts, 120
Baked French Fries, 179
Barley and Brussels Sprouts, 149
Basic White Bread, 29
Black Bean and Couscous Salad with Jalapeño-Lemon Dressing, 121
Black Beans and Barley, 149
Broiled Shrimp Skewers, 176
Brown Sugar-Balsamic Marinated Strawberries, 178
Brussels Sprouts with Tomato, Olives, and Bacon, 143
Cabbage, Onion, and Pepper Toss, 144

Caraway-Raisin Whole Wheat Bread, 30
Cherry-Almond Biscotti, 33
Chicken Tenders Satay with Peanut Dipping Sauces, 18
Chipotle Red Pepper Soup, 154
Citrus Cran-Apple Relish, 173
Cornmeal Pancakes, 27
Cranberry-Spiced Pepper Jelly, 15
Creamy Chipotle Shrimp Bisque, 162
Creamy Veggie Dip, 165
Cucumber Mint Relish, 79
Dijon-Cracked Pepper Drop Biscuits, 26
Ginger-Lime Bars, 32
Green Bean Casserole, 142
Kalamata-Herb Cream Cheese, 14
Lemon-Dill Potato Salad, 121
Lemon-Glazed Sugar Cookies, 33
Maple-Pecan Grapefruit, 180
Melon Agua Fresca, 20
Mocha-Dark Chocolate Chunk Brownies, 32
Parmesan Polenta, 150
Peach Shortcake, 178
Pear Chutney, 87
Polenta with Fontina, 171
Raspberry Lemonade Sorbet, 50
Roasted Sweet Potatoes, 167
Root Beer Floats, 165
Rosemary and Kalamata Focaccia, 28
Salad Primavera, 119
Simple Black-Eyed Pea and Corn Salad, 177
Strawberry Smoothie, 174
Stuffed New Potatoes, 16
Summer Corn and Tomatoes, 146
Triple Chocolate Mocha Latte, 19
Warm Potato and Sausage Salad, 121
Watermelon with Mint Syrup, 174
Zesty White Beans and Tomatoes, 143

3 POINTS value

Apple Strudel, 34
Apricot Greens and Swiss with Ginger Vinaigrette, 118
Artichoke-Pepperoncini Pasta Salad, 123
Banana Pudding Ice Cream Cupcakes, 50
Barley and Vegetable Chopped Salad, 122
Berry and Mousse Pastries, 34
Brown Sugar-Crusted Sweet Potato Casserole, 173
Caesar Salad, 176
Cheesy Cheddar Mashed Potatoes, 178
Chicken Wonton Soup, 163
Corn and Pecan Pilaf, 145
Cranberry Rice Salad, 123
Creamed Spinach, 177
Creamy Rice Pudding with Dried Cherries, 40
Dill and Cheddar Loaf, 29
Edamame Salad, 120
Frozen Hazelnut Cappuccino, 171
Gingered Butternut Squash Soup, 156
Gingered Peach Fruit Soup, 152
Gorgonzola and Chive Mashed Potatoes, 147
Grapefruit and Avocado Salad, 180
Korean Beef with Spicy Cabbage, 84
Lemon Artichoke Risotto, 150
Lemon Grass Vegetable Stew, 153
Maple-Pecan Sweet Potatoes, 147
Orange-Flavored Hot Chocolate, 19
Orange-Kissed Berry Pilaf, 150
Overnight Caramel-Pecan Bread, 28
Parmesan Twist, 29
Pear, Prosciutto, and Pine Nut Salad, 119
Picadillo Empanadas, 17
Roast Beef on Rye Sandwiches, 129
Roasted Italian Pork Tenderloin, 94
Roasted Poblano and Potato Gratin, 146
Roasted Vegetable and White Bean Soup, 161
Skillet Ham with Pineapple-Ginger Salsa, 94
Smoked Salmon Omelet, 178
Sweet Corn Spoonbread, 28
Triple Chocolate Sundae, 175
Turkey Sausage Patties, 167

4 POINTS value

Apple Cider Crisp, 34
Asian Burgers, 180
Asian-Style Crab Cakes, 58
Bacon-Egg-Arugula Sandwiches, 130
Banana Breakfast Smoothie, 20
Beef Minestrone, 162
Cajun Catfish, 175
Caribbean Grilled Turkey Kabobs, 107
Chicken and Spinach Pizza, 96
Chicken Thighs Piccata-Style, 103
Classic Mushroom and Cheese Omelets, 73
Coconut Rice, 80
Cranberry Pecan Buns, 30
Creamy Coconut Shrimp, 60
Crunchy Pecan Greens with Fresh Berries, 119
Curried Mussels, 59
Dijon Steak with Orange-Balsamic Sauce, 85
Filet Mignon with Rosemary-Port Sauce, 85
Fresh Lemon and Pepper Linguine, 176
Fresh Tuna Burgers with Mango-Jalapeño Jam, 129
Fried Rice with Asparagus and Eggs, 78
Glazed Apricot Scones, 27
Greek Chicken Salad Pita, 132
Grilled Grouper Tacos, 54
Grilled Pork Chops with Orange-Olive Relish, 87
Grilled Provolone and Vegetable Pizza, 62
Ham and Cheese Grill, 180
Herbed Roasted Chicken, 104
Lime-Marinated Flank Steak, 83
Loose Meat Sandwiches, 130
Mediterranean Pizza with Whole Wheat Crust, 63
Mexican-Style Chicken, 102
Mint Brownie Ice Cream Bars, 50
Mixed Seafood Grill with Lemon Butter, 58
Mushroom and Onion Quesadillas, 64
Open-Faced Eggplant-Olive Sandwiches, 126
Open-Faced Salmon Salad Sandwiches, 128
"Osso Bucco"-Style Chicken, 170
Peaches and Cream Oatmeal, 176
Pear Upside-Down Cake with Pecans, 38
Pesto-Crusted Flounder, 179
Pork with Grapefruit-Mint Salsa, 93
Risotto with Spinach and Mushrooms, 76
Salmon Salad, 123
Scallops with Mild Creamy Ginger Sauce, 59
Seared Fish with Tomato-Tarragon Salsa, 52
Southwest Chicken Pizza, 96
Spicy Andouille Posole, 163
Spicy Pork with Black Bean and Tomatillo Salsa, 93
Thai Curry Shrimp, 60
Tiramisù, 40
Toasted Coconut Banana Muffins, 26
Turkey Cutlets with Puttanesca Sauce, 108
Turkey Scaloppine in Cranberry-Port Sauce, 106
Two Potato Chowder, 155
Veal Cutlets with Wine-Braised Mushrooms, 86
Yellow Pepper Chipotle Chicken, 102

5 POINTS value

Apple Slaw and Ham Sandwiches, 131
Apple-Stuffed Pork Loin with Maple-Mustard Sauce, 88
Baby Lima Bean Soup with Crispy Sage, 153
Baked Salmon with Creamy Onion Sauce, 56
Baked Vegetable Penne, 75
Bean and Roasted Vegetable Burritos, 64
Beef Tenderloin Steak with Cherry-Port Sauce, 84
Bow Tie Pasta and Kalamata Olive Toss, 74
Cinnamon Beef over Couscous, 83
Classic French Onion Soup, 154
Creamy Spinach and Mushroom Alfredo, 74
Cumin Lamb Chops with Pear Chutney, 86
Dark Chocolate and Raspberry Layer Cake, 37
Dark Chocolate Crème Brûlée, 49
Fresh Vegetable Po' Boys, 127

Frittata with Whole Wheat Spaghetti and Spinach, 73
Greek Frittata, 74
Greek Pasta Salad, 175
Grilled Caramel-Banana Sundaes, 169
Lemonade Pudding Pie in Biscotti Crust, 36
Lemon Grouper with Tomato-Dill Sauce, 54
Margherita Pizza, 62
Marsala-Style Chicken, 99
Mediterranean Couscous and Lentil Salad, 122
Molasses-Bourbon Grilled Salmon, 168
Mustard-Glazed Halibut with Warm Scallions, 55
Oriental Hens, 108
Oven-Roasted Halibut, 55
Pan-Seared Salmon with Honey-Balsamic Sauce, 56
Pan-Seared Scallops and Bacon Salad, 124
Pan-Seared Snapper with Garlic-Herb Vinaigrette, 57
Pastitsio, 82
Pizza with Chicken, Artichokes, and Basil, 96
Poached Salmon with Spring Vegetables, 57
Pumpkin-Cranberry Custard with Maple Cream, 49
Quick Peach and Raspberry Pies, 36
Red Curry Tofu Stir-Fry, 80
Risotto with Spinach and Shrimp, 60
Roast Beef and Blue Cheese Salad, 175
Roasted Pepper and Corn Chowder, 154
Rosemary Chicken with White Beans, 100
Southwestern Tilapia, 58
Southwestern Turkey Burgers, 132
Spaghetti with Fresh Basil Meat Sauce, 83
Striped Bass en Papillote, 52
Stuffed Pasta Shells with Tofu Mushroom Sauce, 76
Teriyaki Amberjack Skewers, 52
Turkey Meat Loaf with Roasted Red Bell Pepper Sauce, 105
White Beans Oreganata, 79

6 *POINTS* value

Baked Shells with Three Cheeses, 75
Balsamic Chicken and Rice Skillet, 103
Blue Cheese and Steak Quesadilla, 174
Breakfast Sandwich, 174
Butternut Squash Stuffed with Orange Couscous, 77
Cajun Chicken, 100
Carrot Cake with Cream Cheese Frosting, 38
Cheddar and Blue Cheese Twice-Baked Potatoes, 77
Chicken and Rice Enchiladas, 97
Chicken and Vegetable Garden Wraps, 131
Chocolate-Toffee Pudding Cake, 39
Creamed Chicken with Noodles, 98
Curried Pumpkin Stew with Roasted Pepitas, 156
Filet Mignon with Sherry-Mushroom Sauce, 86
Fresh Lemon Greens on Red Pepper Focaccia, 128
Grilled Double Cheese and Tomato Sandwiches, 126
Grilled Mozzarella Chicken Sandwiches, 132
Hearty Chicken and Dumplings, 104
Holiday Herbed Pork Roast, 172
Lemon-Caper Chicken, 181
Mahimahi Fingers with Creamy Dill Tartar Sauce, 56
Mushroom Quiche, 166
Oat Grain-Feta Salad, 122
Pan-Fried Flounder, 53
Pan-Fried Tofu with Coconut Rice, 80
Pan-Seared Polenta with Mediterranean Vegetables, 78
Peach Preserves Pound Cake, 39
Pecan-Crusted Chicken Fingers with Dijon-Maple Sauce, 98
Pork and Garbanzo Bean Chili, 162
Provolone Panini Sandwiches, 127
Pumpkin Cheesecake, 37
Scallop Vermicelli with Spinach, 59
Skillet Chicken and Biscuits, 97
Skillet Sausage Casserole, 94

Skillet Turkey Parmesan, 106
Spaghetti Pie, 164
Spicy Chicken Tortillas, 99
Tofu and Chickpea Patties with Cucumber Mint Relish, 79
Tomato-Basil-Stuffed Chicken Breasts, 101
Turkey Sausage and Pasta Bake, 107
Vegetarian Tortilla Pizza, 63

7 *POINTS* value

Artichoke, Mushroom, and Prosciutto Calzones, 130
Chicken and Black Bean Taco Salad with Chipotle Dressing, 124
Cornmeal- and Pecan- Crusted Catfish, 53
Cranberry-Orange Chicken, 102
Pear and Creamy Swiss Cheese on Walnut Bread, 126
Stuffed Chicken Breasts with Marsala Cream Sauce, 101
Turkey and Bean Enchiladas, 105

8 *POINTS* value

Shrimp Po'Boys, 128

VEGETABLE COOKING CHART

Vegetable	Servings	Preparations	Cooking Instructions
Asparagus	3 to 4 per pound	Snap off tough ends. Remove scales, if desired.	To steam: Cook, covered, on a rack above boiling water 8 to 12 minutes. To boil: Cook, covered, in a small amount of boiling water 6 to 8 minutes or until crisp-tender.
Broccoli	3 to 4 per pound	Remove outer leaves and tough ends of lower stalks. Wash; cut into spears.	To steam: Cook, covered, on a rack above boiling water 15 to 18 minutes.
Carrots	4 per pound	Scrape; remove ends, and rinse. Leave tiny carrots whole; slice large carrots, or cut into strips.	Cook, covered, in a small amount of boiling water 8 to 10 minutes (slices) or 12 to 15 minutes (strips).
Cauliflower	4 per medium head	Remove outer leaves and stalk. Wash. Leave whole, or break into florets.	Cook, covered, in a small amount of boiling water 10 to 12 minutes (whole) or 8 to 10 minutes (florets).
Corn	4 per 4 large ears	Remove husks and silks. Leave corn on the cob, or cut off tips of kernels, and scrape cob with dull edge of knife.	Cook, covered, in boiling water to cover 10 minutes (on cob) or in a small amount of boiling water 8 to 10 minutes (cut).
Green beans	4 per pound	Wash; trim ends, and remove strings. Cut into 1½-inch pieces.	Cook, covered, in a small amount of boiling water 12 to 15 minutes.
Potatoes	3 to 4 per pound	Scrub; peel, if desired. Leave whole, slice, or cut into chunks.	To cook: Cook, covered, in a small amount of boiling water 30 to 40 minutes (whole) or 15 to 20 minutes (slices or chunks). To bake: Bake at 400° for 1 hour or until done.
Snow peas	4 per pound	Wash; trim ends, and remove tough strings.	Cook, covered, in a small amount of boiling water 3 to 5 minutes. Or cook over high heat in reduced-calorie margarine or in pan coated with cooking spray 3 to 5 minutes, stirring constantly.
Squash, summer	3 to 4 per pound	Wash; trim ends. Leave whole, slice, or chop.	To steam: Cook, covered, on a rack over boiling water 10 to 12 minutes (sliced or chopped). To boil: Cook, covered, in a small amount of boiling water 8 to 10 minutes (slices) or 15 minutes (whole).
Squash, winter *(including acorn, butternut, hubbard, and spaghetti)*	2 per pound	Rinse; cut in half, and remove all seeds.	To boil: Cook, covered, in boiling water 20 to 25 minutes. To bake: Place cut side down in shallow baking dish; add ½ inch water. Bake, uncovered, at 375° for 30 minutes. Turn and season, or fill; bake 20 to 30 minutes or until tender.